P.M. Grant, C.F.N. C
B. Mulgrew, J.H. Dri

Analogue and Digital
Signal Processing and Coding

Chartwell-Bratt   **Studentlitteratur**

British Library Cataloguing in Publication Data
Analogue and digital signal processing and coding
    1. Signals. Processing
    I. Grant, R. M.
    621.38' 043

ISBN 0-86238-206-8

© P M Grant, C F N Cowan, B Mulgrew, J H Dripps and Chartwell-Bratt Ltd, 1989

Chartwell-Bratt (Publishing and Training) Ltd
ISBN 0-86238-206-8

Printed in Sweden,
Studentlitteratur, Lund
ISBN 91-44-29581-2

1 2 3 4 5 6 7 8 9 10 | 1993 92 91 90 89

CONTENTS

PREFACE

This text has been compiled from the lecture notes associated with an industrial course on signal processing and coding techniques run by staff of the Electrical Engineering Department at the University of Edinburgh. The course has been presented at a number of company premises in the UK since its original inception at Ferranti plc. in 1982. The set of notes contained in this text are specific to a version of the course compiled in video tape form in 1988. Copies of these 20 (45-55 minute) tapes are available for purchase or hire through EUMOS Ltd., University of Edinburgh, 16 Buccleuch Place, Edinburgh. It should however, be noted that whereas the text is essential to make full use of the video tapes, the text has been designed in such a way that it may be used as an independent study guide without recourse to the accompanying video course.

It has been assumed in writing this text that the reader will be a graduate level applied scientist or equivalent with reasonable competence in mathematics and have some background in signal theory appropriate to engineering electronics. The first part of the book, chapters 1 to 4, covers basic theoretical concepts such as Laplace and z-transforms, Fourier transforms etc. The following section, chapters 5 to 7, covers the design of digital frequency filters, both finite and infinite impulse response types. Optimal time domain estimation techniques such as Wiener, Kalman and adaptive filters are covered in chapters 8 to 10. The next major section of the book, chapters 11 to 13, covers the area of spectral estimation and includes material on the design of discrete and fast Fourier transforms and modern spectral analysis. This is followed in chapters 14 to 17 by a consideration of coding techniques including forward error correcting codes and data reduction techniques for voice and image data transmission. The final section of the text, chapters 18 to 20, provides a treatment of some of the practical aspects of the realisation of signal processing systems. This is done with chapters covering the implementation of analogue filters and digital signal processor designs. A specific case study on the use of matched filters in the application areas of radar and wideband communications is also included.

The objective of the book is to provide a broad coverage of the subject of analogue and digital signal processing with a bias towards the practical aspects of actual implementations. Apart from the specific technical detail this should allow the reader to assimilate the basics of the subject area and obtain a realistic perspective on the techniques which will allow him to approach an application area and readily identify likely routes to problem solutions. In this way we hope to have provided a text which is useful to both project engineers and their managers in addition to the academic community.

The authors are indebted to a large number of people and organisations who have made the production of this work possible. First we must acknowledge two successive heads of the Department of Electrical Engineering at University of Edinburgh, Professors Jeffrey Collins and John Mavor, who have been responsible for initiating many of the earlier studies in analogue signal processing. This has stimulated the formation of a significant research group in signal processing techniques and it is with ongoing research activities in this area that we have an environment conducive to the pursuance of a project of this scale. We are also grateful to Ferranti plc., and in particular Ron McMurtrie, who provided the initial testing ground for the development of this course and indeed it was he who was initially responsible for suggesting that we might commit the course to video tape. Edith Field, as the training manager for EUMOS Ltd., was responsible for much of the organisational work attached to the course and we are indebted to her for her efforts in monitoring these activities.

A great many friends and colleagues should be mentioned here for their contributions and we must apologise for the omissions. However, we must acknowledge Peter Woods of the television centre at Heriot-Watt University for the preparation of graphics, Steve McLaughlin of Edinburgh University for the preparation of some key simulation results used in the text. Finally, we would like to thank the secretarial staff of the University of Edinburgh and in particular Joan Burton, Jacqui Anderson, Linda Young and Nicola Wahlberg for their extensive efforts in preparing and editing much of the early typescript for this text.

GLOSSARY

ADC	Analogue to Digital Convertor
ADM	Adaptive Delta Modulation
ADPCM	Adaptive Differential PCM
AIC	Akaike Information Criteria
ALU	Arithmetic Logic Unit
AM	Amplitude Modulation
AMF	Analogue (CCD or SAW) Matched Filter
AMT	Active Memory Technology
AR	Auto-regressive
ARQ	Automatic Request Repeat
ARMA	Autoregressive Moving Average
ASK	Amplitude-Shift Keying
AU	Arithmetic Unit
BCD	Binary Coded Decimal
BCH	Bose Chaudhri Macquenghem (code)
BER	Bit Error Rate
BLMS	Block LMS
BPF	Band Pass Filter
CAD	Computer Aided Design
CAT	Criterion Autoregressive Transfer
CCD	Charge Coupled Device
CFAR	Constant False Alarm Rate
CML	Current Mode Logic
CMOS	Complementary Metal Oxide Semiconductor
CODEC	Coder and Decoder
CPU	Central Processing Unit
CZT	Chirp Z Transform
DAC	Digital to Analogue Convertor
DAP	Distributed Array Processor
DCT	Discrete Cosine Transform
DES	Data Encryption Standard (USA)
DFT	Discrete Fourier Transform
DIF	Decimation in Frequency
DIT	Decimation in Time

DM   Delta Modulation
DMA   Direct Memory Access
DMF   Digital Matched Filter
DPCM   Differential Pulse Code Modulation
DPSK   Differential-Phase-Shift Keying
DSP   Digital Signal Processing
DWHT   Discrete Walsh Hadamard Transform

ECCM   Electronic Counter Counter Measures
ECG   Electrocardiographic
ECL   Emitter Coupled Logic
EMI   Electromagnetic Interference
EPROM   Erasable Programmable Read Only Memory
ESM   Electronic Support Measures
EVR   Eigenvalue Ratio

FAD   Filter and Detect
FDMA   Frequency Division Multiple Access
FECC   Forward Error Correcting Code
FET   Field Effect Transistor
FFT   Fast Fourier Transform
FH   Frequency Hopping
FIR   Finite Impulse Response
FM   Frequency Modulation
FPE   Final Prediction Error
FPLA   Field Programmable Logic Array
FSK   Frequency Shift Keying
FTR   Functional Throughput Rate

GaAs   Gallium Arsenide

HMOS   High Performance MOS
HPF   High Pass Filter

IC   Integrated Circuit
IDT   Interdigital Transducer (SAW)
IIR   Infinite Impulse Response
IOP   Input/Output Port
ISI   Intersymbol Interference

JAGUAR(V)   Jamming Guarded VHF radio
JTIDS   Joint Tactical Information Distribution System

KLT   Karhunen Loeve Transform

LMS   Least Mean Square
LPC   Linear Predictive Coder
LPF   Low Pass Filter
LSTTL   Low Power Schotky Transistor - Transistor Logic
LS   Least Squares
LSB   Least Significant Bit
LSI   Large Scale Integration

MA   Moving Average

MEDL	Marconi Electronic Devices Ltd (UK)
MESFET	Metal Semiconductor (Gate) Field Effect Transistor
MIPs	Million of Instructions per second
MMSE	Minimum MSE
MOPs	Millions of Operations per second
MOS	Metal Oxide Semiconductor
MOST	Metal Oxide Semiconductor Transistor
MSB	Most Significant Bit
MSE	Mean Square Error
MSK	Minimum-Shift Keying
NRZ	Non Return to Zero
NMOS	N Channel Metal Oxide Semiconductor (Transistor)
O/P	Output
OOK	On Off keying
PAM	Pulse Amplitude Modulation
PCB	Printed Circuit Board
PCM	Pulse Code Modulation
PDF	Probabilty Density Function
PE	Prediction Error
PLL	Phase Locked Loop
PLA	Programmable Logic Array
PM	Phase Modulation
PN	Pseudo Noise
PPM	Pulse Position Modulation
PRF	Pulse Repetition Frequency
PRI	Pulse Repetition Interval
PROM	Programmable Read Only Memory
PSD	Power Spectral Density
PSK	Phase Shift Keying
PT	Prime Transform
PTF	Programmable Transversal (FIR) Filter
PWM	Pulse Width Modulation
Q	Quality Factor
QPSK	Quadrature Phase Shift Keying
QAM	Quadrative Amplitude Modulation
QMF	Quadrative Mirror Filter
RAM	Random Access Memory
RLC	Resistor, Inductor Capacitor
RLS	Recursive Least Squares
ROM	Read Only Memory
RX	Receive
S&H	Sample and Hold
SAW	Surface Acoustic Wave
SBC	Straight Binary Counter
SBC	Sub-band Coding
SG	Stochastic Gradient
SIMD	Single Instruction Multiple Data
SKYNET	British Spread Spectrum System

SNR	Signal to Noise Ratio
SO	Self Orthogonalising
SOS	Silicon on Sapphire
ST-X	Cut of Quartz substrate for SAW device
TDM	Time Division Multiplexing
TDMA	Time Division Multiple Access
TB	Time Bandwidth Product
TSB	Tri-State Buffer
TWT	Travelling Wave Tube
TX	Transmit
UHF	Ultra High Frequency
ULA	Uncommitted Logic Array
VCO	Voltage Controlled Oscillator
VHF	Very High Frequency
VHPIC	Very High Performance Integrated Circuits
VHSIC	Very High Speed Integrated Circuits
VLSI	Very Large Scale Integration
VOCODER	Voice Coder

INTRODUCTION

Both analogue and digital approaches are widely used in signal processing but there is a growing trend towards the deployment of digital techniques. This arises because conventional analogue techniques usually incur drift and accuracy problems and they are fundamentally less flexible than a digital approach. Digital processing offers:

*   no short-term drift with temperature and/or minor supply voltage fluctuations;

*   no long-term (aging) drift;

*   high reproducibility i.e. no variation of component value or characteristics from processor to processor;

*   low parts count, fewer interconnections and higher reliability;

*   accuracy determined purely by the number of bits used in input signal quantisation and internal arithmetic.

The advantages of the digital approach are thus higher accuracy and capability to deal with more complex algorithms combined with the ability to easily reconfigure or reprogramme the processor. The disadvantages are higher costs, but these are reducing each year with advances in VLSI improving chip complexity and speed. At the present time DSP components are generally limited to audio bandwidth (~ 10 kHz), while sophisticated array processors can comfortably handle video bandwidth (~ 10 MHz) signals.

These notes also cover analogue processing because of the significant capabilities of discrete-time sampled-data integrated charge-coupled devices (CCD's) which can perform filtering and Fourier transformation up to video bandwidth. The surface acoustic wave (SAW) devices, which are continuous, complex, analogue processors can undertake similar processing functions, at bandwidths from 100 kHz to greater than 100 MHz. Thus the performance (or speed) of the faster of these analogue systems will not be overtaken for several years by digital techniques, and it may take even longer to achieve their processing capability at the same cost as present day analogue processors. However, at speech bandwidths, digital techniques now predominate with several general purpose DSP microprocessor or microcomputer designs now being commercially available.

The applications for signal processing occur in many areas of electronics. They are currently being applied widely in telecommunications, for example, in the touch-tone dialing system where each button on a telephone generates a pair of tones which must be received, filtered and decoded at the central exchange. There are many dedicated telephone lines for transmitting binary data at 24, 48 and 96 kbit/s. Sampling speech at 8 k sample/s with 8 bit words produces a bit rate of 64 kbit/s which is unsuitable for data links. However if instead of transmitting the sampled speech, a time sample of speech is modelled as the output of a digital filter excited by an appropriate noise input the parameters of the filter can be transmitted with low accuracy to yield a low density digital speech signal. Signal processing is thus being used increasingly in speech coding, automatic speaker recognition systems to recognise the human voice, and also in speech synthesis. Other key applications in telecommunications include the use of signal processing for equalisation, to compensate for distortion in bandlimited and multipath transmission paths and for cancellation of the echos caused by imbalances in the two to four wire hybrid transformers employed in telephony systems.

In test equipment, spectrum analysers and other processor based equipments can measure noise spectra, cross correlation, cepstra, transfer functions, coherence functions, histograms, phase distortion and many other features. Although the equipment may operate at microwave frequencies these microprocessor based instruments perform filtering, thresholding and distortion measurement, directly on the low bandwidth digitised signals.

In biomedical analysis the harmonic analysis of ECG and EEG can be studied for anomalies to make blood velocity and volumetric measurements via acoustic Doppler methods. Acoustic imaging is used in prenatal care and obstretics, and digital filters and data compression are widely used in acoustic and X-Ray image enhancement, as well as in tomographic reconstruction systems.

In radar and sonar systems signal processing is used for antenna beam-forming, matched filtering for pulse compression, tracking filters, trajectory modelling and phase compensation as well as clutter suppression, target identification and dimension measurement. Radar systems have undergone a revolution in capabilities due to advances in signal processing with almost all new equipments being built and designed round digital filters, FFT's or some form of digital-analogue processors. These new radars are usually smart and flexible (with multi-mode capabilities) and their personality can easily be altered by reprogramming the processor.

Further, seismic processing, industrial (chemical process) control and many other applications all involve signal processing techniques in some form or other. Signal processing is thus a developing field which will be applied more extensively in a wider range of applications as the constituent processors progressively reduce in cost and increase in capability.

Chapter 1
LAPLACE AND z-TRANSFORMS

1.1 INTRODUCTION

This chapter encompasses a brief review of the subject of signal analysis using Laplace and z-transform theory. It is not intended that this should be a complete and rigorous treatment, rather a sufficient coverage is provided to enable the reader to comprehend the use of these transforms in signal processing. Further background reading can be found in texts such as [Oppenheim Willsky & Young, Kuo, Rabiner & Gold].

1.2 COMPLEX FREQUENCY

The representation of signals in the complex frequency domain is key to the understanding of Laplace and z-transforms. Here we may represent a generalised cisoidal signal, $x(t)$ by:

$$x(t) = A \ e^{st} \tag{1.1}$$

where $s = \sigma + j\omega$ is the complex frequency, σ represents signal growth or decay, and ω represents continuous angular frequency. Figure 1.1 shows 3 particular cases of signals represented in this way. In Figure 1.1(a) the signal is a continuous, undamped, sinusoid as shown in the vertical axis projection, so for this case the signal vector x simply has a constant amplitude and constant rotational velocity, ω. The other 2 cases shown in Figures 1.1(b) and 1.1(c) are for exponentially decreasing and increasing sinusoids respectively. Here an additional velocity component, parallel to the signal vector, exists indicating signal growth or decay (this is the σ component of the complex frequency). It should be noted that when σ is negative the signal is decreasing (therefore real and bounded), but when σ is positive the signal increases to ∞ (i.e. it is unstable).

The five basic types of cisoidal signal described by equation (1.1) are summarised in Table 1.1.

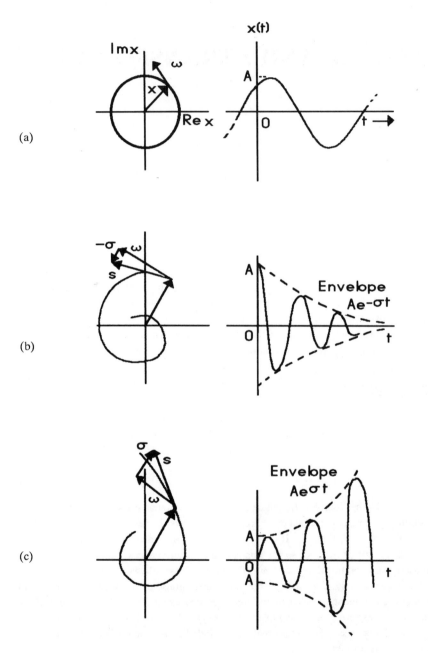

Figure 1.1   Representation of generalised cisoidal signals in the complex frequency domain: (a) an undamped sinusoid; (b) an exponentially decreasing sinusoid; (c) an exponentially increasing sinusoid.

$\sigma = 0$	undamped sinusoid
$\omega = 0$	exponential signal
$\omega = \sigma = 0$	constant (d.c.) signal
$\sigma > 0$	sinusoid increasing in amplitude
$\sigma < 0$	sinusoid decreasing in amplitude

Table 1.1 Cisoidal signals.

We will find that it is the real, σ, component in the complex frequency description which sets it apart from the Fourier description (described in chapter 2). Because of the real component a Laplace description of a signal is capable of describing transient signals as opposed to steady state cisoids.

1.3 THE LAPLACE TRANSFORM

The Laplace transform $G(s)$ of a signal $f(t)$ can be obtained by evaluating the integral:

$$G(s) = \int_0^\infty f(t)\, e^{-st}\, dt \tag{1.2}$$

which is only valid for $t \geq 0$. This allows one to characterise the signal or response of a network $f(t)$ by the complex s-plane representation. Considering the function $f(t) = e^{-\alpha t}$ as an example.

$$G(s) = \int_0^\infty e^{-\alpha t} e^{-st}\, dt \tag{1.3}$$

$$= \int_0^\infty e^{-(s+\alpha)t}\, dt$$

$$= \frac{-1}{s+\alpha} [e^{-(s+\alpha)t}]_0^\infty = \frac{1}{s+\alpha}$$

This function can be easily represented by using the pole-zero description of the signal. If we consider a more general Laplace transform:

$$G(s) = \frac{A(s-z_1)(s-z_2)(s-z_3)\ldots}{(s-p_1)(s-p_2)(s-p_3)\ldots} \tag{1.4}$$

Now $G(s)$ goes to zero when $s = z_1, z_2$, or z_3 and it goes to infinity when $s = p_1, p_2, p_3$ etc. So we say that z_1, z_2 etc are the zeros of $G(s)$ and p_1, p_2 etc are its poles. Poles are either real or they occur in complex conjugate pairs, and the same is true of zeros. Thus a pole at $s = \alpha + j\beta$ is matched by one at $s = \alpha - j\beta$, and *this is always the case if the signal is a real function of time.*

Poles and zeros are normally plotted on an Argand (complex plane) diagram, Figure 1.2, which shows the pole zero locations for the function

$$G(s) = \frac{4(s^2 - 2s)}{s^2 + 2s + 10}$$

This has zeros at $s = 0, 2$ and poles at $-1 \pm j3$. The Fourier spectrum, $G(j\omega)$, is obtained directly by replacing s by $j\omega$ in $G(s)$. This for $G(s) = \frac{1}{(s+\alpha)}$ gives $G(j\omega) = \frac{1}{(j\omega+\alpha)}$. The denominator is represented by a vector in the s-plane drawn from the pole $(-\alpha)$ to a point on the imaginary axis representing a particular value of ω as shown in Figure 1.3. The length of this vector represents the magnitude of $(j\omega+\alpha)$ and the angle with the real axis is its phase. As $(j\omega+\alpha)$ is in the denominator then $G(j\omega)$ is proportional to the reciprocal of $(j\omega+\alpha)$. Thus $G(j\omega)$ is a maximum when $(\alpha+j\omega)$ is a minimum $(\omega=0)$, and $G(j\omega)$ is a minimum at $\omega=\infty$. The phase angle alters from 0 at $\omega=0$, to 90° at $\omega=\infty$ (and -90° at $\omega=-\infty$), see Figure 1.3.

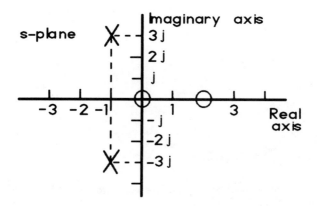

Figure 1.2   Poles and zeros of $G(s) = \dfrac{4(s^2-2s)}{s^2+2s+10}$.

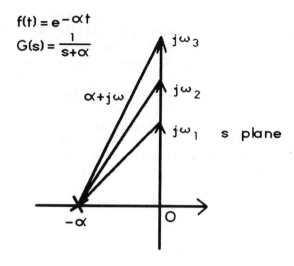

$$f(t) = e^{-\alpha t}$$

$$G(s) = \frac{1}{s+\alpha}$$

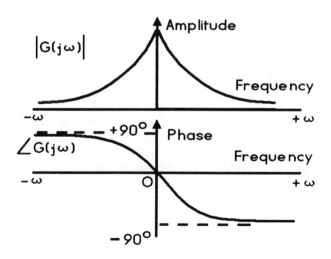

Figure 1.3 $G(j\omega)$ derived from the transform $G(s) = \dfrac{1}{s+\alpha}$.

In the general case the magnitude of the spectrum $G(j\omega)$ is obtained by taking the products of the lengths of the various vectors drawn from the zeros to the relevant frequency (ω) value on the imaginary axis and dividing this by the product of the pole vectors. The phase is found by summing the phases of the individual zero vectors minus the sum of the phases of the individual pole vectors (see Figure 1.4). Thus it is obvious that a pole close to the imaginary axis gives rise to a maximum in the spectrum or frequency response as ω approaches a value equal to the pole's imaginary part (i.e. $\omega = \beta$ for $s = \alpha + j\beta$) while a zero gives rise to a minimum in the response. Examples illustrating this are shown in Figure 1.5. As a pole in the right half of the s-plane gives rise to a time function growing without limit, they cannot be encountered in the real physical world therefore poles are constrained to the left hand s-plane, while zeros can occur anywhere.

1.4 THE z-TRANSFORM

In the case of sampled data signals we may represent a signal as:

$$f(t) = \sum_{n=0}^{\infty} x(t)\, \delta(t - nT) \tag{1.5}$$

where $x(t)$ is continuous in t, and $\delta(t - nT)$ is the Dirac delta function. The Laplace transform is thus given by:

$$G(s) = \int_0^{\infty} \left(\sum_{n=0}^{\infty} x(t)\, \delta(t - nT) \right) e^{-st}\, dt \tag{1.6}$$

$$= x_0 + x_1 e^{-sT} + x_2 e^{-s2T} + \cdots$$

where $x_i = x(iT)$. In the Laplace domain this represents a transform with an infinite number of poles and zeroes (this is essentially due to spectral aliasing because of the sampling). This means that the information contained in the band $s = +\dfrac{\pi}{T}$ to $-\dfrac{\pi}{T}$ is replicated in the band $s = \dfrac{\pi}{T}$ to $3\dfrac{\pi}{T}$ and $s = -\dfrac{\pi}{T}$ to $-3\dfrac{\pi}{T}$ etc. This redundancy of information may be compressed by employing the z-transform which maps the region of the s-plane vertical axis between $\pm\dfrac{\pi}{T}$ to a circle of unit radius in the "z-plane". All the information to the left of the s-plane imaginary axis then maps inside the unit circle, with the right half plane transforming to outside the z-plane unit circle (Figure 1.6). This is done by applying the substitution :

$$e^{sT} \to z$$

giving

$$G(z) = x_0 + x_1 z^{-1} + x_2 z^{-2} + \ldots \tag{1.7}$$

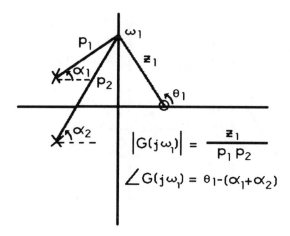

$$\left|G(j\omega_1)\right| = \frac{z_1}{P_1 P_2}$$

$$\angle G(j\omega_1) = \theta_1-(\alpha_1+\alpha_2)$$

Figure 1.4 General definition of $G(j\omega)$ from the s-plane.

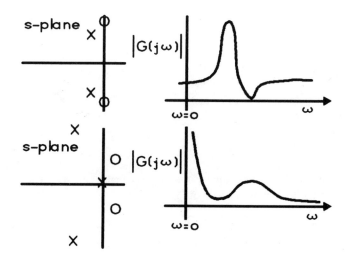

Figure 1.5 Examples of spectra with corresponding Laplace transforms.

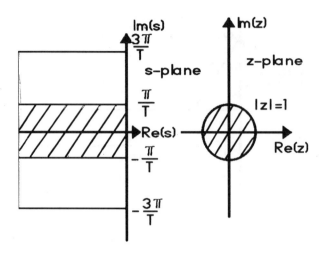

Figure 1.6   Mapping from Laplace to z-plane.

where z^{-1} is the shift operator denoting one sample delay of T secs. $G(z)$ thus represents directly the impulse response of a network (the actual values of the signal samples under examination). Taking an example :

$$G(z) = \frac{z}{(z-\alpha)} \tag{1.8}$$

$$= \frac{1}{(1-\alpha z^{-1})}$$

$$= 1+\alpha z^{-1}+\alpha^2 z^{-2}+\ldots \tag{1.9}$$

The form of equation (1.8) yields directly the physical realisation shown in Figure 1.7 with equation (1.9) giving the impulse response of Figure 1.8.

The significance of the z transform is that it removes the repetitive form of the Laplace transform which repeats with period $2\frac{\pi}{T}$ rad/sec. The s-plane imaginary axis $s=j\omega$ becomes $z = e^{j\omega T} = cos(\omega T) + jsin(\omega T)$ which traces out the unit circle on the z-plane. All the left hand s-plane maps inside the unit circle and the right hand is outside the circle, Figure 1.5. Substituting into $z = cos(\omega T) + jsin(\omega T)$ shows that $\omega = 0$ is equivalent to $z = 1$, $\omega = \frac{\pi}{2T}$

Realization

$$G(z) = \frac{1}{1 - \alpha z^{-1}}$$

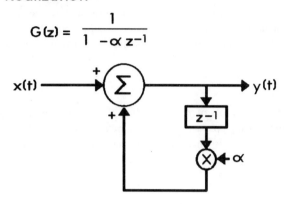

Figure 1.7   Physical realisation of $G(z) = \frac{z}{z - \alpha}$.

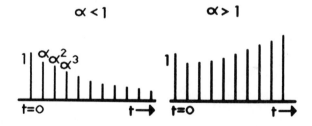

Figure 1.8   Time function corresponding to $G(z) = \frac{z}{z - \alpha}$.

is $z = j$, $\omega = \frac{\pi}{T}$ is $z = -1$, $\omega = 3\frac{\pi}{T}$ is $z = -j$ and $\omega = 2\frac{\pi}{T}$, the sampling frequency, corresponds again to $z = 1$. As with the Laplace transform the z-plane response allows us to investigate the approximate $|G|$ and $\angle G$ by inspection, Figure 1.9. This repetitive sampling in the s-plane repeats itself on the unit circle in the z-plane. For example consider the function

$$G(z) = 1 - z^{-8} = \frac{z^8 - 1}{z^8}$$

This has 8 zeros given by the roots of $z^8 = 1$ and an 8th order pole at $z = 0$. Figure 1.10 shows the corresponding z-plane pole zero diagram, impulse response and spectrum magnitude, and Figure 1.11 the equivalent responses when the zero at $z = 1$ is removed. This simple example allows us to see how some simplistic filter design (low pass) may be achieved with little knowledge of classical systems theory.

1.5 SUMMARY

In this chapter Laplace and z-transform analysis of signals and system responses has been introduced. In subsequent chapters the concepts of time and frequency domain analysis will be developed further.

$$G(z) = \frac{z}{(z - \frac{1}{2} - j\frac{1}{2})(z - \frac{1}{2} + j\frac{1}{2})}$$

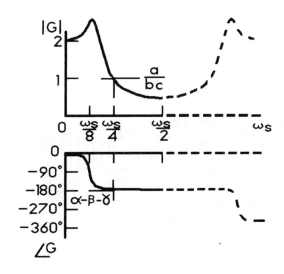

$$\omega T = \frac{\pi}{2} \text{ radians}$$
$$(\omega = \frac{\omega_s}{4})$$

$$\left| G(e^{j\omega T}) \right| = \frac{a}{bc}$$

$$\angle G(e^{j\omega T}) = \alpha - (\beta + \gamma)$$

Figure 1.9   Derivation of spectra from the z-plane.

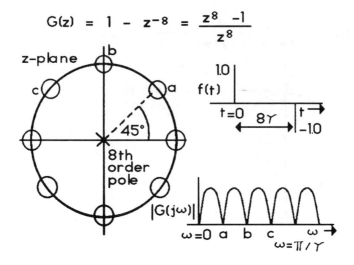

Figure 1.10   Pole-zero plot for $G(z) = 1 - z^{-8}$ with the corresponding time function and spectrum.

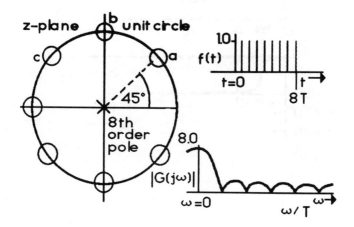

Figure 1.11   As Figure 1.10 with the zero at $z = 1$ removed.

Chapter 2
FOURIER SERIES
AND
FOURIER TRANSFORMS

2.1 FOURIER SERIES

The exponential Fourier series expansion [Oppenheim Willsky & Young] of a periodic signal $f(t)$ is defined as:

$$f(t) = \sum_{n=-\infty}^{\infty} F(n) e^{j2\pi n f_o t} \tag{2.1}$$

where $\omega_o = 2\pi f_o = \dfrac{2\pi}{T}$, and T is the period of the signal $f(t)$. This states that $f(t)$ can be expressed as a linear combination or weighted sum of phasors at frequencies $f = nf_o = 0, \pm f_o, \pm 2f_o, \ldots\ldots$ where the weighting factors, $F(n)$, are given by:-

$$F(n) \triangleq \frac{1}{T} \int_{-T/2}^{T/2} f(t) e^{-j2\pi n f_o t} \, dt \tag{2.2}$$

This implies that a periodic signal (over $\pm T/2$) contains only those frequency components which are integer multiples of the fundamental frequency $f_o = \dfrac{1}{T}$, i.e. all frequencies are harmonics of the fundamental, Figure 2.1. This gives rise to certain properties of the Fourier representation of periodic signals.

1. Implies that $f(t)$ is periodic over the interval $\pm T/2$,

2. All frequencies are harmonics of the fundamental i.e. spectral lines spaced by f_o,

3. The d.c. component of $f(t)$ is measured by the $F(0)$ term,

4. If $f(t)$ is real and even, i.e. $f(-t) = f(t)$ then $F(n)$ is purely real,

5. If $f(t)$ is real and odd, i.e. $f(-t) = -f(t)$ then $F(n)$ is purely imaginary.

To illustrate the application of Fourier series let us evaluate the line spectrum of the rectangular pulse train shown in Figure 2.2. Here

$$f(t) = A, \quad |t| \leq \frac{\tau}{2} \tag{2.3}$$

$$= 0, \quad |t| > \frac{\tau}{2}$$

i.e. $f(t)$ has amplitude A and duration τ, and waveform repeats with period T. We can evaluate $F(n)$ by integrating over the interval $-T/2$ to $+T/2$ for this repetitive waveform.

$$F(n) = \frac{1}{T} \int_{-T/2}^{T/2} f(t) e^{-jn\omega_o t} \, dt \tag{2.4}$$

$$= \frac{1}{T} \int_{-\tau/2}^{\tau/2} A \, e^{-jn\omega_o t} \, dt$$

$$= \frac{-A}{jn\omega_o T} \left(e^{-jn\omega_o \tau/2} - e^{jn\omega_o \tau/2} \right)$$

$$= \frac{A}{jn\omega_o T} \sin(n\omega_o \tau/2) \, 2j \tag{2.5}$$

(N.B. $\int e^{\alpha t} \, dt = \frac{1}{\alpha} e^{\alpha t}$ and $e^{j\phi} - e^{-j\phi} = 2j \sin(\phi)$.)

Hence

$$F(n) = \frac{A\tau}{T} \frac{\sin(n\omega_o \tau/2)}{(n\omega_o \tau/2)}$$

$$= \frac{A\tau}{T} \frac{\sin(x)}{x} \tag{2.6}$$

where $x = n\omega_o \tau/2$.

Thus the real part of the Fourier series, which defines the line spectrum, has values spaced apart by $f_o = \frac{1}{T}$ and the envelope is controlled by the $\frac{\sin(x)}{x}$ function. The zeroes of the $\frac{\sin(x)}{x}$ function are controlled by the value of pulse width τ. Figure 2.3(a) shows the resulting line spectrum as would be displayed on a spectrum analyser. Examination of the phase of the Fourier series, Figure 2.3(b) for this real and even signal shows the 180° phase shift in alternate lobes of the $\frac{\sin(x)}{x}$ response, as the true response is negative for alternate lobes. Reducing the width of the pulse, τ, alters the $\frac{\sin(x)}{x}$ envelope response, Figure 2.4, and produces a spectrum with higher frequency components. Hence the necessity for wide

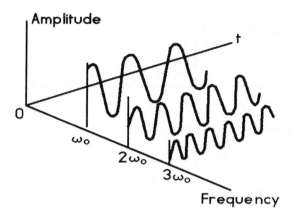

Figure 2.1   Analysis of a periodic signal as a weighted sum of harmonically related sinusoids.

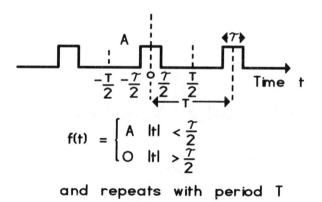

$$f(t) = \begin{cases} A & |t| < \dfrac{\tau}{2} \\ O & |t| > \dfrac{\tau}{2} \end{cases}$$

and repeats with period T

Figure 2.2   Rectangular pulse waveform.

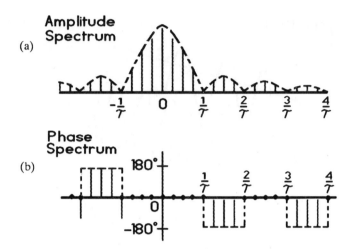

Figure 2.3   Fourier series spectrum for the rectangular pulse waveform: (a) amplitude
spectrum; (b) phase spectrum.

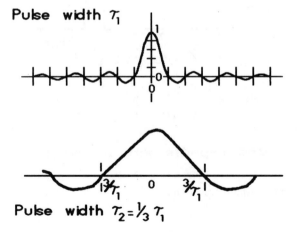

Figure 2.4   Spectra showing the effect of altering the pulse width in the rectangular pulse
waveform.

bandwidth to pass shorter duration pulses.

As an example consider the envelope of the spectrum of the gated pulse:

In the limit as $x \to 0$ radians, $\dfrac{\sin(x)}{x} \to \dfrac{x}{x} = 1$.

The first zero occurs at $\dfrac{\sin(\pi)}{\pi}$ i.e. when $n\omega_o \tau/2 = \pi$

or equivalently when $2\pi f \tau/2 = \pi$, that is at a frequency $f = \dfrac{1}{\tau}$.

The second zero occurs at $\dfrac{\sin(2\pi)}{2\pi}$, i.e. $f = \dfrac{2}{\tau}$.

The occupied bandwidth is therefore inversely proportional to the width of the pulse, τ. For example $\tau = 1$ ms gives a 1st zero at ± 1 kHz whereas $\tau = 1$ μs gives a 1st zero at ± 1 MHz.

2.2 THE FOURIER TRANSFORM

The Fourier transform may be considered as a development of the Fourier series where the period T is progressively increased reducing the fundamental frequency making the spectrum more dense. The overall shape of the spectrum is not altered as this is controlled by the shape of the waveform. As T becomes very large the discrete lines merge and the spectrum becomes continuous to give the direct or forward Fourier transform $F(\omega)$, this is illustrated in Figure 2.5.

$$F(\omega) = \int_{-\infty}^{+\infty} f(t)\, e^{-j\omega t}\, dt \qquad (2.7)$$

There is also a related expression called the inverse Fourier transform which recovers the original time domain waveform.

$$f(t) = F^{-1}(F(\omega)) = \frac{1}{2\pi} \int_{-\infty}^{+\infty} F(\omega)\, e^{j\omega t}\, d\omega \qquad (2.8)$$

The Fourier transform may alternatively be considered as a restriction of the Laplace transform to the $j\omega$ axis, i.e. replacing s by $j\omega$ in:

$$F(s) = \int_{0}^{\infty} f(t)\, e^{-st}\, dt \qquad (2.9)$$

A table of some typical Fourier transform pairs [Spiegel] is given in Table 2.1 with a graphical illustration in Figure 2.6.

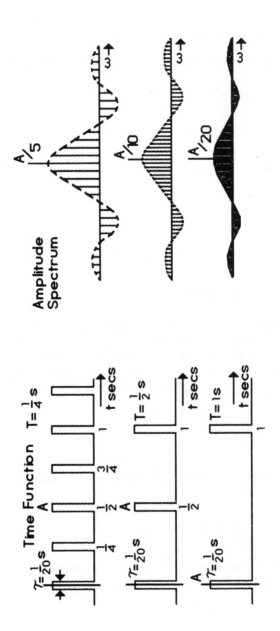

Figure 2.5   Spectra for various repetition frequencies of the rectangular pulse waveform.

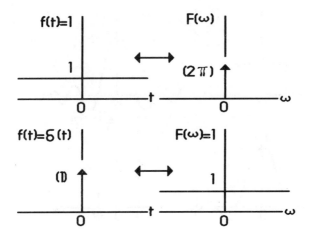

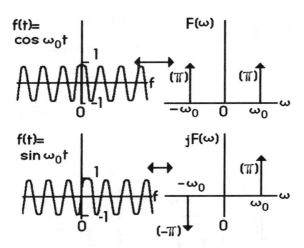

Figure 2.6(a)   Fourier transform pairs for some common signal types.

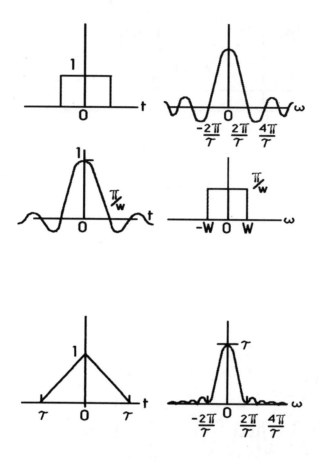

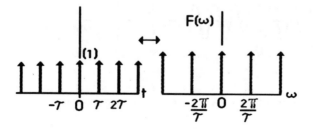

Figure 2.6(b)   Fourier transform pairs for some common signal types.

$f(t)$	$F(\omega)$
$\delta(t)$ (impulse)	1
1	$2\pi\delta(\omega)$
$e^{\pm j\omega_o t}$	$2\pi\delta(\omega \overline{+} \omega_o)$
$cos(\omega_o t)$	$\pi[\,\delta(\omega-\omega_o) + \delta(\omega+\omega_o)\,]$
$sin(\omega_o t)$	$-j\pi[\,\delta(\omega-\omega_o) - \delta(\omega+\omega_o)\,]$
$rect(t)$	$\dfrac{sin(\omega/2)}{\omega/2}$
$rect\left(\dfrac{t}{\tau}\right)$	$\tau\,\dfrac{sin(\omega\tau/2)}{\omega\tau/2}$
$\dfrac{\omega}{2}\dfrac{sin(\omega t/2)}{\omega t/2}$	$rect(\omega/2)$
$\Lambda(t)$ (triangular)	$\left(\dfrac{sin(\omega/2)}{\omega/2}\right)^2$
$\Lambda\left(\dfrac{t}{\tau}\right)$	$\tau\left(\dfrac{sin(\omega\tau/2)}{\omega\tau/2}\right)^2$
$\sum_n \delta(t-nT)$ (impulse train)	$\dfrac{2\pi}{T}\sum_n \delta(\omega-\dfrac{2\pi n}{T})$

Table 2.1 Functions of time and their Fourier transforms.

2.3 THE DISCRETE FOURIER TRANSFORM

In a similar manner to the development of the Fourier transform we may derive its equivalent form for sampled data, known as the discrete Fourier transform (DFT) [Rabiner & Gold]. Starting with the z-transform:

$$X(z) = \sum_{n=o}^{N-1} x_n\, z^{-n} \qquad\qquad (2.10)$$

and constraining this to the z-plane unit circle yields

$$X(m) = \sum_{n=0}^{N-1} x_n \, e^{-j\frac{2\pi mn}{N}}, \qquad 0 < m < N-1$$

which maps a set of N time sampled signals into N transformed points which provide the discrete Fourier transform, Table 2.2. The DFT is discussed further in chapter 11.

	Continuous-Time	Sampled Data
Discrete Frequencies	$F(n) = \dfrac{1}{T} \displaystyle\int_{-T/2}^{T/2} f(t) \, e^{-jn\omega_o t} \, dt$ $f(t) = \displaystyle\sum_{n=-\infty}^{\infty} F(n) \, e^{jn\omega_o t}$ *Fourier Series*	$F(m) = \displaystyle\sum_{n=0}^{N-1} f(n) \, e^{-j\frac{2\pi nm}{N}}$ $f(n) = \dfrac{1}{N} \displaystyle\sum_{m=0}^{N-1} F(m) \, e^{j\frac{2\pi mn}{N}}$ *Discrete Fourier Transform*
Continuous Frequency	$F(\omega) = \displaystyle\int_{-\infty}^{\infty} f(t) \, e^{-j\omega t} \, dt$ $f(t) = \dfrac{1}{2\pi} \displaystyle\int_{-\infty}^{\infty} F(\omega) \, e^{j\omega t} \, d\omega$ *Fourier Transform*	*Discrete-Time Fourier Transform*

Table 2.2 Transform techniques applied to continuous and sampled time and frequency.

TUTORIAL Laplace, z and Fourier Transforms.

1.   For the function $G(z) = \dfrac{z^2 + 2z + 1}{z^3}$ sketch the z plane pole zero diagram and the time and frequency domain responses, the latter in amplitude and phase.

2.   Sketch the pole zero configuration for the function $G(z) = \dfrac{(1-z^4)}{(1+z^2)z^2}$, and check your result by simplifying the function directly. What form does the time domain response take for the above function $G(z)$?

3. Sketch the time domain waveforms and frequency spectra for an on-off keyed pulse train on a 10 kHz carrier frequency with 1 ms pulse duration at the following pulse repetition periods, 10 ms, 2 ms, 1.1 ms (the Fourier transform of rectangular pulse may be assumed).

4. (a) Find the Fourier transform of the signal $f(t) = e^{-at}$ which exists for $t > 0$.

(b) Extend this into the signals

$$f(t) = \begin{cases} e^{at}, & t < 0 \\ e^{-at}, & t > 0 \end{cases}$$

and (c)

$$f(t) = \begin{cases} -e^{at}, & t < 0 \\ e^{-at}, & t > 0 \end{cases}$$

$$\left[\frac{1}{a + j\omega}, \frac{2a}{a^2 + \omega^2}, \frac{-2j\omega}{a^2 + \omega^2} \right] \quad (\int e^{at} dt = \frac{1}{\alpha} e^{at})$$

5. The network shown in (a) of the Figure below is known as a *shunt peaking* network. Show that the impedance has the form

$$Z(s) = \frac{K(s - z_1)}{(s - p_1)(s - p_2)}$$

and determine z_1, p_1, and p_2 in terms of R, L and C. If the poles and zero of $Z(s)$ have the locations shown in (b) of the figure with $Z(j0) = 1$ find the values for R, L and C.

(a)   (b)

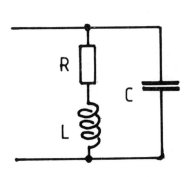

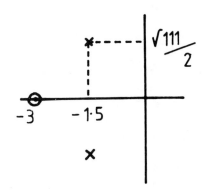

Chapter 3
FREQUENCY AND TIME DOMAIN ANALYSIS

3.1 INTRODUCTION

The oscilloscope permits a time domain observation of signals and system responses. Many phenomena are traditionally analysed in the time domain. The impulse response of a filter, the step response of a servo system and the electrocardiographic (ECG) waveform produced by heart muscle activity are three common examples. There are also many phenomena which yield more useful information when observed in the frequency domain on a spectrum analyser or the joint application of time and frequency domain analysis may be appropriate. Time domain observation of the output from an AM radio station may easily reveal overmodulation while frequency domain observation will more easily yield information about carrier frequency and signal bandwidth. The engineer will choose to analyse the phenomena in whichever domain most easily reveals the information which he requires. He does not find different information in the two domains merely different manifestations of the same information. A system or signal can be characterised completely in the time domain and its frequency domain characterisation deduced by a Fourier or Laplace transform of the time domain function. Application of the inverse transform will bring the description back into the time domain.

3.2 SIGNAL ANALYSIS IN THE TIME AND FREQUENCY

Arbitrary signals, even if they are periodic, are too difficult a subject for theoretical analysis since we cannot write mathematical expressions for them in either domain. Consider a short section of recorded speech made periodic by playback on a continuous tape loop. Formulation of a theoretical equation is a hopeless task although the signal may be easily studied at a practical level using an audio frequency spectrum analyser. For the purposes of practical analysis we confine ourselves to signals which are easily generated such as the periodic waveforms obtained from a function generator with the very simplest type, the sinewave, being the most useful. For example frequency responses (Bode plots) are plotted for the practical characterisation of systems in terms of their steady state response to sinusoids. In mathematical analysis however there is a signal closely related to the sinusoid which is simpler to manipulate and hence even more useful than the sinusoid. That is the exponential function $e^{j\theta}$.

3.3 PHASOR REPRESENTATION OF SIGNALS

The function $e^{j\theta}$ describes a unit amplitude vector at an angle θ in a polar coordinate system. When $\theta = \omega t$ the vector rotates at ω radians/second. A rotating vector is called a phasor. The complex conjugate of $e^{j\omega t}$ is $e^{-j\omega t}$, an identical phasor rotating in the opposite (clockwise) direction. The vector sum of this pair moves along the real axis of a complex plane (Figure 3.1(a)). If this resultant is applied to the y input of an oscilloscope and viewed on a suitable timebase we see a cosinewave of peak amplitude 2. i.e.

$$\frac{1}{2} (e^{j\omega t} + e^{-j\omega t}) = cos (\omega t) \tag{3.1}$$

If we multiply the complex conjugate of $e^{j\omega t}$ by -1 and sum vectorially we produce a resultant whose amplitude varies sinusoidally along the imaginary axis of the complex plane, i.e.

$$\frac{1}{2} (e^{j\omega t} - e^{-j\omega t}) = j \, sin (\omega t) \tag{3.2}$$

Hence we should regard a real sinusoidal signal (in this case $cos (\omega t)$) as the vector sum of two complex conjugate phasors. The pair of identities (3.1) and (3.2) are the Euler equations [Spiegel]. At this point we should consider the concept of negative frequencies.

The phasor $e^{j\omega t}$ rotates in an anticlockwise direction in the complex plane of Figure 3.1. It represents a positive frequency $+\omega$. Its complex conjugate rotates in the opposite (clockwise) direction and may be regarded as representing a negative frequency $-\omega$. This model leads to two sided frequency spectra for signals as can be seen from Figure 3.2 which shows the phasor representation of $cos (\omega t)$ (Figure 3.2(a)) and $jsin (\omega t)$ (Figure 3.2 (b)) respectively in the frequency domain. Note the impulses represent *phasors not sinewaves*. You cannot have a negative frequency sinewave, but you can have a negative frequency phasor as defined above. The plot is actually the Fourier transform of the signals $F(x(t))$ and constitutes a complex Fourier series expansion for the time domain expression. In this case the expansion is somewhat trivial as it only involves 2 terms. Figure 3.3 shows a phasor construction of the first half cycle of a square wave using appropriately scaled and phased complex conjugate pairs. Only the first few harmonics are shown for simplicity. This is a graphical illustration of the representation of a simple periodic time domain waveform in terms of a complex Fourier series expansion using phasors. In general the complex Fouriers series expansion of $f(t)$ is:-

$$f (t) = \sum_{n = -\infty}^{\infty} F(n) \, e^{jn \omega_o t} \tag{3.3}$$

where

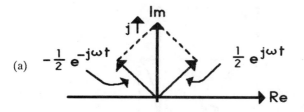

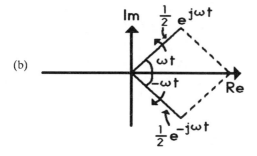

Figure 3.1   Phasor diagrams showing the construction of (a) a sinusoid and (b) a cosinusoid.

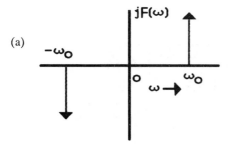

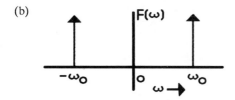

Figure 3.2   Spectra of (a) a sinusoid and (b) cosinusoid.

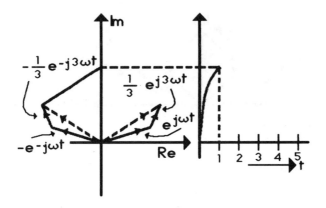

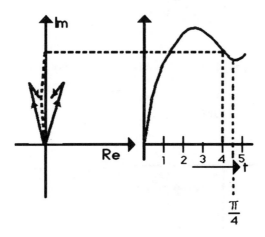

Figure 3.3   Phasor construction of a square wave using a 2-term Fourier series expansion

$$F(n) = \frac{1}{T} \int_{-T/2}^{T/2} f(t) e^{-jn\omega_o t} \, dt \qquad (3.4)$$

$F(n)$, the nth Fourier coefficient, is the amplitude of the complex conjugate phasor pair rotating at $n\omega_o$ rad./sec. For the case of Figure 3.2(a) where $f(t) = cos(\omega_o t)$ then $F(1) = F(-1) = +\frac{1}{2}$ and $F(n) = 0, n \neq \pm 1$ [Oppenheim Willsky & Young].

3.4 ORTHOGONALITY

Each element of the expansion of $f(t)$ is orthogonal to every other element in the expansion. i.e. by the definition of orthogonality when $f(t)$ is equivalent to the nth Fourier coefficient then:-

$$\frac{1}{T} \int_{-T/2}^{T/2} e^{jm\omega_o t} e^{-jn\omega_o t} \, dt = \begin{cases} 1, & m = n \\ 0, & m \neq n \end{cases} \qquad (3.5)$$

This is a useful property for any series expansion of a function since it enables each coefficient to be evaluated independent of every other coefficient. Thus the Fourier series expansion of a periodic function is in terms of an orthogonal set of "basis" functions.

There are many sets of orthogonal functions which could be used in series expansions. The Walsh functions are one example. Figure 3.4 shows sets of orthogonal Fourier and Walsh basis functions. The advantage of a transform or mapping based on Walsh functions is that they have binary magnitudes which simplifies multiplication (chapter 17). Unfortunately the transform domain is not the "frequency" domain which we enter with the Fourier transform. This complicates signal interpretation in the transform domain but if fast convolution is the ultimate aim this is no drawback.

The principle of orthogonality is not confined to orthonormal basis function sets such as the set of harmonically related sinewaves used in Fourier series expansions. Orthogonality is an important concept in signal design for transmission systems. They key concept in this context is that the cross correlation coefficient between two waveforms zero if they are orthogonal.

3.5 CROSSCORRELATION AND AUTOCORRELATION

This concept is widely used when dealing with two random processes in order to determine if they are independent or if there is some connection between them. The cross correlation coefficient is denoted by $r_{fg}(\tau)$:-

$$r_{fg}(\tau) = \int_{-\infty}^{\infty} f^*(t) g(t + \tau) \, dt \qquad (3.6)$$

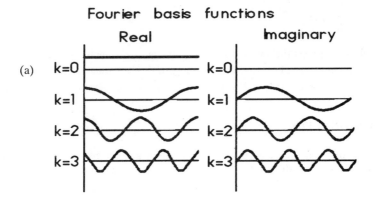

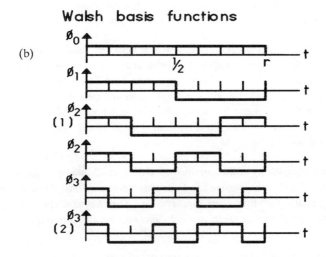

Figure 3.4   Orthogonal basis functions: (a) Fourier basis functions; (b) Walsh basis functions.

$$= E[f^*(t)\,g(t + \tau)]$$

where $E[\,.\,]$ is the statistical expectation operator, $f(t)$ and $g(t)$ are two random processes or two (periodic) waveforms, the superscript * denotes the complex conjugate operation and τ is a shift parameter used to slide the two waveforms through each other when looking for a match or correlation peak. If the process is applied to two versions of the same waveform (i.e. transmitted and locally generated versions) then the process is referred to as autocorrelation and receivers based on this principle are known as correlation receivers. Correlation receivers are also referred to as matched filters since they maximise the signal to additive noise ratio at the instant of recognition of the received waveform. This feature makes them very useful for the detection and recognition of signals which are masked by additive noise (chapter 20).

As an example of the use of autocorrelation consider the periodic square wave shown in Figure 3.5(a) with autocorrelation function $r_{xx}(\tau)$ shown in Figure 3.5(b). Figure 3.5(c) shows a bandlimited random noise waveform $n(t)$ with autocorrelation function $r_{nn}(\tau)$ (Figure 3.5(d)). If these two waveforms are added to give $y(t) = x(t) + n(t)$ (Figure 3.5(e)) and the autocorrelation function of this waveform is obtained (Figure 3.5(f)) we see that the autocorrelation function of the square wave is clearly recognisable even though the square wave was "buried" in the additive noise. A drawback with the use of autocorrelation to find the square wave is that the autocorrelation function of the noise is also present in the output and our template or reference signal is also contaminated by noise.

A correlation receiver looking for a known signal in additive noise would normally use crosscorrelation of the received noisy signal against a clean replica generated in the receiver. Assume the transmitted signal $x(t)$ to be the random waveform shown in Figure 3.6(a). Assume that it is time delayed to t_o secs. and added to a second random waveform $n(t)$ (i.e. noise or another message) to produce $y(t) = x(t - t_o) + n(t)$. Figure 3.6(b) shows $y(t)$. Crosscorrelation of $y(t)$ with $x(t)$ produces $r_{xy}(\tau)$ (Figure 3.6(c)). The correlation peak or instant of recognition of the received signal by the receiver is clearly visible and the delay may be measured. It is the characteristic of a random or noisy signal that its autocorrelation function has the shape, Figure 3.6(c). Other synthetic or pseudo noise signals are designed to reflect this autocorrelation function, chapter 20.

Autocorrelation and crosscorrelation are powerful signal analysis tools in analytical and practical work. It is interesting to note that the power spectrum of a signal is the Fourier transform of its autocorrelation function, chapter 13. Alternatively the autocorrelation function is the inverse Fourier transform of power spectrum. These are useful relationships when characterising random signals and noise.

3.6 SIGNALS AND SYSTEMS

So far we have looked at signals and their characteristics in the time and frequency domains. It is equally important to be able to predict what will happen to a signal when it is

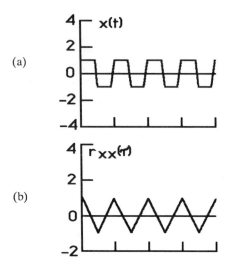

Figure 3.5   Square wave: (a) time domain representation; (b) autocorrelation function.

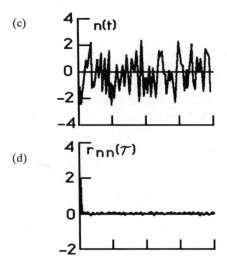

Figure 3.5   White noise: (c) time domain representation; (d) autocorrelation function.

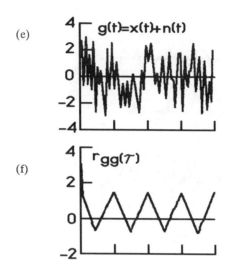

(e)

(f)

Figure 3.5   Square wave plus white noise: (e) time domain representation; (f) autocorrelation function.

passed through a system such as a filter. For simplicity we must confine ourselves to linear systems which do not vary with time. This covers the majority of commonly encountered analogue circuits with rectifiers (envelope detectors) and all forms of mixers being notable exceptions. These are nonlinear devices and our theory does not apply.

3.7 CONVOLUTION

In addition to characterising a network via its frequency response or transfer function we can also characterise it by its impulse response, i.e. response to a unit impulse. Exciting a network by the unit impulse:-

$$i(t) = \delta(t - \tau)$$

where τ represents a delay variable, gives and output $h(t)$ known as the network impulse response which characterises the network. The output $g(t)$ for any other input waveform $f(t)$ is given by the *convolution* of $f(t)$ with $h(t)$ i.e.

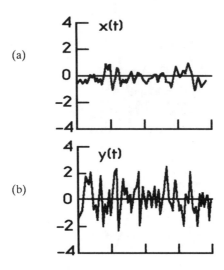

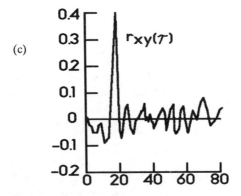

Figure 3.6   Crosscorrelation of a random signal plus noise: (a) random signal; (b) random signal plus noise; (c) crosscorrelation of (a) with (b).

$$g(t) = \int_{-\infty}^{+\infty} f(\tau)\, h(t-\tau)\, d\tau$$

This convolution integral is often written as

$$g(t) = f(t) * h(t)$$

The convolution integral can be represented graphically as a progressive sliding of the input signal $f(t)$ over the impulse response $h(t)$ for different relative delays between the two waveforms and integrating or summing the overlapped voltages. It should be noted that convolution is very similar to correlation except that one of the waveforms is time reversed. An important property of the Fourier transform is that it reduces the convolution integral operator to an algebraic product (multiplication). Thus to obtain the convolution of $f(t)$ with $h(t)$, we can transform $h(t)$ into $H(\omega)$ and $f(t)$ into $F(\omega)$, multiply the transformed signals to obtain the output $G(\omega)$ i.e.

$$G(\omega) = F(\omega)\, H(\omega)$$

and inverse transform $G(\omega)$ to obtain the time domain output $g(t)$.

Figure 3.7 shows the application of this technique in the simple case of evaluating the response of a low-pass filter to a rectangular pulse. This may be done by either convolving the input with the filter impulse response or by multiplying their respective spectra and inverse transforming the resultant spectrum.

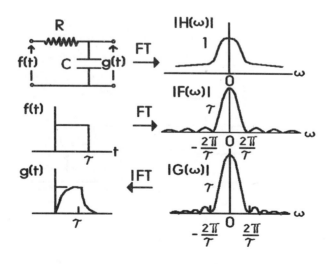

Figure 3.7   Magnitude response of a low-pass filter

TUTORIAL Frequency and Time Domain Analysis

1. Sketch the convolution $f_1(t) * f_2(t)$ of the following waveforms.

(a) $f_1(t), f_2(t)$

(b) $f_1(t), f_2(t)$

(c) $f_1(t)$

$f_2(t)$

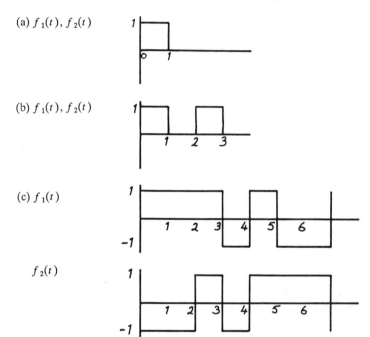

2. Sketch the convolution of each of the following waveforms with $h(t)$.

(a) $f_1(t)$

(b) $f_2(t)$

(c) $f_3(t)$

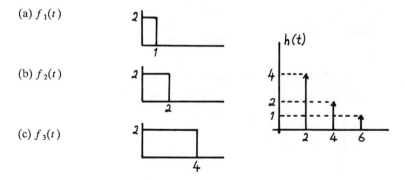

3. Derive and sketch the transfer function for a simple RC low-pass filter. Find the response of this circuit to an input pulse amplitude A volts and width τ secs using time domain analysis.

Chapter 4
SAMPLING, ALIASING
AND
DATA CONVERSION

4.1 INTRODUCTION

In this chapter the important subjects of analogue to digital conversion (ADC) and digital to analogue conversion (DAC) are addressed. This is an area which involves skills and techniques from both the analogue and digital domains. The chapter begins with explanations of the sampling process, the Nyquist criterion for sampling low-pass and band-pass processes and the aliasing phenomenon. Analogies are then invoked for ADC's and DAC's followed by a discussion of sample and hold (S & H) devices and six different converter types. Finally non-ideal ADC's and their effects in signal processing applications are considered.

As digital signal processing replaces analogue processing the need arises for analogue to digital and digital to analogue conversion either side of the digital processor. The advantages of digital processors are flexibility (programmability), they are stable (repeatable) and they tend to have large dynamic range in relation to their analogue counterparts. For instance, digital audio tape recorders have a typical 72 dB dynamic range as opposed to some 45 dB for analogue recorders. Analogue processing, on the otherhand, often has a considerable size and power advantage over its digital counterpart.

4.2 SAMPLING AND ALIASING

Figure 4.1(a) shows an arbitrary analogue voltage signal. In Figure 4.1(b) a sampling waveform is illustrated as a uniform train of equally spaced impulses. Conceptually the sampled version of the analogue signal, Figure 4.1(c), is obtained by multiplying the waveforms of Figure 4.1(a) and Figure 4.1(b) together. The analogue signal can be reconstructed from the sampled version using a reconstruction (low-pass) filter. The reconstructed version is shown in Figure 4.1(d). For the case of perfect reconstruction the only difference between Figure 4.1(a) and Figure 4.1(d) would be a slight processing delay. Perfect reconstruction, however, requires a brick-wall (perfect low-pass) filter. This is impossible to realise in practice, so we have to accept a realisable approximation. If a perfect, brick-wall filter could be achieved it would have a sinc function $(sin(x)/x)$ impulse response and so the reconstructed analogue signal of Figure 4.1(d) would simply be a weighted sum of sinc functions, each one being raised on the corresponding sample from Figure 4.1(c). The question arises, at what rate should sampling occur and is there a minimum sample rate?

The guiding rule here is known as the Nyquist criterion which has two forms. The more common form is called the Nyquist baseband criterion. The baseband criterion (4.1) states that we must sample at a rate which is as least twice the highest frequency in the signal.

$$f_s \geq 2f_m \qquad\qquad\qquad\qquad (4.1)$$

Where f_s is the sample rate and f_m is the maximum frequency component of the baseband signal. Ensuring the validity of (4.1) requires use of analogue filters known as anti-aliasing filters. There is an equivalent statement for narrow band-pass processes. For the band-pass process case, the sample rate, f_s, is given by the inequality:

$$f_s \geq 2f_B \qquad\qquad\qquad\qquad (4.2)$$

where f_B is the bandwidth of the band-pass process. The consequences of not meeting the the Nyquist criteria are discussed with the aid of Figure 4.2.

Figure 4.2 shows a typical low-pass signal spectrum with a single sided bandwidth B Hz. The sampling pulse train is shown with period T. The sampling process, as previously stated, can be regarded as a multiplication of the sampling impulse train and the time domain waveform. When the two waveforms are multiplied in the time domain, this is equivalent to convolving their Fourier transforms in the frequency domain. If the Fourier transform of the signal (shown here in power spectrum form) is convolved with the Fourier transform of the sampling impulse train (which itself is an impulse train with impulses at f_s, $2f_s$ etc), then one of the three cases shown in Figure 4.2(a), Figure 4.2(b) and Figure 4.2(c) will result. If the sample rate is greater than $2B$ (that is, if the sampling rate exceeds the Nyquist sampling rate), then the result is Figure 4.2(a) which consists of replicas of the baseband spectrum at baseband, f_s, $2f_s$, $3f_s$ etc. Notice that, since the Nyquist sampling rate is exceeded there is a "guard-band", which ensures no overlap between the spectra. If, on the other hand if sampling is at the Nyquist rate (sample rate equals twice the bandwidth of the signal), then the resulting situation is shown in the Figure 4.2(b). Here, the successive spectra are just touching so the guard-band width has reduced to zero. This situation is still acceptable providing perfect reconstruction filtering is employed. This is, in practice, not achievable. The third case, shown here in Figure 4.2(c), is where the sample rate is less than $2B$. Here the sampling rate has not meet the Nyquist sampling criterion and the adjacent spectra overlap. This is a disastrous situation because, once it happens, it is irretrievable.

There are two common pitfalls to be avoided in signal conversion. The first is trying to use a sampled-data type anti-aliasing filter (such as a switch-capacitor filter). This, being a sampled data system in its own right, requires an anti-aliasing filter. The second pitfall lies in not using an adequate reconstruction filter following a DAC. This is a particular temptation

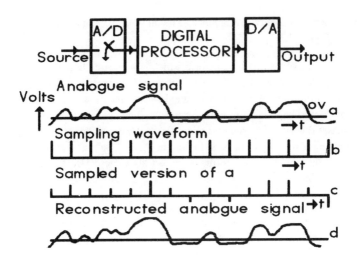

Figure 4.1   Sampling and reconstructing an analogue waveform.

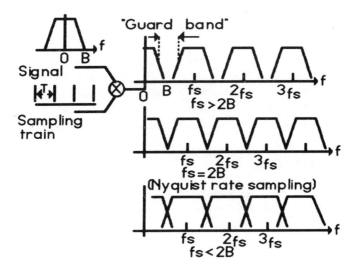

Figure 4.2   The Nyquist criterion viewed in the frequency domain.

where the signal has been highly oversampled. The aliasing phenomenon is now considered in the time domain (Figure 4.3).

Figure 4.3 shows five cycles of a sinewave which is substantially under sampled producing just 6 samples. The Nyquist criterion has not been met. When the sinewave is reconstructed, the reconstruction filter output will follow the low frequency sinusoid illustrated. In this example the input signal has aliased to a much lower frequency. In fact, the region between nf_s and $(n+1)f_s$ aliases down to the primary region d.c. (0 Hz) to f_s for all n. Furthermore, for a single ADC sampling a real signal there is folding at $f_s/2$. That is, a sinewave at a frequency just below the sampling rate aliases to a frequency just above zero Hz. Aliasing is a property of the sampling process and is not confined to ADC's. The generality of the problem is illustrated in Figure 4.4.

Figure 4.4 shows an example of a sampled data system in the form of a pulse-Doppler radar. The radar transmitter is ground based and transmits a train of pulses with a pulse repetition interval (PRI) as indicated. The objective is to determine the component of velocity of the aircraft in the direction of the radar. This velocity is $V \cos(\theta)$ where V is the velocity of the aircraft and θ is the angle between the aircraft's velocity vector and a line from the aircraft to the radar. The Doppler shift on the backscattered radar signal is denoted by f_d as shown on the diagram and λ is the wavelength of the radar signal. Assume θ is zero, so that the aircraft is flying directly towards to radar, that it has a velocity of 300 metres per second (which is approximately 600 miles per hour) and that $\lambda = 0.03$ metres. We find that the Doppler shift created by the target motion is approximately 20 kHz. Since this is a sampled data system, as the transmission is not continuous but pulsed, then the minimum sampling rate is 40 kHz to prevent aliasing of the target velocity. This means that the PRI must be the inverse of (at least) 40 kHz.

Figure 4.5 illustrates a typical digital processing system. An analogue input is being fed to a S & H device. The output of this is fed to an ADC which would typically be 16-bit or less. This, in turn, feeds the digital processor which would typically incorporate 16 or 32-bit fixed point or floating point arithmetic. The output from the digital processor is fed to a DAC and finally, the DAC output is passed through a reconstruction filter before analogue display.

4.3 ADC/DAC ANALOGIES

Figure 4.6 shows a DAC being modelled as a simple potentiometer connected between zero volts and a reference voltage (V_{ref}), which represents the full scale output from the device. The digital input to the DAC is normally an 8,10,12,14 or 16-bit word and is shown operating the wiper of the potentiometer to create an analogue output which is a digitally controlled fraction of V_{ref}. This reflects the simplicity of the DAC process compared with the ADC process which is now modelled.

The model for the ADC (Figure 4.7) incorporates this DAC model in a feedback loop. This is typical of ADC converter realisations in practice. Figure 4.7 shows an analogue input to

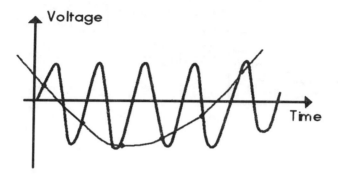

Figure 4.3   Aliasing caused by undersampling.

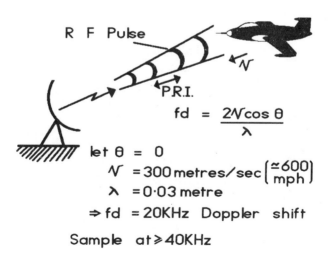

$$fd = \frac{2 \mathcal{N} \cos \theta}{\lambda}$$

let $\theta = 0$

$\mathcal{N} = 300$ metres/sec $\left(\begin{array}{c}\approx 600 \\ \text{mph}\end{array}\right)$

$\lambda = 0.03$ metre

$\Rightarrow fd = 20$KHz Doppler shift

Sample at $\geqslant 40$KHz

Figure 4.4   The Nyquist criterion applied to a pulse-Doppler radar.

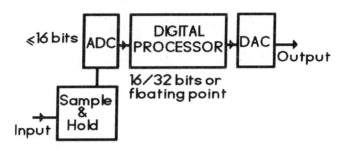

Figure 4.5   A typical digital signal processing facility.

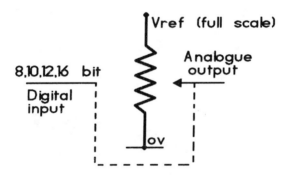

Figure 4.6   A simple digital-to-analogue converter analogy.

a comparator. The output of the comparator feeds a code selector which in turn controls a DAC. This DAC is part of a feedback loop to the comparator. Thus the ADC process is iterative which explains why it is approximately an order of magnitude slower than the corresponding DAC process.

4.4 ADC/DAC LAYOUT CONSIDERATIONS

Consider the ADC shown in block form in Figure 4.8. It has an analogue input with respect to the analogue ground (Grnd). The analogue reference gives the ADC its knowledge of the standard voltage which it compares with the input. "Start conversion" is an input control line which tells the ADC when to start the conversion process. "Status" is an output control line which indicates end of conversion (output data ready to be transferred). The DAC block is a mirror of the ADC block. It has a digital input which is normally latched into the DAC by a strobe signal. Again, it has an analogue reference, an analogue output and an analogue ground. Notice the number of "ground" pins on these devices. There may be a power ground, a digital ground and an analogue ground. The connection of these is critical if full performance of the device is to be achieved. A common method of connection is to regard the ADC as a bridge between the analogue "world" and the digital "world". Analogue circuitry is built on an analogue earthplane and digital circuitry on a digital earthplane. The analogue ground (Grnd) is connected to the analogue earthplane, and the digital ground to the digital earthplane. A potential link between the two earthplanes is created close to the analogue ground input to the ADC. This minimises the amount of noise from the digital circuitry which gets into the analogue circuitry and the ADC. We should recall that the least significant bit (LSB) of a 16-bit converter is approximately one part in 32,000 of the analogue reference which may only be 2.5 volts. In fact, most 16-bit converters only claim to have 14-bit accuracy in the absolute sense and most 14-bit converters only claim to have 12-bit accuracy.

4.5 SAMPLE AND HOLD DEVICES

Figure 4.9 shows a sinusoidal input to a S & H device. The control input controls the processes of tracking and holding this analogue signal. The conversion cycle begins on the negative edge of the control signal with the S & H device going into its acquisition mode to acquire the input signal. The output of the S & H device follows the path shown and after a time, known as the acquisition time, the voltage on the hold capacitor will be sufficiently close to the analogue input voltage to terminate the acquisition process. On the rising edge of the control input the device goes into hold mode after which conversion begins. Following this rising edge there is a delay while the field effect transistor (FET) switch controlling charging of the capacitor switches off. This delay is known as the aperture time. There are two components to the aperture time, the aperture delay and the aperture jitter. Of the two, the aperture delay is systematic and is not a problem. The aperture jitter, however, is non-systematic and is, in fact, related to the analogue voltage being acquired. This causes the generation of harmonic components which is a problem in high dynamic range systems. S & H devices are available in modular and integrated form and we would expect to pay as much for a

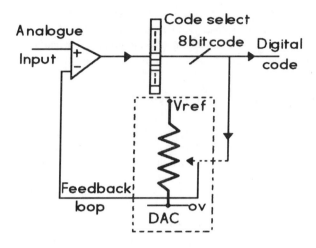

Figure 4.7   An analogue-to-digital converter analogy.

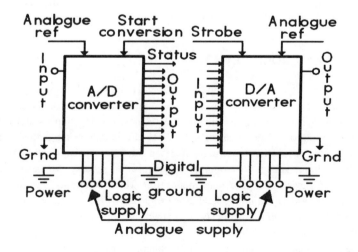

Figure 4.8   Supply, signal and control lines associated with converters.

S & H device as for the ADC which follows it.

With a S & H device the user is required to supply the hold capacitor since its value is a tradeoff between acquisition time and droop rate. Droop occurs, as illustrated in Figure 4.9, during the hold period when charge from the capacitor leaks away. Obviously, it is desirable to minimise the droop rate while the conversion process is continuing and the best way to achieve this is to use a large hold capacitor. Unfortunately, a large capacitor takes longer to charge up and, as a result, requires a longer acquisition time. Hence the tradeoff, which is application dependent. A potential pitfall lies in the choice of the hold capacitor type. Dielectric absorption of charge leads to droop. Absorption rate varies dramatically with the type of capacitor as shown in Figure 4.10. Here we see four capacitor types with varying amounts of dielectric absorption. The ceramic capacitor is the worst, followed by paper and micra. The polystyrene capacitor is the best of the four and is a good choice. It exhibits a very low dielectric absorption rate.

4.6 ADC TYPES

The following 6 ADC types are discussed in the section:

*   sequential comparison;

*   continuous tracking;

*   successive approximation;

*   parallel flash;

*   serial-parallel;

*   dual slope.

The first converters to be considered are the sequential comparison and continuous tracking types. Although they are mainly of academic interest, they are simple and they do illustrate well the main ADC techniques.

Sequential Comparison Converter

Figure 4.11 shows the sequential comparison converter. This comprises of a comparator, an up-counter and a DAC. The DAC is in a feedback loop, which is typical of several ADC types. The analogue input signal is positive unipolar. The conversion cycle is shown in Figure 4.12. The reset pulse starts the conversion process by clearing the counter to zero. A clock then increments the counter in an upward direction and the DAC produces an analogue staircase approximation to a ramp in response to the increasing output from the counter. The comparator maintains a constant comparison between the analogue input voltage and the DAC output. The analogue input signal is shown as being constant here, since it is held in a S & H

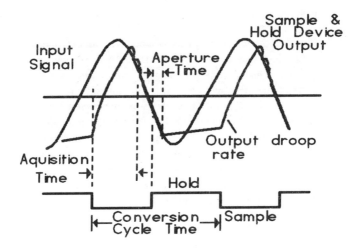

Figure 4.9   Illustration of sample and hold waveforms and parameters.

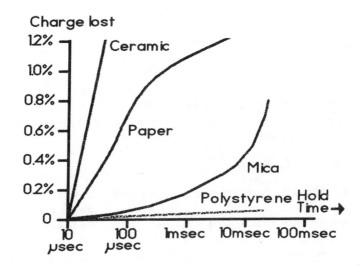

Figure 4.10   Dielectric absorption as a function of time for a range of capacitor types.

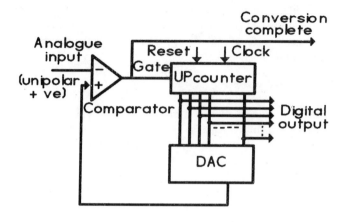

Figure 4.11   Sequential comparison ADC.

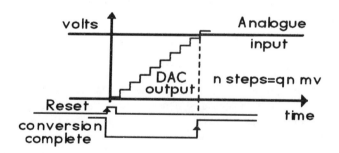

Figure 4.12   Sequential comparison conversion cycle.

device. When the digital ramp (or staircase) exceeds the analogue input voltage, the comparator output changes state and freezes the count in the counter. This signifies the end of conversion. This comparator output can also be used to provide the conversion complete signal, shown at the bottom of this diagram.

The Continuous Tracking Converter

Figure 4.13 illustrates the continuous tracking converter. This technique is similar to but faster than the previous sequential comparison type. The only difference between the sequential comparison and the continuous tracking types is the replacement of the up-counter in the former with an up-down counter in the latter. This leads to removal of the requirement to reset the counter to zero at the beginning of each conversion process. A typical conversion process for the continuous tracking converter is shown in Figure 4.14. Here an arbitrary analogue signal voltage is being tracked by the up-down counter. If the input signal is below the digital output, as seen by the comparator at the DAC output, then the counter is put into count down mode. This example illustrates a case where the analogue input signal is coming down in voltage and the counter counts down four times sequentially. Then there is a period where the analogue input stays constant. During this period the counter flips up and down by one LSB. As the analogue input signal begins to rise again the counter counts upwards to track it. If the analogue input signal rises too quickly, the ADC output cannot follow it. This phenomenon is known as slope-overload and is similar to the slope-overload which occurs in delta modulators for the digital encoding of speech. The sequential comparison and continuous tracking types are mainly of academic interest. The next type is, however, currently the most widely used ADC converter.

The Successive Approximation Converter

Here, as shown in Figure 4.15, the familiar DAC is again present in the feedback loop, but the counters of the previous examples are replaced with control logic and a successive approximation register. The technique used here is to seek the analogue input in a manner analogous to the Newton method of successive bi-section for finding the roots of polynomials. That is, the span of the search field is halved at each step. This is illustrated in Figure 4.16. Here the conversion range from MIN to MAX voltage is depicted and an input voltage is shown just above half range. On the first clock pulse following the signal to start conversion the most significant bit (MSB) in the successive approximation register is put to logic '1'. This causes the output of the DAC to jump to half fullscale. The comparator compares this DAC output voltage with the analogue input voltage and if it finds the analogue input above this voltage, then it retains the MSB at logic '1', as shown here, and on the next clock pulse the second MSB is put a logic '1'. With the MSB already at logic '1' this, in turn, causes the output from the DAC to jump to three-quarters of the full-scale. Again the comparator compares this new threshold with the input voltage and if the input voltage were above this threshold then this second MSB would be left at logic '1'. In this particular example the input voltage is below this new threshold and hence the second MSB is put back down to logic 'zero'. Either way, the next clock pulse tries the third MSB. With each successive clock pulse we are halving the

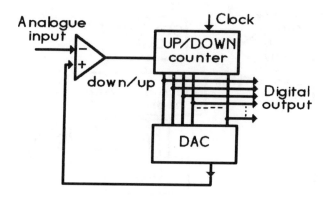

Figure 4.13   Continuous tracking ADC.

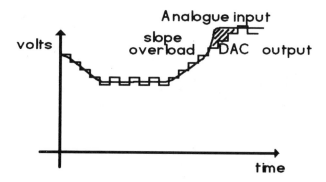

Figure 4.14   Continuous tracking conversion process.

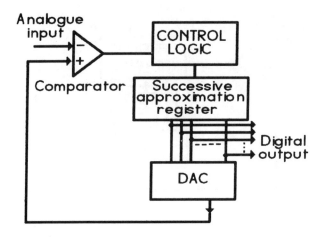

Figure 4.15   Successive approximation ADC.

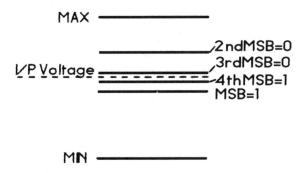

Figure 4.16   Illustration of successive approximation conversion process.

range of conversion. The whole process requires $n+1$ clock pulses for an n bit conversion.

The Parallel Flash Converter

Figure 4.17 illustrates this type with a simple 2-bit converter example. Parallel flash is the fastest conversion technique, with all circuitry being fabricated on a single chip. A reference voltage (V_{ref}) is fed to a potential divider chain comprising equal value resistances. This divider chain creates a set of reference voltages which are equally spaced from zero volts to V_{ref}. For the case of an n-bit converter we require 2^n resistors to produce $2^n - 1$ thresholds. In this example, for clarity, only a 2-bit converter is shown, so there are only 3 thresholds. These are, respectively, $0.25V_{ref}$, $0.5V_{ref}$ and $0.75V_{ref}$. Each threshold goes to a comparator where it is compared with the analogue input voltage, which is fed to all the comparators. If the analogue input voltage to a comparator is above its reference input then its output is at logic '0'. If the analogue input is below its reference voltage its output is at logic '1'. The resulting threshold code is fed decoding logic. This decoding logic converts the threshold code into the requisite n-bit binary code for output from the ADC.

The Serial-Parallel Converter

This is a relatively new type of converter and is rapidly gaining in popularity since it does not require an external clock and it avoids the biggest problem with the n-bit parallel flash converter, that of fabricating $2^n - 1$ comparators on a chip. The serial-parallel converter shown in Figure 4.18 has the further advantage that is has its own on-board S & H devices. In this case two capacitors each charge to the input voltage at the start of the conversion cycle. During conversion time, the voltage on the upper capacitor is fed to a 4-bit parallel flash ADC. The latter, of course, only requires fabrication of 15 comparators and gives a 4-bit output. This 4-bit output is fed to a 4-bit DAC which produces an analogue voltage, one of sixteen possible voltage levels. This voltage is subtracted from the version of the V_{in} held on the lower S & H capacitor. Thus the analogue input voltage is reduced, or localised, to one-sixteenth of the total conversion range at the output of this subtractor. The residue is fed to the second 4-bit converter whose analogue input reference is one-sixteenth of V_{ref} (the overall full range). This 4-bit parallel flash converter performs the fine conversion of the least significant 4-bits. The outputs from both converters are fed into a latch and tristate buffers. Note that as the error is quantised in the second DAC, the first DAC although comprising only 4-bits has to have the accuracy of a full 8-bit design. Expensive variants of this design can incorporate digital correction when the constituent converters have more bits than required at the output. Low-cost devices with conversion times in the region of 1μs to 2μs are available at 8-bit precision, while sophisticated devices achieve 12-bit conversion at 10 to 20 MHz sampling rates.

Dual Ramp Converter

Figure 4.19 illustrates the slowest of all converters, the dual ramp converter. Here, an analogue input voltage from a S & H device is fed to a perfect integrator. At the start of the conversion process the integrator is zeroed, (the capacitor voltage set to zero). Under the influence of the input voltage (unipolar positive) the inverting integrator will ramp downwards.

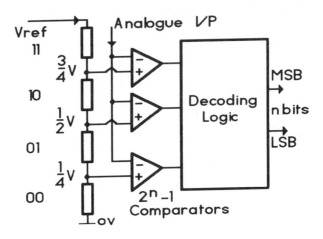

Figure 4.17   Parallel flash converter (2-bit example).

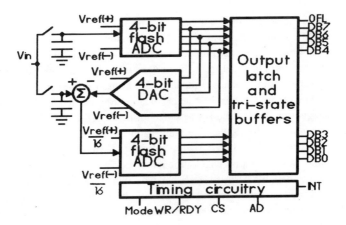

Figure 4.18   Serial-parallel converter (8-bit example).

Figure 4.20 illustrates the conversion process. Here three cases are depicted: Figure 4.20(a) a small input voltage v_1, Figure 4.20(b) a larger voltage v_2, and Figure 4.20(c) a large voltage v_3. The integrator ramps downwards for a predetermined time T. This would normally be 20 milliseconds to minimise any mains hum that may be present on the signal. The mains hum would integrate out over this period (a case of orthogonality by period of integration). At the end of the integration period, the switch at the input to the integrator switches over to the negative reference voltage, (V_{ref}). To this point the capacitor has been discharged at an unknown rate for a known time T. The capacitor is now re-charged at a known rate (under the influence of V_{ref}) for an unknown time. During this time, which is proportional to the input voltage, the comparator will enable the counter to count upwards. The counter, having started at zero, will accumulate a digital count which is proportional to the input voltage. The main use of this type of converter is in digital multimeters and digital panelmeters.

4.7 NON-IDEAL CONVERTERS

Figure 4.21 illustrates the main problems with non-ideal converters. In terms of linearity, an ideal converter has a linear staircase transfer function. The most common deviation from this ideal case is the monotonic non-linearity. A monotonic non-linearity is characterised by a transfer function which deviates from linear but whose slope does not change along its span. A non-monotonic non-linearity is also illustrated. Here, in one region there is a decreasing output in response to an increasing input. This tends to occur at input voltages where many or all of the outputs from the DAC are switching together (from all zeros to all ones for instance) and is due to an accumulation of errors at the switching nodes. Some problems caused by ADC non-linearities will now be considered. The effects of these problems are best illustrated in the frequency domain after applying a discrete Fourier transform.

Effect of Monotonic Non-Linearity

This is illustrated by performing a two-tone test. The ADC is fed with the sum of two sinusoids with amplitudes A_1 and A_2. The transfer function for the converter may be modelled by a power series.

$$V_{out} = \alpha_0 + \alpha_1 V_{in} + \alpha_2 V_{in}^2 + \alpha_3 V_{in}^3 \tag{4.3}$$

An ideal device would have a linear transfer function with all α's being zero, except α_1, which should be 1.0. In this case $V_{out} = V_{in}$. Assume the case where $\alpha_0 = \alpha_3 = 0$ and $\alpha_1 = 1.0$ but α_2 (the coefficient of the second order term) is 0.005. What effect does this have on the output of the ADC? Harmonic and intermodulation terms are created as shown in Table 4.1. The amplitudes of all of these terms are proportional to α_2, the coefficient of the term creating the non-linearity. This would, of course, be a monotonic non-linearity. All output components are shown in Figure 4.22. The only components which should be present are at f_1 and f_2. Another problem lies in the gain balancing of ADCs in cases where the input signals are complex (real and imaginary).

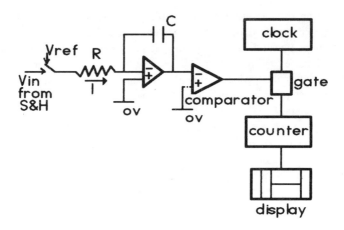

Figure 4.19   Dual ramp converter.

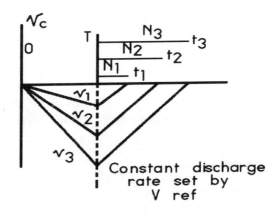

Figure 4.20   Dual ramp converter cycle.

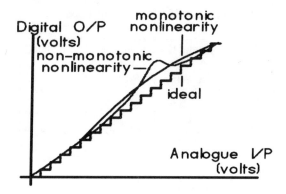

Figure 4.21   Transfer characteristics for ideal and non-ideal ADC/DAC's.

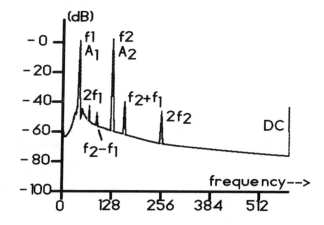

Figure 4.22   Illustration of harmonic and intermodulation products caused by a monotonic non-linearity.

Harmonics		Intermods	
Frequency	Amplitude	Frequency	Amplitude
d.c.	$\alpha_2 \dfrac{(A_1+A_2)}{2}$	f_2+f_1	$\alpha_2 A_1 A_2$
$2f_1$	$\alpha_2 \dfrac{A_1}{2}$	f_2-f_1	$\alpha_2 A_1 A_2$
$2f_2$	$\alpha_2 \dfrac{A_2}{2}$		

Table 4.1 Harmonic and intermodulation products for the monotonic non-linearity example.

ADC Gain Mismatch in I/Q Processors

Figure 4.23 illustrates the problem. The I (inphase) channel is the real channel, while the Q (quadrature) channel is the imaginary channel. The situation occurs in radar and communications. Assume, in this example, that the ADC in the I channel has a gain of 0.99 while the ADC in the Q channel has a gain of 1.00. Also assume that the outputs from these ADC's are going to a discrete Fourier transform (DFT) processor producing a 1024 point transform, since this problem is best viewed in the frequency domain (chapters 11 and 18). Figure 4.24 illustrates what happens to a single sine/cosine pair of unit amplitude. An image is created which is symmetrically disposed about half the sample rate with respect to the input frequency. If the input signal is in bin 127 the image will be 128 bins below the sample rate (bin 1023). This image is only 43 dB below the test signal in this example. Since 16-bit fixed point arithmetic has a dynamic range potential of 96 dB, this is a very visible signal.

4.8 MODELLING THE QUANTISATION PROCESS

Figure 4.25 illustrates that quantisation is a linear process. Assume a two-tone input signal, $A_1 cos(\omega_1 t) + A_2 cos(\omega_2 t)$. This signal is fed to the quantiser which is modelled here simply as a device which adds "quantisation" noise. The quantisation noise has a variance of $q^2/12$, assuming that one quantum step at the ADC output is of amplitude q. This noise has a flat probability density function (PDF) between $-q/2$ and $q/2$. The signal plus the quantisation noise was fed to a DFT processor to see the effect. In this example a 6-bit converter (including sign) has been assumed, so that $q = 1/32$ in a range from -1.0 to 1.0. Since $A_1 = 1/2$ and $A_2 = 1/64$, A_2 is only half the height of the least significant bit (LSB) for this converter. In the absence of noise or of the larger signal, this small signal of amplitude A_2 could not pass through the converter. The noise and/or the large signal act as a carrier taking

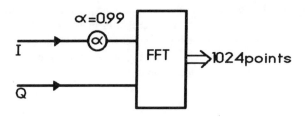

Figure 4.23   Model for amplitude imbalance between a pair of ADC's on the I and Q inputs of a fast Fourier transform unit.

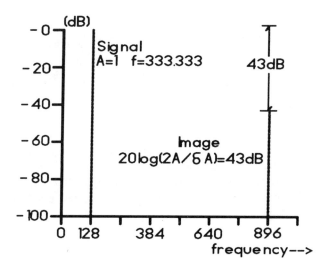

Figure 4.24   Image of a signal caused by a 1% imbalance following Figure 4.23.

the small signal over the ADC threshold (LSB). In this example the smaller signal should be 30.1 dB below the larger signal and indeed this is verified in Figure 4.26. This is confirmation of the validity of the linear model and indeed this model can be used for computer simulations of quantisation noise and its effects in cases where small signals are carried over the LSB threshold by larger signals or by external additive noise.

4.9 SUMMARY

In this chapter the sampling process was discussed and the Nyquist baseband and band-pass criteria were stated. The problem of aliasing was explained. Two simple analogues for ADCs and DACs in terms of potentiometers were introduced. The S & H and its requirements were studied as were six different converter types. Finally, problems arising from non-ideal converters as a result of non-linearities were considered and the validity of a linear model for the quantisation process was demonstrated.

TUTORIAL   Sampling, Aliasing and Data Conversion

1.   A simultaneous comparison method analogue to digital converter is to provide a 3-bit two's complement representation of a bipolar input signal in the range $\pm V_0$. Assuming that reference voltages $+V_0$ and $-V_0$ are available, draw a resistor chain which would provide the required comparator reference voltages. (Ignore the extra negative number available with two's complement notation).

2.   Describe briefly, with the aid of time and frequency domain diagrams, what is meant by aliasing in sampled data systems. Calculate the minimum pulse repetition rate for a pulse-doppler airborne radar in an aircraft with a velocity of 300 m/s, assuming that the radar is required to unambiguously detect targets with velocities up to 350 m/s. You may assume that $\lambda = 0.03$ m.

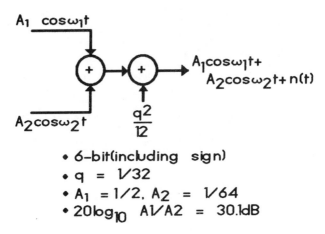

Figure 4.25   A linear model of the quantisation process.

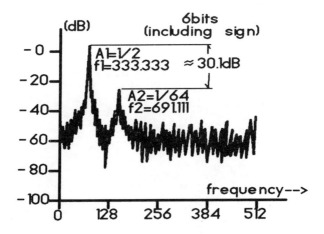

Figure 4.26   Power spectrum of the sum of two sinewaves where the smaller sinewave was below the input threshold of the converter.

Chapter 5
CONTINUOUS ANALOGUE FILTER DESIGN

5.1 INTRODUCTION

The commonly required types of frequency filter fall into four main groups, i.e. low-pass, high-pass, band-pass and band-stop. The technique used to design these filters is to specify a prototype low-pass filter function which is normalised to provide a cut-off frequency at 1 rad/sec and then apply transformations to achieve the actual desired cut-off frequencies and filter type. In this chapter some common approximations used for the design of prototype low-pass filters are discussed [Zverev]. The transformations used to realise the practical filter functions are then presented [Kuo].

The ideal, brick-wall, low-pass filter prototype is one which has a unit amplitude frequency response from d.c. to 1 rad/sec with the response dropping to zero thereafter (see Figure 5.1). This may be defined in terms of the following squared magnitude transfer function:

$$H(j\omega)\,H(-j\omega) = |H(j\omega)|^2 = \frac{1}{1 + F(\omega^2)} \tag{5.1}$$

where

$$F(\omega^2) = \begin{cases} 0, \ 0 < \omega < 1 \\ \infty, \ \omega > 1 \end{cases} \tag{5.2}$$

Since $F(\omega^2)$ is a polynomial in ω^2.

$$F(\omega^2) = \lim_{n \to \infty} \omega^{2n}$$

to satisfy the lower condition in (5.2). It is not practically feasible to form a polynomial of this type (∞ order) since an infinite number of real reactive components would be required. Therefore approximations to $F(\omega^2)$ are made.

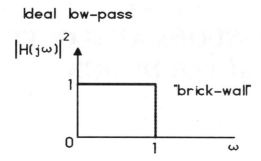

Figure 5.1   Ideal "brick-wall" low-pass filter.

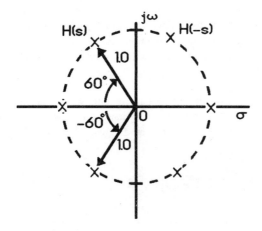

Figure 5.2   Butterworth pole positions for order 3.

5.2 BUTTERWORTH APPROXIMATION

The approximation for $F(\omega^2)$ due to Butterworth is given by:-

$$F(\omega^2) = \omega^{2n} \tag{5.3}$$

This yields the following squared magnitude transfer function:

$$|H(j\omega)|^2 = \frac{1}{1 + \omega^{2n}} \tag{5.4}$$

$$\rightarrow H(j\omega) = \frac{1}{\sqrt{(1 + \omega^{2n})}} \tag{5.5}$$

where n is a positive integer. To localise the poles of this function let $p = j\omega$. Therefore (5.5) becomes:-

$$H(p) = \frac{1}{(1 + p^{2n})^{1/2}} \quad \text{for } n \text{ even} \tag{5.6}$$

$$H(p) = \frac{1}{(1 - p^{2n})^{1/2}} \quad \text{for } n \text{ odd} \tag{5.7}$$

therefore for n even the poles are given by:

$$(1 + p^{2n})^{1/2} = 0$$

$$p^{2n} = -1 = e^{\pm j\pi}$$

$$p = e^{\pm j\pi/2n} = e^{\pm j\pi/4}, e^{\pm j\pi/8}, e^{\pm j\pi/12} \cdots$$

for n odd the poles are given by:

$$(1 - p^{2n})^{1/2} = 0$$

$$p^{2n} = 1 = e^{\pm j2\pi}$$

$$p = e^{\pm j\pi/n} = e^{\pm j\pi}, e^{\pm j\pi/3}, e^{\pm j\pi/5} \cdots$$

The poles of the Butterworth filter all lie in the left-hand s-plane with a locus which is a circle of unit radius whose centre is the s-plane origin. A plot of the poles of this function for the case $n = 3$ is shown in Figure 5.2. Note that the poles are spaced by π/n radians. Odd order filters have a negative real pole while even order filters have only complex conjugate pole pairs.

The Butterworth function produces a magnitude frequency response which is termed as 'maximally flat'. The parameter, n, determines how close to the ideal frequency response the approximation comes. Plots of magnitude frequency response for various values of n are shown in Figure 5.3. As an example of the derivation of a Butterworth transfer function for the case of $n = 3$ is given here:-

$$H(s)\,H(-s) = \frac{1}{1+(-s^2)^3}$$

$$= \frac{1}{1 - s^6}$$

$$= \frac{1}{(1 + 2s + 2s^2 + s^3)(1 - 2s + 2s^2 - s^3)}$$

$$\rightarrow H(s) = \frac{1}{(1 + 2s + 2s^2 + s^3)} \qquad (5.8)$$

Although the derivation of $H(s)$ is fairly simple in this case the form of $H(s)$ becomes more complicated as n increases beyond $n = 3$. Tables of the polynomial coefficients may be found in many texts and are listed for the first 5 orders in Table 5.1.

n	a_1	a_2	a_3	a_4	a_5
1	1				
2	2	1			
3	2	2	1		
4	2.613	3.414	2.613	1	
5	3.236	5.236	5.236	3.236	1

$$H(s) = \frac{1}{a_n s^n + a_{n-1} s^{n-1} + \cdots a_1 s + 1}$$

Table 5.1 Butterworth polynomials.

Although these values may be used in the synthesis of continuous ladder-type networks it is more common to realise high-order filters as a cascade of 1st and 2nd order filter sections. It is then required to factor the denominator polynomial of $H(s)$ and again tables of these factored forms may be found in numerous texts. The first 5 orders are listed in Table 5.2.

n	Butterworth Polynomials
1	$s + 1$
2	$s^2 + \sqrt{2}s + 1$
3	$(s^2 + s + 1)(s + 1)$
4	$(s^2 + 0.76536s + 1)(s^2 + 1.84776s + 1)$
5	$(s + 1)(s^2 + 0.6180s + 1)(s^2 + 1.6180s + 1)$

Table 5.2 Butterworth polynomials (factored form).

5.3 CHEBYSHEV APPROXIMATION

This approximation for $F(\omega^2)$ is the so-called "equal ripple" approximation, i.e. it has a pass-band ripple of constant amplitude with maximum band edge roll-off rate. A plot of Chebyshev filter response is shown in Figure 5.4. The transfer function, $H(j\omega)$, for the Chebyshev filter is given by:

$$H(j\omega) = \frac{1}{(1 + \epsilon^2 C_n^2(\omega))^{1/2}} \tag{5.9}$$

where $C_n(\omega)$ is the Chebyshev polynomial of order n which is defined by

$$C_n(\omega) = \begin{cases} \cos(n \cos^{-1}\omega), & |\omega| \leq 1 \\ \cosh(n \cosh^{-1}\omega), & |\omega| > 1 \end{cases} \tag{5.10}$$

The definition of the Chebyshev polynomial in (5.10) means that rather than having poles with a circular locus on the s-plane a Chebyshev filter has poles with an elliptical locus (see Figure 5.5). The actual values of the polynomials, $C_n(\omega)$, may be found from the following recursion formula,

$$C_n(\omega) = 2 \omega C_{n-1}(\omega) - C_{n-2}(\omega)$$

where $C_0(\omega) = 1$ and $C_1(\omega) = \omega$. Thus for example

$$C_2(\omega) = 2\omega^2 - 1$$

$$C_3(\omega) = 4\omega^3 - 3\omega$$

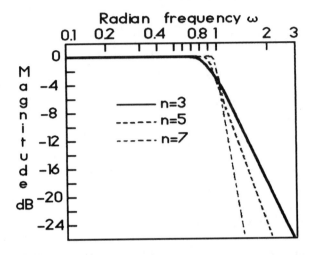

Figure 5.3   Frequency-amplitude responses for various Butterworth low-pass filter orders.

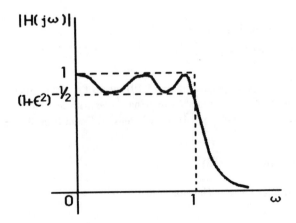

Figure 5.4   Chebyshev approximation for the low-pass filter.

$$C_4(\omega) = 8\,\omega^4 - 8\,\omega^2 + 1, \quad etc.$$

A comparison of 3rd order Butterworth and Chebyshev filter responses is shown in Figure 5.6.

Many other types of filter response approximation are available, e.g. linear phase, approximations based on Bessel polynomials. Figure 5.7 shows some of these normalised responses along with phase (group delay) characteristics for these filters. Bessel filters provide least phase distortion (for a simple design) but their roll off rate to the stop band is inferior to Butterworth. Chebyshev provides fastest roll off (best rejection for a given number of filter stages) but its phase response is inferior to the other designs and this is also dependent on the specified level of pass band ripple. If ripple can also be tolerated in the stop band then elliptic filter designs can be contemplated.

5.4 FILTER TRANSFORMATIONS

In order to synthesise the actual required filter it is necessary to transform the low-pass prototype by restructuring the pole/zero locations in the s-plane. In the case of a low-pass Butterworth design with a desired cut-off frequency of Ω_p this means expanding the circle forming the locus of the poles to radius Ω_p instead of unity (see Figure 5.8). In the case of a bandpass Butterworth with upper cut-off Ω_u and lower cut-off Ω_l the transform is rather more complex (see Figure 5.9). Here the pole locus is readjusted in radius and shifted up the $j\omega$ axis, with a mirrored set of poles on the negative axis.

These transformations are actually implemented by substituting different functions (shown in Table 5.3) for the complex frequency variable s in the prototype transfer function.

Filter Type	Substitute for s
Lowpass	$\dfrac{s}{\Omega_p}$
Highpass	$\dfrac{\Omega_p}{s}$
Bandstop	$\dfrac{s\,(\Omega_u - \Omega_l)}{(s^2 + \Omega_u\Omega_l)}$
Bandpass	$\dfrac{(s^2 + \Omega_u\Omega_l)}{s\,(\Omega_u - \Omega_l)}$

Table 5.3 Prototype filter transformations.

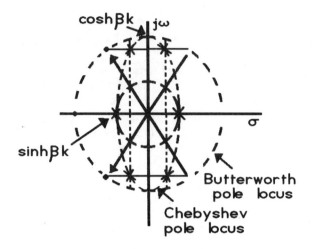

Figure 5.5   Chebyshev pole positions for order 3.

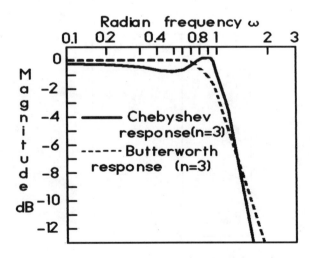

Figure 5.6   Comparison of 3rd order Butterworth with 3rd order Chebyshev low-pass responses.

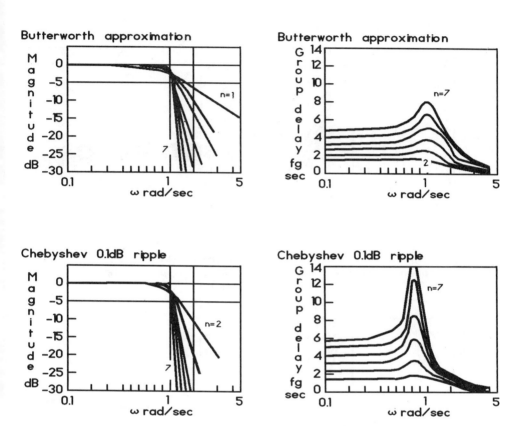

Figure 5.7(a)   Magnitude and group delay responses for various filter approximations.

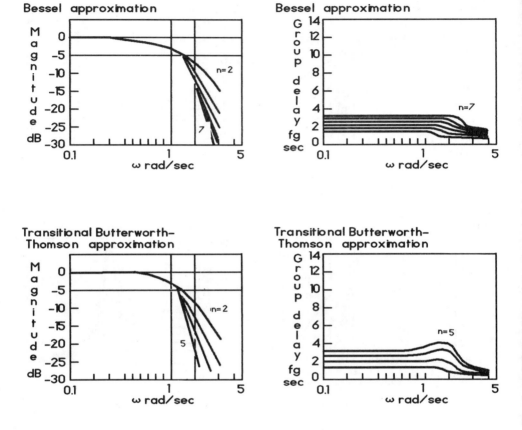

Figure 5.7(b)   Magnitude and group delay responses for various filter approximations.

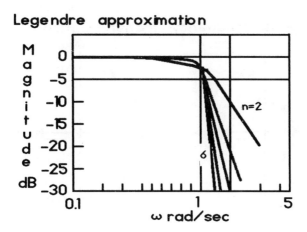

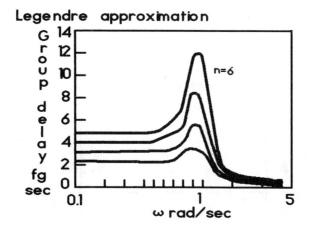

Figure 5.7(c)   Magnitude and group delay responses for various filter approximations.

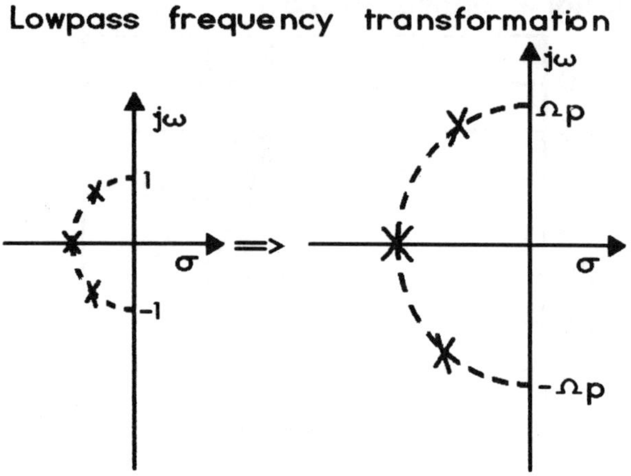

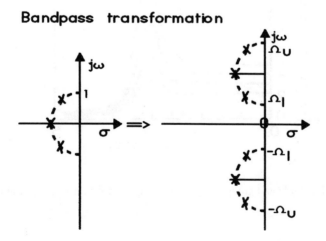

Figure 5.8   Low-pass filter pole transformation.

Figure 5.9   Band-pass filter pole transformation.

The basic filter design process may be summarised as:

(1) Choose the low-pass prototype which satisfies the design criteria for band-edge roll-off, pass-band ripple and phase response.

(2) Apply required filter transformation to yield the actual desired transfer function.

Chapter 6
INFINITE IMPULSE RESPONSE DIGITAL FILTERS

6.1 INTRODUCTION

There are five main reasons for the use of digital filters as opposed to analogue filters of either the passive or active type.

(i)   It is extremely difficult to realise RLC filters with low cut-off frequencies. However, in the case of digital filters, cut-off frequency is determined entirely by the clock frequency. It is, therefore, possible to realise filters with very low cut-off frequencies without adversely affecting filter performance.

(ii) Digital filters may be time division multiplexed to process many signals with a single filter.

(iii) In contrast to analogue filters the frequency domain characteristics of a digital filter may be easily changed. This permits, for instance, the processing of one signal with a low-pass filter and another signal by a band-pass simply by time division multiplexing the input signal and altering the frequency characteristics using a set of coefficients stored in RAM.

(iv) Digital filters do not suffer from the aging characteristics of analogue filters.

(v)   The problem of impedance matching does not exist with digital filters.

The disadvantages of digital filters are remarkably few. The most significant of these has, historically, been the relatively high cost of digital filters. However, with the increasing use of special-purpose LSI circuits and fast microprocessor architectures this advantage on the part of analogue filters is being rapidly eroded.

6.2 GENERAL DIGITAL FILTER DESCRIPTION

Any order M linear discrete system can be expressed by the order M difference equation

$$y(nT) = \sum_{i=0}^{N} a_i \, x[(n-i)T] - \sum_{i=1}^{M} b_i \, y[(n-i)T] \tag{6.1}$$

The difference equation is very important in the sense that it illustrates the fact that the present output $y(nT)$ of a linear discrete system is a linear combination of the weighted present and N past inputs to the system as well as M weighted past outputs. The design of the digital filter consists of selecting the constants a_i and b_i.

If at least one of the coefficients b_i is non-zero then the filter is classified as a recursive filter. If, however, all the coefficients b_i are identically zero, then the filter is called a non-recursive filter. Note here that the recursive filters have an infinite memory since the present output is a function of the past outputs, and they result in infinite impulse response (IIR) filters. Non-recursive filters have no memory of the past outputs and they result in finite impulse response (FIR) filters, whose impulse response duration is controlled by the overall non-recursive filter delay [Bozic, Williams].

Figure 6.1 shows the direct realisation of the order M difference equation. Direct programming uses $N+M+1$ shift registers, each with a bit length equal to the word length of input data, one accumulator and $N+M+1$ data storage units (ROM's) again each with a bit length equal to the desired coefficient word length of the filter. However, it is possible to reduce the number of delay units to M (assuming $M > N$), to give the canonical realisation, Figure 6.2.

The two other significant digital filter realisations are the series and parallel cascade, Figure 6.3 and 6.4. In these realisations each section $K_n(z)$ is designed as either a first or second order polynomial and the overall difference equation is obtained by parallel or series cascade interconnections of these lower order sections. The basic filter type used in such a cascade is the so-called biquadratic filter shown in Figure 6.5.

6.3 DIRECT IMPLEMENTATION OF z TRANSFER FUNCTION

The derivation of the canonical form of the IIR digital filter may be obtained as follows;

$$H(z) = \frac{Y(z)}{X(z)} = \frac{N(z)}{D(z)} = \frac{\sum\limits_{i=0}^{N} a_i z^{-i}}{(1 + \sum\limits_{i=1}^{M} b_i z^{-i})} \tag{6.2}$$

where $N(z) = \sum\limits_{i=0}^{N} a_i z^{-i}$ and $D(z) = (1 + \sum\limits_{i=1}^{M} b_i z^{-i})$.

For input signal $X(z)$ the output is given by:

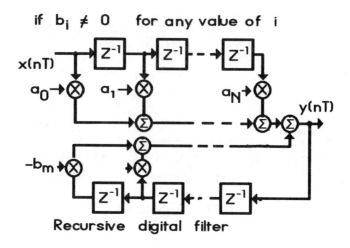

Figure 6.1   Direct realisation of the digital filter difference equation.

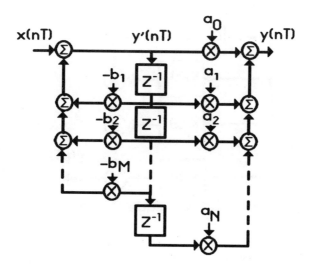

Figure 6.2   Canonical form of the digital filter difference equation.

$$H(z) = \frac{N(z)}{D(z)} = \frac{A(z)\ B(z)\ C(z)}{W(z)\ X(z)\ Y(z)\ \ldots}$$

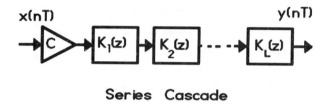

Series Cascade

Figure 6.3   Series cascade of lower order filters.

$$H(z) = \frac{N(z)}{D(z)} = \frac{A(z)}{W(z)} + \frac{B(z)}{X(z)} + \frac{C(z)}{Y(z)} +$$

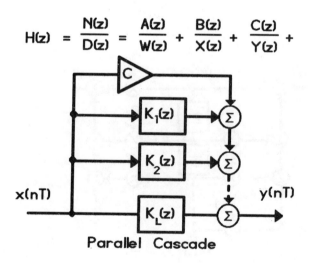

Parallel Cascade

Figure 6.4   Parallel cascade of lower order filters.

$$Y(z) = \frac{N(z)}{D(z)} X(z) \tag{6.3}$$

Let

$$Y'(z) = \frac{X(z)}{D(z)}$$

then

$$Y(z) = H(z) Y'(z)$$

or in sampled data notation:

$$y'(n) = x(n) - \sum_{i=1}^{M} b_i \, y'(n-i), \tag{6.4}$$

and

$$y(n) = \sum_{i=0}^{N} a_i \, y'(n-i) \tag{6.5}$$

(N is not necessarily equal to M)

For example if:

$$H(z) = \frac{z^2 - 0.2z - 0.08}{z^2 + 0.5}$$

$$H(z) = \frac{1 - 0.2z^{-1} - 0.08z^{-2}}{1 + 0.5z^{-2}}$$

$$Y(z) (1 + 0.5z^{-2}) = X(z) (1 - 0.2z^{-1} - 0.8z^{-2})$$

Inverse z transform

$$y(nT) + 0.5y(nT - 2T) = x(nT) - 0.2 \, x(nT - T) - 0.08 \, x(nT - 2T)$$

$$y(nT) = x(nT) - 0.2x(nT - T) - 0.08 \, x(nT - 2T) - 0.5y(nT - 2T)$$

This is the linear difference equation giving $y(nT)$ as a function of present and past input and output samples.

6.4 INFINITE IMPULSE RESPONSE FILTERS

Digital filter designs can be based on analogue prototype frequency response functions e.g. Butterworth and Chebyshev lowpass filter functions, as described in chapter 5 and in [Kuo].

1   The bilinear transformation can be used to obtain the required function of z

2   Analogue prototype step and impulse responses can be sampled to yield other z transfer
        functions

No single transform exists to perfectly map $G(s)$ to $G(z)$. They all suffer some defect;
aliasing, frequency warping etc. [Jackson]. Three practical methods are:

*   Impulse Invariant - produces a $G(z)$ whose impulse response is identical to a sampled
        version of $g(t)$.

*   Matched z-transform - poles and zeros of $G(s)$ are directly mapped into poles and zeroes
        of $G(z)$.

*   Bilinear z-transform - the whole left half s-plane is mapped into the unit circle in the z-
        plane in one go. i.e. the whole $|G(j\omega)|$ is telescoped into the range $\omega = 0$ to $\dfrac{\omega_s}{2}$.

6.5 THE BILINEAR z-TRANSFORM

        Only the example of digital filter design using the bilinear z-transform will be considered
here as this is the most frequently used technique. This transformation makes use of a
mapping of the complete imaginary s-plane axis between $\pm\infty$ onto the z-plane unit circle
[Bozic, Peled & Liu]. To facilitate this the continuous transformation:

$$\omega_a = \frac{2}{T} tan\left(\frac{\omega_d T}{2}\right) \tag{6.6}$$

is used which maps the continuous analogue frequency variable ω_a into a modified frequency
variable ω_d. This has the effect of compressing the entire frequency spectrum of a function
described in terms of ω_a into a finite interval (see Figure 6.6). The warping algorithm is stated
in terms of the variable s by:

$$s = \frac{2}{T} \frac{j\, sin\left(\dfrac{\omega_d T}{2}\right)}{cos\left(\dfrac{\omega_d T}{2}\right)} \tag{6.7}$$

which may be rewritten as:

$$s = \frac{2}{T} \frac{(1-e^{-j\omega_d T})}{(1+e^{-j\omega_d T})} \tag{6.8}$$

appling the standard z-transform $z = e^{s_d t}$ yields:

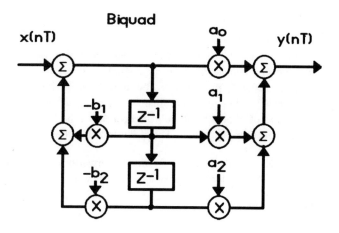

Figure 6.5   The biquadratic digital filter.

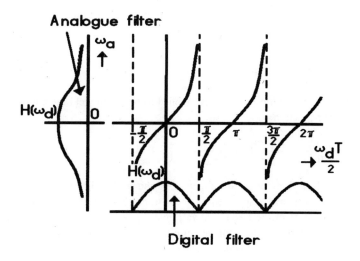

Figure 6.6   Spectral compression due to the bilinear z-transform.

$$s = \frac{2(1-z^{-1})}{T(1+z^{-1})} \tag{6.9}$$

The relationship of equation (6.9) is the bilinear z-transform which yields the digital filter function $H(z)$ from a given analogue filter function $H(s)$ by direct use of the substitution. However, due to the frequency warping introduced by (6.6) the same transfer function shape is not obtained and the analogue function must first be "pre-warped" used (6.6) in order to maintain the proper position of critical break point frequencies. The frequency warping effect of the tan function may be seen in Figure 6.7. This is illustrated in the following example.

Example Design the digital equivalent of a 2nd order Butterworth lowpass filter with cut off frequency of $\omega_d = 10^2$ rad/sec and sampling frequency $\omega_s = 10^3$ rad/sec.

Solution The analogue prototype filter is given by:

$$H(s) = \frac{1}{s^2 + \sqrt{2}s + 1} \tag{6.10}$$

The prewarping substitution of equation (6.6) is first applied to the critical cut-off frequency ω_d to yield:

$$\omega_a = \left(\frac{2}{6.28 \times 10^{-3}}\right) \tan\left[10^2 \times \frac{(6.28 \times 10^{-3})}{2}\right] = 103.3 \; rad/sec$$

This figure is then used to denormalise the prototype filter function of (6.10) giving:

$$H(s_d) = \frac{1}{\left(\dfrac{s}{103.3}\right)^2 + \dfrac{\sqrt{2}s}{103.3} + 1} \tag{6.11}$$

The bilinear z-transform (6.9) is now applied to (6.11) to yield the equivalent digital filter transfer function:

$$H(z) = \frac{0.067z^{-2} + 0.135z^{-1} + 0.067}{0.413z^{-2} - 1.141z^{-1} + 1} \tag{6.12}$$

The physical realisation of this function is shown in Figure 6.8 with the actual magnitude and phase responses obtained from this filter in Figures 6.9(a) and 6.9(b). The effect of the frequency warp may be seen here as introducing a sharper roll-off rate after the defined critical cut-off frequency, and also some peaking at the band edge. A plot of the analogue prototype in this case is shown in Figure 6.9(c).

The frequency responses shown in Figure 6.10 show a 3rd order Butterworth low-pass with $\omega_d = \omega_s/10$ using both the bilinear and impulse invariant design techniques. It may be seen from this that although the impulse invariant technique holds closer to the original analogue prototype response it never attains the level of attenuation of the bilinear design due to spectral imaging.

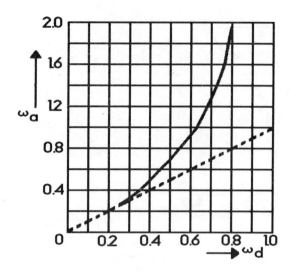

Figure 6.7   Frequency warping effect of the bilinear z-transform.

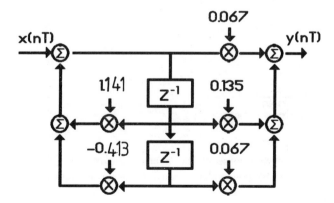

Figure 6.8   Physical realisation of a 2nd order Butterworth filter with cut-off frequency $\omega_s/10$.

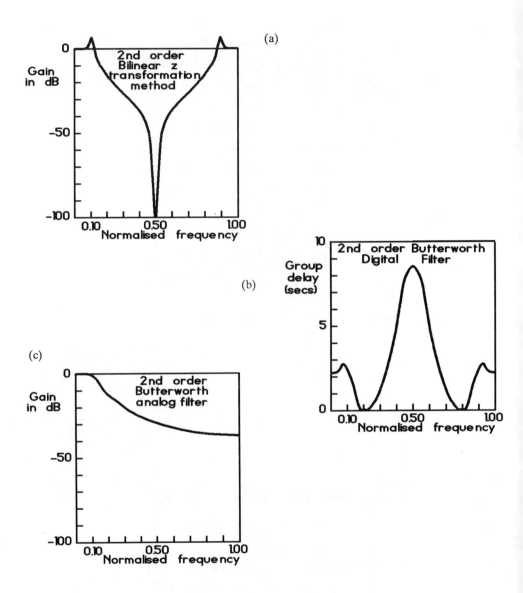

Figure 6.9   Frequency response of the filter in Figure 6.9: (a) magnitude frequency
response; (b) group delay response; (c) analogue prototype response.

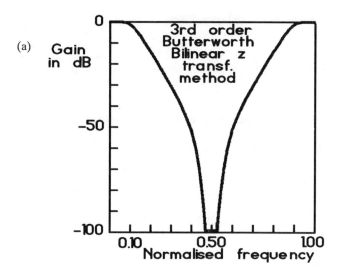

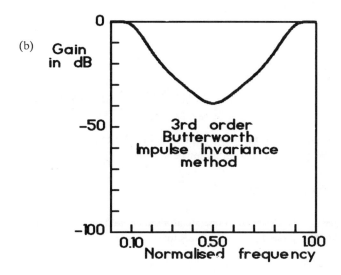

Figure 6.10 Frequency response for a 3rd order Butterworth low pass filter response: (a) bilinear z-transform design; (b) impulse invariant design.

TUTORIAL Infinite Impulse Response Digital Filters.

1.   The transfer functions of two digital filters are: (i) $\dfrac{z}{z - \frac{1}{2}}$ and (ii) $\dfrac{z^2}{z^2 + \frac{1}{2}}$. For each example:

(a) determine the locations in the z-plane of the filter's poles and zeros.

(b) determine whether or not the filter is stable.

(c) sketch the steady-state frequency response of the filter between $\omega = 0$ and $\omega = \omega_s/2$, and comment. Derive exact values for the magnitude and phase at $\omega = \omega_s/4$.

(d) determine the linear difference equation that defines the time-domain response of the filter.

(e) compute the first five samples of the impulse response of the filter.

(f) draw a block diagram of a suitable hardware realisation.

2.   Use the bilinear transformation method to design a digital filter based on the prototype function $F(s) = \dfrac{s\tau}{1+s\tau}$. Assume that the desired 3 dB frequency is: (i) much lower than Nyquist frequency, e.g. $\ll \omega_s/100$ and (ii) at $\omega_s/4$.

$$\left[\quad (i)\ F(z) = \frac{z-1}{2z} \quad (ii)\ F(z) = \frac{2\tau(z-1)/T}{(1+2\tau/T)\left[z + \left(\dfrac{1-2\tau/T}{1+2\tau/T}\right)\right]} \quad \right]$$

3.   Use the bilinear z-transform to design an infinite impulse response digital low pass filter based on the third order Butterworth prototype function:

$$G(s) = \frac{1}{(s^2+s+1)(s+1)}$$

The digital filter is to be designed to operate at a sample rate of 8 kHz with a 3 dB cut off frequency at 2 kHz. Show that $G(z)$ reduces to:

$$\frac{(z+1)^3}{6z\left(z-j\dfrac{1}{\sqrt{3}}\right)\left(z+j\dfrac{1}{\sqrt{3}}\right)}$$

Sketch the z-plane pole-zero diagram and the expected shape of the magnitude of the digital filter frequency response from d.c. to 8 kHz. Calculate from $G(z)$ the individual multiplier weight values, and show clearly on a block diagram where the different weights are employed.

4. A second-order Butterworth prototype filter having a -3 dB lowpass cutoff at 1 rad/sec is defined by

$$G(s) = \frac{1}{s^2 + \sqrt{2}s + 1}$$

Using the bilinear z-transform show that an equivalent sampled-data filter sampling at 8000 Hz with a cutoff at 100 Hz has the pulse transfer function

$$G(z) = \frac{0.098\ z^2 + 0.195\ z + 0.098}{z^2 - 0.942\ z + 0.333}$$

and derive a linear difference equation for this sampled-data filter.

Chapter 7
FINITE IMPULSE RESPONSE DIGITAL FILTERS

7.1 INTRODUCTION

Finite impulse response (FIR) filters are non-recursive i.e. all the b coefficients are zero (Figure 6.2). They offer the possibility of a linear phase characteristic and are unconditionally stable but they require more stages of delay and multiply than an infinite impulse response (IIR) filter with a similar passband specification. In this chapter both time and frequency descriptions of FIR filters will be examined. Symmetry conditions to ensure linear phase response will be outlined and design techniques for linear phase FIR filters will be presented. Finally there will be a discussion of the effects of finite precision arithmetic on the performance of FIR filters.

7.2 TRANSFER FUNCTION AND FREQUENCY RESPONSE

Removing the b coefficients from the general difference of equation (6.1) yields an N-coefficient FIR filter.

$$y(nT) = \sum_{i=0}^{N-1} a_i \, x[(n-i)T]$$

Since only constant sampling rate processors will be considered the sampling period T can be removed for simplicity.

$$y(n) = \sum_{i=0}^{N-1} a_i \, x(n-i) \tag{7.1}$$

This structure is illustrated in Figure 7.1. Equation (7.1) represents the convolution of the finite impulse response sequence $\{a_n\}$ with input sequence $\{x(n)\}$. To obtain the transfer function, $H(z)$, of the FIR filter take the z-transform of both sides of equation (7.1).

$$Y(z) = \sum_{i=0}^{N-1} a_i \, X(z) \, z^{-i}$$

$$= X(z) \sum_{i=0}^{N-1} a_i \, z^{-i}$$

Hence:

$$H(z) = \frac{Y(z)}{X(z)} = \sum_{i=0}^{N-1} a_i \, z^{-i} \tag{7.2}$$

In order to find the poles and zeros this polynomial must be expressed in powers of z greater than or equal to zero.

$$H(z) = a_0 \, z^0 + a_1 \, z^{-1} + \; .... \; + a_{N-1} \, z^{-(N-1)}$$

$$= \frac{z^{N-1}}{z^{N-1}} \left(a_0 \, z^0 + a_1 \, z^{-1} + \; .... \; + a_{N-1} \, z^{-(N-1)} \right)$$

$$= \frac{a_0 \, z^{N-1} + a_1 \, z^{N-2} + \; .... \; + a_{N-1} \, z^0}{z^{N-1}}$$

Therefore $H(z)$ has $N-1$ zeros and $N-1$ poles. All the poles are at the origin in the z-plane and hence FIR filters are unconditionally stable.

The frequency response, $H(\omega)$, of the FIR filter is obtained by replacing z in equation (7.2) with $e^{j\omega T}$.

$$H(\omega) = \sum_{n=0}^{N-1} a_n \, e^{-jn\omega T} \tag{7.3}$$

In fact equation (7.3) is a Fourier series expansion of the function $H(\omega)$ which is a periodic function (Figure 7.2) of ω with period $2\pi/T$ radians per second (i.e. the sampling frequency is $1/T$ Hz). Hence the Fourier coefficients a_n may be calculated by integrating in the frequency domain over one period of the function, $H(\omega)$.

$$a_n = \frac{T}{2\pi} \int_0^{2\pi/T} H(\omega) \, e^{jn\omega T} \, d\omega \tag{7.4}$$

7.3 LINEAR PHASE FILTERS

If a filter has linear phase then its frequency response, $H(\omega)$, may be written as the product of a real amplitude response function, $H_A(\omega)$, and a complex exponential term, $e^{-j\alpha\omega T}$.

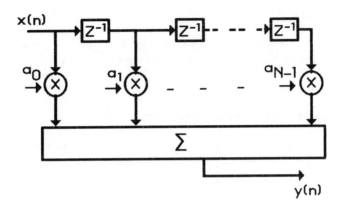

Figure 7.1   Finite impulse response (non-recursive) filter.

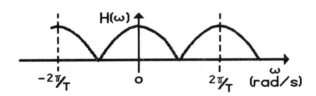

Figure 7.2   Frequency response.

$$H(\omega) = H_A(\omega)\, e^{-j\alpha\omega T}$$

The complex exponential term represents a time delay of αT seconds. Because $H_A(\omega)$ is real, the phase response of the filter is determined by the exponential term.

$$arg\{H(\omega)\} = -\alpha\omega T$$

The phase response is a linear function of frequency i.e. linear phase.

The question then arises as to what sort of impulse response has a real amplitude response as required for $H_A(\omega)$. Consider a digital filter with a real impulse response sequence, $\{c_n\}$. In general the frequency response, $H_A(\omega)$, is given by:

$$H_A(\omega) = \sum_{n=-\infty}^{+\infty} c_n\, e^{-jn\omega T}$$

$$= \sum_{n=-\infty}^{+\infty} \left(c_n \cos(n\omega T) - j\, c_n \sin(n\omega T) \right)$$

The imaginary part will disappear if $\{c_n\}$ has even symmetry (Figure 7.3(a)) i.e.

$$c_n = c_{-n} \tag{7.5}$$

in which case

$$H_A(\omega) = \sum_{n=-\infty}^{+\infty} c_n \cos(n\omega T)\ .$$

Because $H_A(\omega)$ is now a weighted sum of even functions of frequency (i.e. $\cos(n\omega T)$) it is also an even function of frequency. The condition, summarised in equation (7.5), which ensures that $H_A(\omega)$ is real also demands that the impulse response sequence is non-causal i.e. physically unrealisable. The non-causal nature of $H_A(\omega)$ is not a problem when dealing with FIR linear phase filters since the delay of αT seconds can be used to convert the non-causal filter into a causal one.

The transfer function, $H_A(z)$, of the non-causal filter illustrated in Figure 7.3(a) is:

$$H_A(z) = \sum_{n=-\infty}^{+\infty} c_n\, z^{-n}$$

The impulse response series, $\{c_n\}$, can be truncated to $2M+1$ terms, where M is a positive integer, without losing the symmetry property of equation (7.5).

$$H_A(z) = \sum_{n=-M}^{M} c_n\, z^{-n}$$

(a)

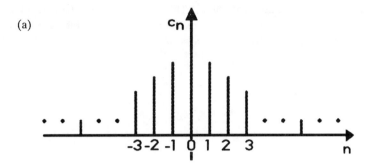

(b)

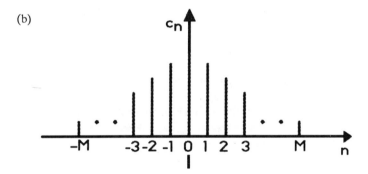

(c)

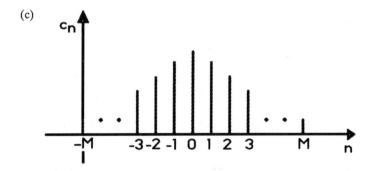

Figure 7.3   Impulse responses: (a) even symmetry (non-causal IIR); (b) even symmetry (non-causal FIR); (c) left shift M times (causal FIR).

$H_A(z)$ now represents a non-causal FIR filter. This filter has $2M+1$ taps, M of which have indices less than zero (i.e. refer to negative time, Figure 7.3(b)). The filter can be made causal by cascading it with a delay of M samples i.e. $\alpha = M$.

$$H(z) = z^{-M} H_A(z)$$

$$= z^{-M} \sum_{n=-M}^{M} c_n z^{-n}$$

$$= \sum_{n=-M}^{M} c_n z^{-(n+M)}$$

The resultant impulse response is illustrated in Figure 7.3(c).

There are, in fact, 4 ways of achieving linear phase FIR filters depending on whether an odd or even number of taps are used or whether the symmetry of the impulse response is odd or even. Only one case has been considered here i.e. an odd number of taps and even symmetry of the impulse response.

7.4 WINDOW DESIGN OF LINEAR PHASE FILTERS

The design of linear phase FIR filters centres on the choice of a set of $2M+1$ coefficients, c_n, to give a desired even amplitude response, $H_D(\omega)$. A set of coefficients can be calculated using equation (7.4) which is simplified because $H_D(\omega)$ is real and has even symmetry.

$$c_n = \frac{T}{2\pi} \int_0^{2\pi/T} H_D(\omega) \, e^{jn\omega T} \, d\omega$$

$$= \frac{T}{2\pi} \left(\int_0^{2\pi/T} H_D(\omega) \cos(n\omega T) \, d\omega + j \int_0^{2\pi/T} H_D(\omega) \sin(n\omega T) \, d\omega \right)$$

$$= \frac{T}{2\pi} \int_0^{2\pi/T} H_D(\omega) \cos(n\omega T) \, d\omega$$

$$= \frac{T}{\pi} \int_0^{\pi/T} H_D(\omega) \cos(n\omega T) \, d\omega \qquad (7.6)$$

Because the number of coefficients is finite (i.e. $n \leq M$) the actual amplitude response, $H_A(\omega)$, will be different from the desired amplitude response, $H_D(\omega)$. The actual amplitude response is provided by equation (7.3) which can be simplified using equation (7.5).

$$H_A(\omega) = \sum_{n=-M}^{M} c_n \cos(n\omega T)$$

$$= c_0 + 2 \sum_{n=1}^{M} c_n \cos(n\omega T) \tag{7.7}$$

The infinite time domain sequence has been effectively multiplied by a rectangular function of time w_n (Figure 7.4).

$$w_n = 1 \qquad |n| \le M$$

$$w_n = 0 \qquad |n| > M$$

The truncation of the time domain function c_n is equivalent to convolving the desired frequency response, $H_D(\omega)$, with the frequency response of the rectangular window i.e. $W(\omega)$.

$$H_A(\omega) = H_D(\omega) * W(\omega)$$

This is illustrated in Figure 7.5. The frequency response of a rectangular window is a $sin(x)/x$ or sinc function. The sidelobes of this sinc function lead to a 'ringing' of the actual frequency response $H_A(\omega)$ at discontinuities of the desired frequency response $H_D(\omega)$. This ringing is known as Gibb's phenomenon and is characteristic of the truncation of a Fourier series. Figure 7.6 shows how the frequency response of a lowpass filter is more closely approximated as the number of taps, N, (and hence the complexity) is increased. For this rectangular window the first sidelobe is only 21 dB below the passband gain value at 0 Hz. A better result is obtained if the impulse response sequence is multiplied by another window function that smoothes the time domain discontinuities and consequently has lower sidelobes in the frequency domain than the sinc function. The choice and design of window functions is a much researched area [Harris]. Some common examples are given below.

Hanning window.

$$w_n = \frac{1}{2}\left(1 + \cos\left(\frac{n\pi}{M}\right)\right)$$

Hamming window (Figure 7.7).

$$w_n = 0.54 + 0.46 \cos\left(\frac{n\pi}{M}\right)$$

Window functions are discussed in more detail in the chapters on the discrete Fourier transform.

The window design of linear phase FIR filters involves 3 steps.

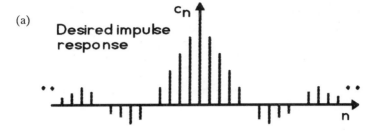

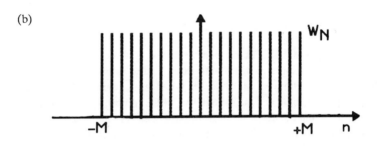

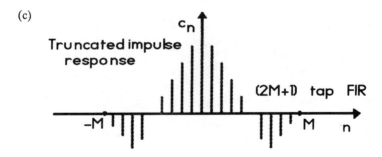

Figure 7.4   Multiplication in the time domain: (a) desired impulse response (infinite); (b) rectangular window; (c) truncated impulse response.

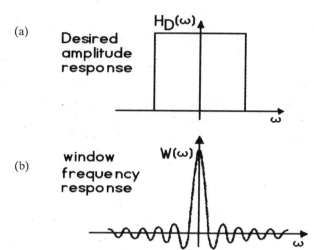

(a) Desired amplitude response $H_D(\omega)$

(b) window frequency response $W(\omega)$

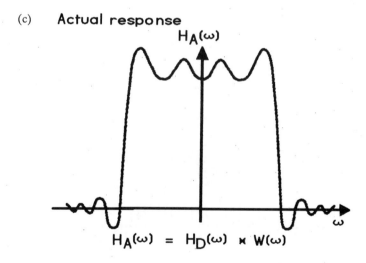

(c) Actual response $H_A(\omega)$

$$H_A(\omega) = H_D(\omega) * W(\omega)$$

Figure 7.5   Convolution in the frequency domain: (a) desired amplitude response; (b) frequency response of rectangular window; (c) actual amplitude response.

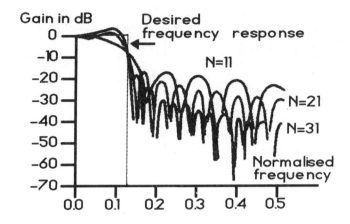

Figure 7.6   Effect of filter length on performance.

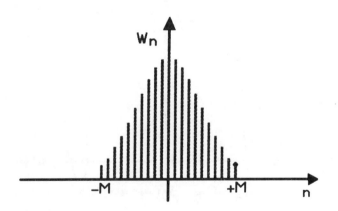

Figure 7.7   Hamming window weighting function.

(i)   For a desired frequency response, $H_D(\omega)$, calculate a set of $2M+1$ coefficients, $\{c_n\}$. Because of the symmetry of the impulse response, equation (7.5), only $M+1$ calculations need to be performed.

$$c_n = \frac{T}{\pi} \int_0^{\pi/T} H_D(\omega) \cos(n\,\omega T)\, d\omega \tag{7.8}$$

(ii) Multiply each point in the impulse response sequence, $\{c_n\}$, by the corresponding point in the window sequence, $\{w_n\}$, to produce a new impulse response sequence, $\{c_n{}'\}$.

$$c_n{}' = w_n\, c_n \tag{7.9}$$

(iii) Finally the actual frequency response, $H_A(\omega)$, of the resultant filter may be calculated in order to compare it with the desired frequency response.

$$H_A(\omega) = c_0{}' + 2 \sum_{n=1}^{M} c_n{}' \cos(n\,\omega T) \tag{7.10}$$

Often the integration in equation (7.8) is straightforward because the desired frequency response is rectangular.

The effect of the window function on filter performance is illustrated in Figure 7.8. For a particular filter length, reducing the stopband ripple tends to increase the width of the transition band. (Filter specifications such as transition band, stopband and passband are summarised in Figure 7.9) The characteristics of some commonly used windows are given in Table 7.1. The choice of window and the selection of the number of taps required to meet a specification is a two stage process.

(i)   Select a window to give a required stopband ripple. e.g. if a stopband ripple of 40 dB was required then a Hanning, Hamming or Blackman window could be used.

(ii) Select N to give the required transition band. Continuing with the above example, if a Hanning window is chosen then

$$\Delta f = \frac{4}{NT}$$

and hence

$$N = \frac{4}{\Delta f\, T} \ .$$

Calculation of N based on Table 7.1 tend to give overestimates. The transition band quoted is merely the width of the mainlobe of the appropriate window in the frequency domain. However it does provide a good starting point for an iterative design procedure. Other window function such as the Kaiser window allow the designer to trade-off stopband ripple for transition band width at a given filter length, N.

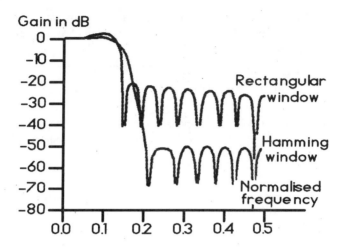

Figure 7.8   Effect of window on performance.

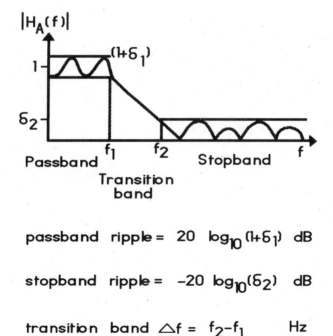

passband ripple = $20 \log_{10}(1+\delta_1)$ dB

stopband ripple = $-20 \log_{10}(\delta_2)$ dB

transition band $\triangle f = f_2 - f_1$ Hz

Figure 7.9   Filter specification.

Window	Transition Band (Hz)	Stopband Ripple (dB)
rectangular	$\dfrac{2}{NT}$	21
triangular	$\dfrac{4}{NT}$	25
Hanning	$\dfrac{4}{NT}$	44
Hamming	$\dfrac{4}{NT}$	53
Blackman	$\dfrac{6}{NT}$	75

Table 7.1 Window characteristics.

7.5 MINIMAX FILTER DESIGN

One design technique which improves significantly on the filter complexity provided by window designs is the minimax technique [Parks & McClellan]. This uses a minimum weighted Chebychev error to approximate the desired frequency response i.e.

$$\underset{\{c_n\}}{minimum} \left\{ \underset{\omega}{maximum} \mid L(\omega) [H_D(\omega) - H_A(\omega)] \mid \right\}$$

The optimal filter design is that set of weight values, $\{c_n\}$, which **minimises** the **maximum** error between the desired frequency response and actual frequency response. Thus it is termed minimax. The positive weighting function, $L(\omega)$, allows the designer to emphasis some areas of the frequency response more than others. The minimisation is performed iteratively using a computer program based on the Remez exchange algorithm (see no.5.1 in [McClellan et al]).

The technique reduces the order of the final filter design significantly. For a low pass filter example with a stopband above 0.18 of the sampling frequency with 50 dB attenuation, and a passband for frequencies below 0.1 of the sampling frequency with a 1 dB ripple, a Hamming weighted frequency domain window design requires a 30 tap filter but achieves a ripple free passband (Figure 7.10(b)). In contrast the minimax design requires a 20 tap filter design to achieve the same performance goal (Figure 7.10(a)). It is thus a very significant filter design technique.

(a)

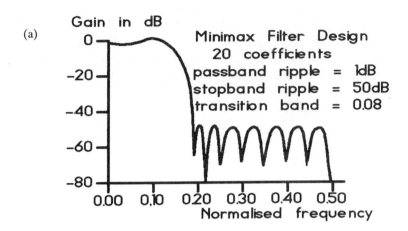

(b)

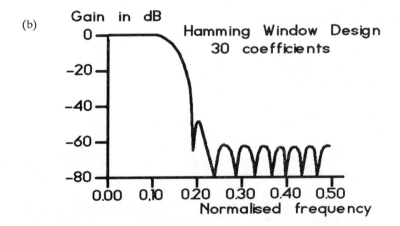

Figure 7.10   Design example: (a) 20 coefficient minimax; (b) 30 coefficient Hamming window.

In practice the number of coefficients, N, or order, $N-1$, of the FIR filter is an important parameter (e.g. in projects where the computational complexity needed to implement a digital filter satisfying given specifications must be determined). For a low pass filter the specifications are summarised in Figure 7.9. Analysis shows that an estimate $\hat{N}$ of the number of coefficients required for a minimax design is given by the following expression [Bellanger].

$$\hat{N} = \frac{2}{3} \frac{1}{T \, \Delta f} \log_{10} \left(\frac{1}{10 \delta_1 \delta_2} \right)$$

The sampling frequency is $1/T$ Hz. The transition band Δf is the most sensitive parameter with the passband, δ_1, and stopband ripple, δ_2, having less significant impact. However it is worth emphasising that according to this estimate the filter complexity is independent of the passband width. Formulae also exist for estimating the order of bandpass filters [Mintzer & Liu].

7.6 FILTER COEFFICIENT ACCURACY

Limited accuracy in the coefficients introduces an error in the frequency response. This effect is illustrated in the graphs of Figure 7.11. The number of bits required in the coefficients can be estimated from the following expression [Bellanger].

$$b_c = 1 + \log_2 \left(\frac{T \, (f_1 + f_2)}{(\delta_m - \delta_0)} \vee \left(\frac{N}{3} \right) \right)$$

where

b_c is the no. of bits used to represent the coefficients (including the sign).

N is the no. of coefficients.

f_1 is the passband edge.

f_2 is the stopband edge.

$\dfrac{1}{T}$ is the sampling frequency.

δ_m is the limit imposed on the amplitude of the ripple.

δ_0 is the amplitude of the ripple of the filter before the no. of bits is limited.

This equation also applies to high pass and low pass filters.

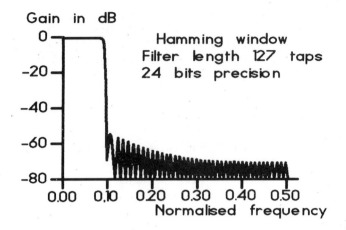

Figure 7.11(a)   Finite precision effects: 24 bit precision.

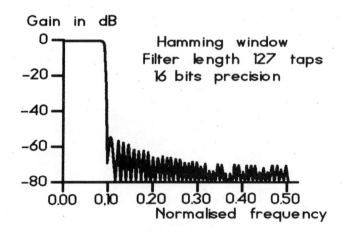

Figure 7.11(b)   Finite precision effects: 16 bit precision.

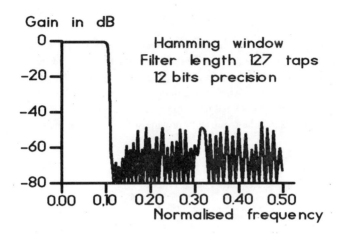

Figure 7.11(c)   Finite precision effects: 12 bit precision.

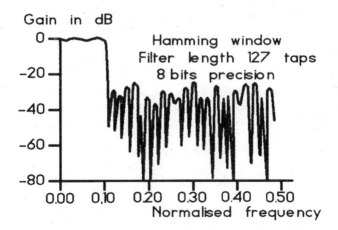

Figure 7.11(d)   Finite precision effects: 8 bit precision.

7.7 SUMMARY

FIR digital filters have the advantage of being unconditionally stable and offer the possibility of a linear phase response. Finite precision effects are simpler to analyse than in IIR designs. Although closed form design techniques are not possible, the window design method can produce reasonable results when computational efficiency is not of prime importance. More efficient designs can be obtained using the minimax technique. The disadvantage of FIR designs is that long filters may be required to provide sharp cut off in the frequency domain.

TUTORIAL Finite Impulse Response Digital Filters.

1. Design a FIR digital low pass filter for an 8 kHz sampling rate whose frequency response has a cosinusoidal shape below 1 kHz.

$$H_D(\omega) = \begin{cases} \cos\left(\dfrac{\omega}{4\times 10^3}\right) & 0 \le \omega < 2\pi\times 10^3 \\ \\ 0 & elsewhere \end{cases}$$

Calculate the values of the filter coefficients for a 15 tap FIR filter. Sketch the actual frequency response from d.c. to 8 kHz. Describe with reference to a block diagram, how such filters can be implemented by multiplexing a single high speed hardware multiplier. [c_0 to c_7 = 0.16, 0.15, 0.12, 0.09, 0.05, 0.021, 0.0, -0.01]

2. Design a 17 tap linear phase filter to approximate a unity gain bandpass response with cut off frequencies at $0.1/T$ and $0.2/T$ incorporating a Hanning window function. [0.0, 0.005, 0.016, 0.0, -0.067, -0.118, -0.05, 0.112, 0.2, 0.112, -0.05, -0.118 etc.]

Chapter 8

WIENER FILTERS

8.1 INTRODUCTION

Norbert Wiener's original work [Wiener] considered the design of continuous time infinite impulse response (IIR) optimal filters for stationary random processes. These filters are optimal in a mean-square error (MSE) sense. This particular definition of optimality is powerful because it leads to closed form solutions for the filter coefficients in terms of the auto- and cross-correlation functions. Other definitions of optimality may lead to estimator structures defined in terms of higher order moments or even probability density functions. In this chapter only discrete-time finite impulse response (FIR) filters are considered as estimators, since they are unconditionally stable (chapter 7). Hence there in no necessity to become involved with the minimum phase spectral factorisation associated with IIR Wiener filter designs. As will be seen the FIR Wiener filter can be derived using purely time domain concepts. In addition a simple example of the application of the Wiener filter will be explored.

8.2 THE MEAN-SQUARE ERROR COST FUNCTION

The structure of a typical linear signal estimation problem is illustrated in Figure 8.1. Given an observed sequence $\{y(n)\}$ which is a distorted and/or noisy version of a signal or information-bearing sequence $\{x(n)\}$, find a linear filter which operates on $\{y(n)\}$ to yield an estimate, $\{\hat{x}(n)\}$, of $\{x(n)\}$. The quality of the estimate is a function, $f(.)$, of the error $\{e(n)\}$, which is the difference between the information-bearing sequence and the estimated sequence (Figure 8.2).

$$e(n) = x(n) - \hat{x}(n) \tag{8.1}$$

The loss function $f(e(n))$ assigns a price or penalty incurred when the estimate is incorrect [Kalman & Bucy]. Clearly the loss function should be: (i) positive

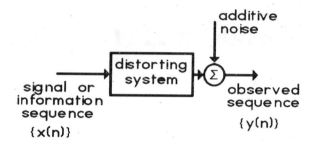

Figure 8.1   The estimation problem.

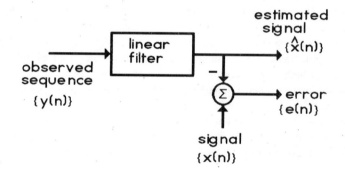

Figure 8.2   Linear estimation.

$$f(e(n)) \geq 0$$

and (ii) non-decreasing.

$$f(0) = 0$$

$$f(e_2) \geq f(e_1) \quad \text{if} \quad e_2 \geq e_1 \geq 0$$

Examples of loss functions with these properties are: e^2, e^4, and $|e|$. A selection of loss functions are illustrated in Figure 8.3. The non-linear threshold type is used in instances where a band of error may be acceptable (i.e. a defined error tolerance exists). In the squared error function, e^2, small errors have less emphasis than in comparison to large errors (in contrast to the modulus cost function, $|e|$, which gives equal weight to all errors). Since either $\{x(n)\}$ or $\{y(n)\}$ may have a random component, $\{e(n)\}$ may be a random sequence. Hence an optimal or best choice for the linear filter is that which minimises a cost function $l(.)$, which is the expected value of the loss function $f(.)$.

$$l(e(n)) = E[f(e(n))]$$

The most commonly used cost function, and the one adopted here, is the mean-square error [Wiener] (MSE) $\xi(n)$.

$$\xi(n) = E[e^2(n)] \tag{8.2}$$

Thus the optimal filter is defined as that filter of the set of all possible linear filters which minimises the MSE.

8.3 THE WIENER FIR FILTER

The output $\hat{x}(n)$ of a causal linear filter may be written as the convolution of the input sequence $\{y(n)\}$ and the impulse response sequence $\{h_n\}$.

$$\hat{x}(n) = \sum_{i=0}^{+\infty} h_i \, y(n-i)$$

This is by definition an IIR filter since it includes terms to $h_\infty y(n-\infty)$. In this chapter only FIR filters are considered. The output of a FIR filter of order $N-1$ may be written as a finite summation of N products since

$$h_n = 0 \quad \text{for} \quad n \geq N, n < 0$$

Thus

$$\hat{x}(n) = \sum_{i=0}^{N-1} h_i \, y(n-i)$$

This finite sum of products may be written more compactly as a vector inner product.

$$\hat{x}(n) = \underline{h}^T \underline{y}(n) = \underline{y}^T(n) \underline{h} \tag{8.3}$$

where $\underline{h}$ is a column vector containing the N non-zero elements of the impulse response sequence $\{ h_n \}$

$$\underline{h} = [h_0 \ h_1 \ \cdots \ h_{N-1}]^T$$

and $\underline{y}(n)$ is a column vector containing the last N elements of the input sequence $\{ y(n) \}$.

$$\underline{y}(n) = [y(n) \ y(n-1) \ \cdots \ y(n-N+1)]^T$$

The superscript T denotes vector or matrix transposition. The structure of a FIR filter is illustrated in Figure 8.4.

If the sequences $\{ x(n) \}$ and $\{ y(n) \}$ are wide sense stationary then substitution of equations (8.1) and (8.3) into (8.2) yields an expression for the MSE cost function

$$\xi = E[\{ x(n) - \underline{h}^T \underline{y}(n) \}^2]$$

$$= E[x^2(n) - 2 \underline{h}^T \underline{y}(n) x(n) + \underline{h}^T \underline{y}(n) \underline{y}^T(n) \underline{h}]$$

$$= E[x^2(n)] - 2 \underline{h}^T \underline{\phi}_{yx} + \underline{h}^T \underline{\phi}_{yy} \underline{h} \tag{8.4}$$

where $\underline{\phi}_{yy}$ is an $(N \times N)$ autocorrelation matrix

$$\underline{\phi}_{yy} = E[\underline{y}(n) \underline{y}^T(n)] \tag{8.5}$$

and $\underline{\phi}_{yx}$ is an N element cross-correlation vector.

$$\underline{\phi}_{yx} = E[\underline{y}(n) x(n)] \tag{8.6}$$

Thus for a FIR filter the MSE cost function has a quadratic form in the impulse response vector $\underline{h}$. The minimum MSE is obtained by differentiating the MSE with respect to each element of the impulse response, h_j, in turn and then setting all the differentials equal to zero simultaneously.

$$\frac{\partial \xi}{\partial h_j} = E[\frac{\partial}{\partial h_j} \{ e^2(n) \}]$$

$$= E[2 e(n) \frac{\partial e(n)}{\partial h_j}]$$

$$= E[2 e(n) \frac{\partial}{\partial h_j} \{ x(n) - \underline{h}^T \underline{y}(n) \}]$$

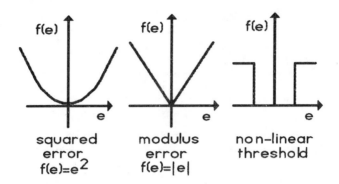

Figure 8.3   Loss functions.

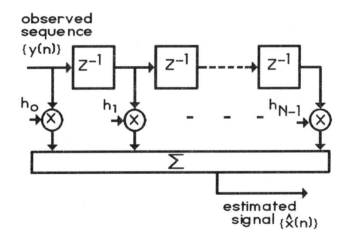

Figure 8.4   A FIR estimator.

$$= E[\,2\,e(n)\,\frac{\partial}{\partial h_j}\{\,-h_j\,y(n-j)\,\}\,]$$

$$= E[\,-2\,e(n)\,y(n-j)\,]$$

$$= 0 \quad \text{for } j = 0,1,...,N-1$$

This set of N scalar equations summarises the principle of statistical orthogonality for a FIR estimator. In words, the output error, $e(n)$, associated with an optimal filter is uncorrelated with any of the observations, $y(n), y(n-1), \cdots y(n-N+1)$, which are currently in the filter. This set of equations can also be written more compactly in vector form by collecting all the differential terms together into a vector which is known as the gradient vector $\underline{\nabla}$.

$$\underline{\nabla} = \begin{bmatrix} \partial\xi/\partial h_0 \\ \partial\xi/\partial h_1 \\ . \\ \partial\xi/\partial h_j \\ . \\ \partial\xi/\partial h_{N-1} \end{bmatrix} = -2\,E \begin{bmatrix} y(n)\,e(n) \\ y(n-1)\,e(n) \\ . \\ y(n-j)\,e(n) \\ . \\ y(n-N+1)\,e(n) \end{bmatrix}$$

$$= -2\,E\left\{ \begin{bmatrix} y(n) \\ y(n-1) \\ . \\ y(n-j) \\ . \\ y(n-N+1) \end{bmatrix} e(n) \right\}$$

$$= -2\,E[\,\underline{y}(n)\,e(n)\,]$$

$$= -2\,E[\,\underline{y}(n)\,(\,x(n) - \underline{y}^T(n)\,\underline{h}\,)\,]$$

$$= -2\,E[\,\underline{y}(n)\,x(n)\,] + 2\,E[\,\underline{y}(n)\underline{y}^T(n)\,]\,\underline{h}$$

$$= 0 \qquad\qquad\qquad\qquad (8.7)$$

Hence:

$$\underline{\nabla} = -2\,\underline{\phi}_{yx} + 2\,\underline{\phi}_{yy}\,\underline{h} = 0$$

The optimum impulse response h_{opt} which minimises the MSE is thus the solution to a set of N simultaneous linear equations.

$$\underline{\phi}_{yy} \, \underline{h}_{opt} = \underline{\phi}_{yx} \tag{8.8}$$

If the power spectral density of the input sequence $\{ y(n) \}$ has no nulls i.e. frequencies where it is zero, then the autocorrelation matrix $\underline{\phi}_{yy}$ is positive definite and hence is nonsingular. Under this condition, the optimum impulse response is unique and is is given by

$$\underline{h}_{opt} = \underline{\phi}_{yy}^{-1} \, \underline{\phi}_{yx} \tag{8.9}$$

The filter defined by (8.9) is the Wiener FIR filter or Levinson filter. The minimum MSE, ξ_{opt}, is obtained by substitution of equation (8.9) in (8.4).

$$\xi_{opt} = E[\, x^2(n) \,] - \underline{h}_{opt}^T \, \underline{\phi}_{yx} \tag{8.10}$$

Equation (8.9) provides a means for designing optimum linear FIR filters. However in order to calculate the impulse response of the optimum filter precise knowledge of the autocorrelation matrix and the cross correlation vector is required.

8.4 A SIMPLE EXAMPLE OF A WIENER ESTIMATOR

In this section a simple example of a Wiener estimator is considered where the signal is a sinusoid with a period of 8.

$$x(n) = \sin\left(\frac{n\pi}{4}\right)$$

The observed signal is a noisy version of this periodic signal.

$$y(n) = x(n) + \eta(n)$$

The term $\eta(n)$ is an element of a white noise sequence with variance σ_η. In order to reduce the algebra the FIR filter is chosen to have 4 coefficients. Thus:

$$\hat{x}(n) = \sum_{i=0}^{3} h_i \, y(n-i)$$

The first step in calculating the coefficients of the Wiener FIR filter is to generate the autocorrelation matrix, $\underline{\phi}_{yy}$.

$$\underline{\phi}_{yy} = E \left\{ \begin{bmatrix} y(n) \\ y(n-1) \\ y(n-2) \\ y(n-3) \end{bmatrix} [\, y(n)\ y(n-1)\ y(n-2)\ y(n-3)\,] \right\}$$

$$= E \begin{bmatrix} y^2(n) & y(n)\,y(n-1) & y(n)\,y(n-2) & y(n)\,y(n-3) \\ y(n-1)\,y(n) & y^2(n-1) & y(n-1)\,y(n-2) & y(n-1)\,y(n-3) \\ y(n-2)\,y(n) & y(n-2)\,y(n-1) & y^2(n-2) & y(n-2)\,y(n-3) \\ y(n-3)\,y(n) & y(n-3)\,y(n-1) & y(n-3)\,y(n-2) & y^2(n-3) \end{bmatrix} \quad (8.11)$$

It should be noted that because the processes involved are stationary all the terms on the right hand side of equation (8.11) may be generated from the first row of the matrix.

$$E[\,y^2(n)\,] = E[\,y^2(n-1)\,] = E[\,y^2(n-2)\,] = E[\,y^2(n-3)\,]$$

$$E[\,y(n)\,y(n-1)\,] = E[\,y(n-1)\,y(n-2)\,] = E[\,y(n-2)\,y(n-3)\,]$$

$$E[\,y(n)\,y(n-2)\,] = E[\,y(n-1)\,y(n-3)\,]$$

Using the above identities equation (8.11) may be simplified.

$$\underline{\phi}_{yy} = E \begin{bmatrix} y^2(n) & y(n)\,y(n-1) & y(n)\,y(n-2) & y(n)\,y(n-3) \\ y(n)\,y(n-1) & y^2(n) & y(n)\,y(n-1) & y(n)\,y(n-2) \\ y(n)\,y(n-2) & y(n)\,y(n-1) & y^2(n) & y(n)\,y(n-1) \\ y(n)\,y(n-3) & y(n)\,y(n-2) & y(n)\,y(n-1) & y^2(n) \end{bmatrix} \quad (8.12)$$

Such a matrix is symmetric Toeplitz. The generation of the elements of this matrix is straightforward in this example since only the diagonal terms are affected by the noise term, $\eta(n)$, and all other terms may be generated from the deterministic signal component, $x(n)$, which has only 8 discrete states, with the specified sampling interval.

$$\phi_{yy}(l) = E[\,y(n)\,y(n-l)\,]$$

$$= E[\,\{x(n) + \eta(n)\}\{x(n-l) + \eta(n-l)\}\,]$$

$$= E[\,x(n)\,x(n-l)\,] + E[\,x(n)\,\eta(n-l)\,] + E[\,x(n-l)\,\eta(n)\,] + E[\,\eta(n)\,\eta(n-l)\,]$$

$$= E[\,x(n)\,x(n-l)\,] + \sigma_\eta\,\delta(l)$$

The term $\delta(l)$ is the dirac function i.e.

$$\delta(l) = 1 \quad \text{if } l = 0$$

$$= 0 \quad \text{if } |l| > 0$$

For a deterministic signal such as $x(n)$ the autocorrelation can be calculated by taking a time average.

$$E[x(n)x(n-l)] = \lim_{L \to \infty} \frac{1}{2L+1} \sum_{n=-L}^{L} x(n)x(n-l)$$

However as $x(n)$ is also periodic with period 8 this expression can be simplified to summation of 8 sample pairs.

$$E[x(n)x(n-l)] = \frac{1}{8} \sum_{n=0}^{7} x(n)x(n-l)$$

$$= \frac{1}{8} \sum_{n=0}^{7} \sin\left(\frac{n\pi}{4}\right) \sin\left(\frac{(n-l)\pi}{4}\right)$$

$$= \frac{1}{2} \cos\left(\frac{l\pi}{4}\right)$$

This calculation is illustrated in Figure 8.5 for $l = 0,1,2$. The actual value of the autocorrelation matrix is:

$$\phi_{yy} = \begin{bmatrix} (\frac{1}{2}+\sigma_\eta) & \frac{1}{2\sqrt{2}} & 0 & \frac{-1}{2\sqrt{2}} \\ \frac{1}{2\sqrt{2}} & (\frac{1}{2}+\sigma_\eta) & \frac{1}{2\sqrt{2}} & 0 \\ 0 & \frac{1}{2\sqrt{2}} & (\frac{1}{2}+\sigma_\eta) & \frac{1}{2\sqrt{2}} \\ \frac{-1}{2\sqrt{2}} & 0 & \frac{1}{2\sqrt{2}} & (\frac{1}{2}+\sigma_\eta) \end{bmatrix}$$

In order to calculate the Wiener weight vector, h_{opt}, the cross-correlation vector, ϕ_{yx}, must also be generated.

$$\phi_{yx} = E\left\{ x(n) \begin{bmatrix} y(n) \\ y(n-1) \\ y(n-2) \\ y(n-3) \end{bmatrix} \right\} = E\left\{ \begin{bmatrix} x^2(n) \\ x(n)x(n-1) \\ x(n)x(n-2) \\ x(n)x(n-3) \end{bmatrix} \right\}$$

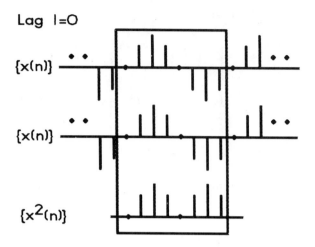

Figure 8.5(a)   Calculation of autocorrelation coefficient, lag $l = 0$.

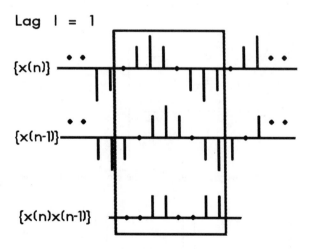

Figure 8.5(b)   Calculation of autocorrelation coefficient, lag $l = 1$.

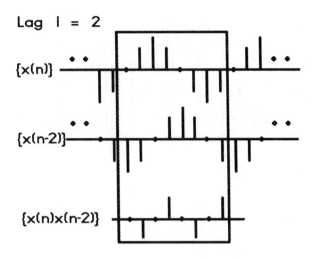

Figure 8.5(c)   Calculation of autocorrelation coefficient, lag l = 2.

The elements of this vector are the correlation coefficients of the periodic sequence, $\{x(n)\}$, and have already been calculated.

$$
\underline{\phi}_{yx} =
\begin{bmatrix}
\dfrac{1}{2} \\[2mm]
\dfrac{1}{2\sqrt{2}} \\[2mm]
0 \\[2mm]
\dfrac{-1}{2\sqrt{2}}
\end{bmatrix}
$$

The Wiener optimum, $\underline{h}_{opt}$, is then obtained by solving 4 simultaneous linear equations.

$$
\begin{bmatrix}
(\frac{1}{2}+\sigma_\eta) & \frac{1}{2\sqrt{2}} & 0 & \frac{-1}{2\sqrt{2}} \\
\frac{1}{2\sqrt{2}} & (\frac{1}{2}+\sigma_\eta) & \frac{1}{2\sqrt{2}} & 0 \\
0 & \frac{1}{2\sqrt{2}} & (\frac{1}{2}+\sigma_\eta) & \frac{1}{2\sqrt{2}} \\
\frac{-1}{2\sqrt{2}} & 0 & \frac{1}{2\sqrt{2}} & (\frac{1}{2}+\sigma_\eta)
\end{bmatrix}
\begin{bmatrix} h_0 \\ h_1 \\ h_2 \\ h_3 \end{bmatrix}
=
\begin{bmatrix} \frac{1}{2} \\ \frac{1}{2\sqrt{2}} \\ 0 \\ \frac{-1}{2\sqrt{2}} \end{bmatrix}
$$

The solution is:

$$
\underline{h}_{opt} =
\begin{bmatrix} h_0 \\ h_1 \\ h_2 \\ h_3 \end{bmatrix}
=
\frac{1}{2(1+\sigma_\eta)}
\begin{bmatrix} 1 \\ \frac{1}{\sqrt{2}} \\ 0 \\ \frac{-1}{\sqrt{2}} \end{bmatrix}
$$

The result for $\underline{h}_{opt}$ is the matched filter in the sinusoidal input case. The minimum MSE may be easily obtained from equation (8.10).

$$
\xi_{opt} = \frac{1}{2} - \frac{1}{2(1+\sigma_\eta)}
$$

$$
= \frac{\sigma_\eta}{2(1+\sigma_\eta)}
$$

Therefore with $\sigma_\eta = 0$ the MSE is zero, and with 0 dB signal to noise ratio (i.e. $\sigma_\eta = 1/2$) the final MSE is 1/6 (with the MSE before the estimation process being 1/2).

If the length of the FIR filter was reduced to 3 coefficients the autocorrelation and cross correlation terms would remain the same. However fewer terms would be required since the autocorrelation matrix is now (3×3)

$$
\underline{\phi}_{yy} =
\begin{bmatrix}
(\frac{1}{2}+\sigma_\eta) & \frac{1}{2\sqrt{2}} & 0 \\
\frac{1}{2\sqrt{2}} & (\frac{1}{2}+\sigma_\eta) & \frac{1}{2\sqrt{2}} \\
0 & \frac{1}{2\sqrt{2}} & (\frac{1}{2}+\sigma_\eta)
\end{bmatrix}
$$

and the cross correlation vector contains only three terms.

$$\underline{\phi}_{yx} = \begin{bmatrix} \dfrac{1}{2} \\[2ex] \dfrac{1}{2\sqrt{2}} \\[2ex] 0 \end{bmatrix}$$

The Wiener optimum is obtained by solving 3 simultaneous equations to yield:

$$\underline{h}_{opt} = \begin{bmatrix} \dfrac{(3 + 4\sigma_\eta)}{4(1 + 2\sigma_\eta)(1 + \sigma_\eta)} \\[3ex] \dfrac{1}{2\sqrt{2}(1 + \sigma_\eta)} \\[3ex] \dfrac{-1}{4(1 + 2\sigma_\eta)(1 + \sigma_\eta)} \end{bmatrix}$$

with corresponding minimum MSE provided by

$$\xi_{opt} = \frac{\sigma_\eta(3 + 4\sigma_\eta)}{4(1 + 2\sigma_\eta)(1 + \sigma_\eta)} \;.$$

It is instructive to compare the performance of the 3 coefficient filter with the 4 coefficient filter. To do this it is simplest to consider a low noise scenario that is when $\sigma_\eta \ll 1/2$. In this case the 3 coefficient filter achieves a minimum MSE of $3\sigma_\eta/4$ compared with the 4 coefficient filter which achieves a min MSE of $\sigma_\eta/2$. Thus in increasing the length of the filter from 3 to 4 coefficients the minimum MSE has been reduced.

8.5 SUMMARY

In this chapter the Wiener FIR filter has been used as an introduction to the concepts of optimal linear MSE estimation. An important property of such estimators is the orthogonality between the error sequence and the observed sequence. This property is used again in chapter 9 in the derivation of the scalar Kalman filter. Because the design of the Wiener filter requires knowledge of the associated autocorrelation and cross correlation functions, is rarely used in practical application. However the importance of the Wiener FIR filter lies in its role in the design of adaptive FIR filters (chapter 10) where it can be used as a benchmark against which performance can be measured.

TUTORIAL Wiener Filters.

1.   A signal source consists of a white noise generator with a variance σ_v^2. Construct the autocorrelation matrix of order 4 and find its inverse.

2.   A signal source consists of a perfect square wave of unit amplitude with additive noise of variance σ_x^2. The signal is sampled by a processor which has a sampling rate exactly 4 times the fundamental frequency of the square wave. This processor is used to define the autocorrelation matrix of the signal (of order 4). Determine the value of this matrix and its inverse.

3.   Given the input signal defined in question 2 it is desired to determine a 4 tap FIR filter which will give an output which is a triangular waveform with a peak amplitude of 4. Determine the impulse response of this filter. If the variance of the input signal is allowed to tend to zero what values do the impulse response elements assume? Why is it necessary to perform this calculation assuming that the signal is noise corrupted in the first instance?

Chapter 9

KALMAN FILTERS

9.1 INTRODUCTION

The Wiener filter, discussed in chapter 8, is finite impulse response (FIR) in nature and optimal only for stationary signals. The Kalman filter [Kalman] on the other hand is usually infinite impulse response in nature and hence can provide the best linear estimate of a signal. Further there is also a capacity for dealing with non-stationary signals. In this chapter the scalar Kalman filter [Bozic] will be derived. This approach highlights the essential features of the Kalman filter and its relationship to the Wiener FIR filter without the necessity of handling the matrix manipulation associated with the full vector form. The vector form of the filter is then developed by analogy to the scalar form, using state-space concepts. It is the vector form of the filter and the related capability to handle multiple-input multiple-output systems that has lead to the popularity of the Kalman filter, finding application in many diverse fields. Some of these applications include radar tracking, inertial navigation and communications channel equalisation. Finally an example is presented of a vector Kalman filter as a communications channel equaliser [Lawrence & Kaufman].

9.2 THE SCALAR KALMAN FILTER

A common data or signal processing problem is to estimate the values of a finite data sequence $\{ x(j) \}$ i.e.

$$x(0), x(1), x(2), \cdots x(j), \cdots x(n)$$

from a second sequence of noisy observations $\{ y(j) \}$,

$$y(0), y(1), y(2), \cdots y(j), \cdots y(n)$$

which are somehow related to the first sequence. A linear estimate, $\hat{x}(n)$, of the sample $x(n)$ may be obtained by forming a weighted sum of all the available observations (Figure 9.1).

$$\hat{x}(n) = \sum_{j=0}^{n} h_j(n) \, y(j)$$

$h_j(n)$ is the *jth* weight used to form an estimate of $x(n)$. Since all the available observations are used in forming the estimate, it has the capability of being the best linear estimate that is possible.

An optimal mean-square error (MSE) estimator is obtained by choosing the weights to minimise the MSE cost function $\xi(n)$.

$$\xi(n) = E[\,(\,x(n) - \hat{x}(n)\,)^2\,] \qquad (9.1)$$

To find the optimal set of weights differentiate the cost function with respect to each weight and set each differential equal to zero simultaneously.

$$\frac{\partial \xi(n)}{\partial h_j(n)} = -2\,E[\,(\,x(n) - \hat{x}(n)\,)\,y(j)\,] = 0 \qquad (9.2)$$

$$for \ j = 0, 1, 2, \cdots n$$

This is the principle of statistical orthogonality i.e. the error in the estimate, $e(n)$, where

$$e(n) = x(n) - \hat{x}(n)\,,$$

is not correlated with any element of the observation sequence from $y(0)$ to $y(n)$. The minimum MSE, $p(n)$, is the value of $\xi(n)$ achieved by the optimal estimator. An expression for $p(n)$ is obtained by combining equations (9.1) and (9.2).

$$p(n) = minimum \ \xi(n)$$

$$= E[\,e^2(n)\,]$$

$$= E[\,e(n)\,(\,x(n) - \hat{x}(n)\,)\,]$$

$$= E[\,e(n)\,x(n)\,] \qquad (9.3)$$

So far the development has been almost identical to the derivation of the Wiener FIR filter presented in chapter 8. The only exception being that the principle of statistical orthogonality has been emphasised rather than the explicit calculation of a set of filter weights.

The difference between the Kalman filter and the Wiener FIR filter becomes more evident when the next observation, $y(n+1)$, becomes available and an estimate, $\hat{x}(n+1)$, of the associated signal sample $x(n+1)$ is required. In order to preserve the best linear estimator property all the available observations from $y(0)$ to $y(n+1)$ must be used in forming the estimate $\hat{x}(n+1)$. An optimal minimum MSE estimate, $\hat{x}(n+1)$, of the data sample $x(n+1)$ can be obtained by forming a weighted sum of all observations from $y(0)$ to $y(n+1)$ (Figure 9.2).

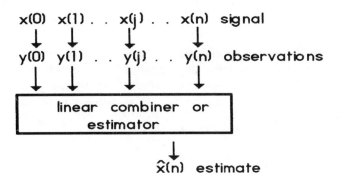

Figure 9.1   The estimation problem.

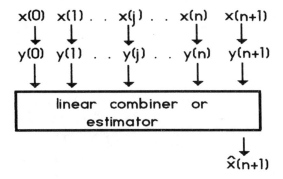

Figure 9.2   A new estimation problem.

$$\hat{x}(n+1) = \sum_{j=0}^{n+1} h_j(n+1) \, y(j)$$

Unlike the Wiener FIR filter this would require the calculation of a completely new set of weights. Also the number of weights would increase as the number of available observations increases. In order to avoid this increase in computation it is natural to ask if it is possible to calculate $\hat{x}(n+1)$ from $\hat{x}(n)$. If such a recursive solution exists it will have the general form

$$\hat{x}(n+1) = b(n+1)\,\hat{x}(n) + k(n+1)\,y(n+1) \tag{9.4}$$

where $b(n+1)$ and $k(n+1)$ are suitable chosen weights.

In order to proceed further it is necessary to make some assumptions about the sequence $\{x(n)\}$. In [Kalman] this sequence is assumed to be a first order Markov process i.e.

$$x(n+1) = a(n+1)\,x(n) + g(n+1) \tag{9.5}$$

where $a(n+1)$ is a time varying feedback coefficient and $g(n+1)$ is white noise with variance $\sigma_g(n+1)$. Each observation, $y(n+1)$, is formed by multiplying $x(n+1)$ by a gain term, $c(n+1)$, and adding a white noise term, $v(n+1)$, with variance $\sigma_v(n+1)$ to the product i.e.

$$y(n+1) = c(n+1)\,x(n+1) + v(n+1) \,. \tag{9.6}$$

The complete arrangement is illustrated in Figure 9.3. In the subsequent discussion only a non time varying Markov model will be considered in order to simplify the notation and the algebra. Thus the time index $(n+1)$ on the parameters $a(n+1)$, $c(n+1)$, $\sigma_g(n+1)$ and $\sigma_v(n+1)$ will be dropped.

The principle of statistical orthogonality is then applied to the Markov signal model in order to calculate values for the coefficients, $b(n+1)$ and $k(n+1)$, associated with the recursive estimate of equation (9.4). Two particular conditions are identified:

(i)   The error, $e(n+1)$, in the new estimate, $\hat{x}(n+1)$, must be orthogonal to all previous observations from $y(0)$ to $y(n)$ e.g.

$$E[\,e(n+1)\,y(n)\,] = 0 \tag{9.7}$$

(ii) The error, $e(n+1)$, in the new estimate, $\hat{x}(n+1)$, must be orthogonal to the latest measurement, $y(n+1)$, i.e.

$$E[\,e(n+1)\,y(n+1)\,] = 0 \tag{9.8}$$

Condition (i) can be used to obtain a relationship between $b(n+1)$ and $k(n+1)$ and hence gain insight into the structure of the optimal recursive estimator. Substituting for $x(n+1)$ and $\hat{x}(n+1)$ using equations (9.5) and (9.4) respectively yields the following result.

$$E[\, e(n+1) \, y(n) \,]$$

$$= E[\, \{ x(n+1) - \hat{x}(n+1) \} \, y(n) \,]$$

$$= E[\, \{ a \, x(n) + g(n+1) - b(n+1) \, \hat{x}(n) - k(n+1) \, y(n+1) \} \, y(n) \,]$$

$$= 0$$

The white noise terms $g(n+1)$ and $v(n+1)$ occur after $y(n)$ in time and hence must uncorrelated with it (e.g. $E[\, g(n+1) \, y(n) \,] = 0$). Finally substitution for $y(n+1)$ using a combination of equations (9.5) and (9.6) yields the following:

$$E[\, e(n+1) \, y(n) \,] = E[\, \{ (1 - k(n+1)) \, a \, x(n) - b(n+1) \, \hat{x}(n) \} \, y(n) \,]$$

$$= 0 \qquad\qquad\qquad (9.9)$$

Equation (9.9) will be satisfied if

$$(1 - k(n+1)) \, a = b(n+1) \qquad\qquad (9.10)$$

in which case

$$E[\, e(n+1) \, y(n) \,] = E[\, e(n) \, y(n) \,] = 0 \, .$$

In words, the relationship between $k(n+1)$ and $b(n+1)$ summarised in equation (9.10) ensures that if the error $e(n)$ is orthogonal to all observations from $y(0)$ to $y(n)$ then the error $e(n+1)$ will also be orthogonal to them.

The structure of the optimal recursive estimator is obtained by substituting equation (9.10) in equation (9.4).

$$\hat{x}(n+1) = (1 - k(n+1)) \, a \, \hat{x}(n) + k(n+1) \, y(n+1)$$

$$= a \, \hat{x}(n) + k(n+1) \, (y(n+1) - c \, a \, \hat{x}(n)) \qquad (9.11)$$

This is a predictor-corrector structure and is illustrated in Figure 9.4. The term $a\hat{x}(n)$ is an estimate of $x(n+1)$ based on all observations from $y(0)$ to $y(n)$ i.e. a prediction. The term $ca\hat{x}(n)$ is a prediction of $y(n+1)$ based on the same set of observations. The correction term or innovation is formed by taking the observation $y(n+1)$ and subtracting from it the prediction $ca\hat{x}(n)$.

Condition (ii) is then used to find a recursion for $k(n+1)$, the Kalman gain. Substituting for $x(n+1)$, $y(n+1)$ and $\hat{x}(n+1)$ using equations (9.5), (9.6) and (9.11) respectively yields the following:

$$E[\, e(n+1) \, y(n+1) \,]$$

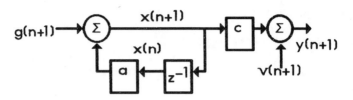

Figure 9.3   First order Markov process.

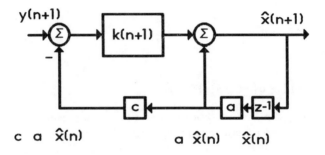

Figure 9.4   Structure of recursive estimator.

$$= E[\{ x(n+1) - \hat{x}(n+1) \} y(n+1)]$$

$$= (1 - k(n+1) c) c \{ a^2 E[e(n) x(n)] + \sigma_g \} - k(n+1) \sigma_v$$

$$= 0 \tag{9.12}$$

The correlation term, $E[e(n)x(n)]$, is recognisable as the minimum MSE, $p(n)$, of equation (9.3). After re-arrangement equation (9.12) provides an expression for the Kalman gain, $k(n+1)$, in terms of the minimum MSE, $p(n)$.

$$k(n+1) = \frac{c \{ a^2 p(n) + \sigma_g \}}{c^2 \{ a^2 p(n) + \sigma_g \} + \sigma_v} \tag{9.13}$$

In order to complete the recursion for $k(n+1)$ an expression for $p(n)$ in terms of $k(n)$ is required. Such an expression can be obtained from equation (9.3) by substituting for $x(n)$ and $\hat{x}(n)$ using equations (9.5) and (9.11) respectively.

$$p(n) = E[e(n) x(n)]$$

$$= (1 - k(n) c) \{ a^2 p(n-1) + \sigma_g \} \tag{9.14}$$

The scalar Kalman filter is defined by equations (9.11), (9.13) and (9.14) and summarised in Table 9.1.

9.3 THE VECTOR KALMAN FILTER

Rarely in practice is the first order Markov model of equations (9.5) and (9.6) sufficient to adequately characterise a signal or process. The solution adopted by Kalman was to employ state space techniques and model the signal as a first order vector Markov process. The resulting system description is then very similar in form to equations (9.5) and (9.6). The only difference being that the scalars used in (9.5) and (9.6) are replaced by vectors and matrices. The great strength of the approach is that the derivation of the vector Kalman filter is very similar to the technique described in section 9.2 and the resulting vector Kalman filter is similar in form to scalar Kalman filter of Table 9.1.

The application of the vector Kalman filter to a high order scalar process is best illustrated by a simple example. Consider a second order autoregressive process defined by:

$$x(n+1) = \alpha x(n) + \beta x(n-1) + g(n+1) \tag{9.15}$$

The observations are formed by:

$$y(n+1) = \gamma x(n+1) + \delta x(n) + v(n+1) \tag{9.16}$$

$\hat{x}(n+1)$	$=$	$a\,\hat{x}(n) + k(n+1)\,(\,y(n+1) - c\,a\,\hat{x}(n)\,)$
$k(n+1)$	$=$	$\dfrac{p_1(n+1)\,c}{c^2\,p_1(n+1) + \sigma_v}$
$p_1(n+1)$	$=$	$a^2\,p(n) + \sigma_g$
$p(n)$	$=$	$(\,1 - k(n)\,c\,)\,p_1(n)$

Table 9.1 Scalar Kalman filter.

Again $g(n)$ and $v(n)$ are white noise processes. Equations (9.15) and (9.16) define a second order system and hence can be described by two state variables.

$$x_1(n) = x(n)$$

$$x_2(n) = x(n-1)$$

Equation (9.15) may be rewritten as a pair of state equations,

$$x_1(n+1) = \alpha\,x_1(n) + \beta\,x_2(n) + g(n+1) \tag{9.17a}$$

$$x_2(n+1) = x_1(n) \tag{9.17b}$$

and as a matrix equation,

$$\begin{bmatrix} x_1(n+1) \\ x_2(n+1) \end{bmatrix} = \begin{bmatrix} \alpha & \beta \\ 1 & 0 \end{bmatrix} \begin{bmatrix} x_1(n) \\ x_2(n) \end{bmatrix} + \begin{bmatrix} g(n+1) \\ 0 \end{bmatrix}$$

or more compactly as

$$\underline{x}(n+1) = \underline{A}\,\underline{x}(n) + \underline{g}(n+1)\,. \tag{9.18}$$

The vector $\underline{x}(n)$ containing the two state variables is the state vector and equation (9.18) is the state transition equation. The observation equation is obtained by re-writing equation (9.16) in matrix form.

$$y(n+1) = [\,\gamma\,\delta\,] \begin{bmatrix} x_1(n+1) \\ x_2(n+1) \end{bmatrix} + v(n+1)$$

$$\underline{y}(n+1) = \underline{C}\,\underline{x}(n+1) + \underline{v}(n+1) \tag{9.19}$$

The second order scalar system of equations (9.15) and (9.16) has now been reformulated as a the first order vector system of equations (9.18) and (9.19). This first order vector system, illustrated in Figure 9.5(a), is similar in structure to the first order scalar system of equations (9.5) and (9.6) and Figure 9.3. The Kalman filter for this vector estimation problem is summarised in the following equations:

$$\hat{x}(n+1) = A\ \hat{x}(n) + K(n+1)\ (\ y(n+1) - C\ A\ \hat{x}(n)\ ) \tag{9.20}$$

$$K(n+1) = P_1(n+1)\ C\ [\ C\ P_1(n+1)\ C^T + Z(n)\ ]^{-1} \tag{9.21}$$

$$P_1(n+1) = A\ P(n)\ A + Q(n+1) \tag{9.22}$$

$$P(n) = (\ 1 - K(n)\ C\ )\ P_1(n) \tag{9.23}$$

where the scalar observation noise σ_v and the system noise variance σ_g have been replaced by matrices $Z(n)$ and $Q(n)$ respectively.

$$Z(n) = E[\ v(n)\ v^T(n)\ ]$$

$$Q(n) = E[\ g(n)\ g^T(n)\ ]$$

Similarly the Kalman gain has been replaced by a matrix, $K(n)$. The structure of the vector Kalman filter is illustrated in Figure 9.5(b). The following section demonstrates an example of the use of the vector Kalman filter in communications equalisation.

9.4 THE VECTOR KALMAN FILTER AS A CHANNEL EQUALISER

The example taken here to illustrate the operation of the Kalman filter is that of channel equalisation [Lawrence & Kaufman]. This is required when a random data sequence is transmitted over a distorting communications channel causing intersymbol interference (ISI) and it is then necessary to filter or equalise the channel to recover the original data sequence. A digital communications channel with intersymbol interference may be modelled by an equivalent discrete time transversal filter with additive white noise at the output. Thus the channel output $y(n)$ may be written in terms of the channel input $g(n)$, which can be assumed to be a white noise process, and the additive noise term $v(n)$ as,

$$y(n) = C^T\ x(n) + v(n) \tag{9.24}$$

where C is the vector of the channel coefficients (Figure 9.6). To ease the notation only a 3-tap channel will be considered hence

$$C^T = [\ c_0\ c_1\ c_2\ ] .$$

The state vector $x(n)$ contains the last 3 inputs to the channel.

(a)

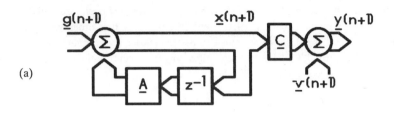

(b)

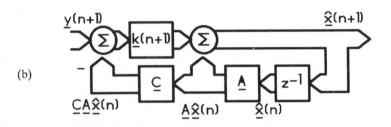

Figure 9.5   State space realisation: (a) first order vector Markov process; (b) vector Kalman filter.

$$\underline{x}^T(n) = [\, g(n)\, g(n-1)\, g(n-2)\,]$$

In other words the state vector contains the contents of the shift register of Figure 9.6. The state transition equation is therefore,

$$\begin{bmatrix} x(n+1) \\ x(n) \\ x(n-1) \end{bmatrix} = \begin{bmatrix} 0\,0\,0 \\ 1\,0\,0 \\ 0\,1\,0 \end{bmatrix} \begin{bmatrix} x(n) \\ x(n-1) \\ x(n-2) \end{bmatrix} + \begin{bmatrix} g(n+1) \\ 0 \\ 0 \end{bmatrix}$$

$$\underline{x}(n+1) = \underline{A}\, \underline{x}(n) + \underline{g}(n+1) \tag{9.25}$$

The observation equation is then obtained directly from (9.24).

The vector state equations (9.24) and (9.25) yield values for the system matrices $\underline{A}$, $\underline{C}$, $\underline{Z}$ and $\underline{Q}$.

$$\underline{A} = \begin{bmatrix} 0\,0\,0 \\ 1\,0\,0 \\ 0\,1\,0 \end{bmatrix}$$

$$\underline{C}^T = [\, c_0\, c_1\, c_2\,]$$

$$\underline{Z} = E[\,\underline{v}\,\underline{v}^T\,] = \begin{bmatrix} \sigma_v\,0\,0 \\ 0\,0\,0 \\ 0\,0\,0 \end{bmatrix}$$

$$\underline{Q} = E[\,\underline{g}\,\underline{g}^T\,] = \begin{bmatrix} \sigma_g\,0\,0 \\ 0\,0\,0 \\ 0\,0\,0 \end{bmatrix}$$

The appropriate Kalman filter is obtained by substitution of these values into equations (9.20) to (9.23). For example equation (9.20) can now be written as a set of scalar equations.

$$\hat{x}(n+1) = \hat{x}(n) + k_0(n+1)\,(\,y(n+1) - c_1\,\hat{x}(n) - c_2\,\hat{x}(n-1)\,) \tag{9.26a}$$

$$\hat{x}(n) = \hat{x}(n-1) + k_1(n+1)\,(\,y(n+1) - c_1\,\hat{x}(n) - c_2\,\hat{x}(n-1)\,) \tag{9.26b}$$

$$\hat{x}(n-1) = \hat{x}(n-2) + k_2(n+1)\,(\,y(n+1) - c_1\,\hat{x}(n) - c_2\,\hat{x}(n-1)\,) \tag{9.26c}$$

where

$$\underline{K}(n+1) = [\, k_0(n+1)\, k_1(n+1)\, k_2(n+1)\,]\,.$$

The filter or equaliser described by (9.26) is illustrated in Figure 9.7 showing how the various matrix products are implemented. It should be noted that it is implied that the distorting channel coefficients, $\underline{C}^T$, are known a-priori.

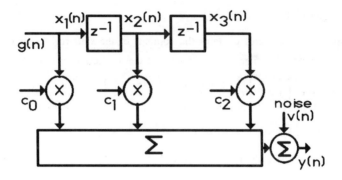

Figure 9.6   Digital communications channel with intersymbol interference (ISI).

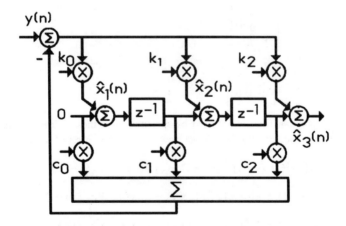

Figure 9.7   Kalman equaliser.

9.5 SUMMARY

The Kalman filter is the best linear estimator for any linear system which can be described as a vector Markov process. Thus the essential first step in the application of the Kalman filter is to form a state space description of the system. The resultant system matrices are then substituted into the Kalman filter equations. Although the Kalman filter is capable of handling the time-varying systems which can be described using state space techniques, the time variations must be embedded in the system matrices and hence their exact form must be known beforehand. The major properties of the Kalman filter are that it provides recursive estimates and that it is capable of handling multiple-input multiple-output systems. Because of these properties it is often found in applications where theoretically it is not an optimum solution e.g. non-linear estimation problems such as radar tracking.

TUTORIAL Kalman Filters

1. A time sequence $\{x(n)\}$ has zero mean and variance σ_x. The generating signal process is first order autoregressive with a white noise signal source, $g(n)$, of variance σ_g and a system parameter a of 0.5. The measurement system has a gain of unity and an additive noise variance of σ_v. Assuming that $\sigma_v = \sigma_g$ derive the steady state value for the Kalman gain of the optimum first order estimator for this process. What is the residual MSE obtained using your filter? $[0.53\ \sigma_v]$

2. A shore based radar system is used to track the movement of ships in the vicinity of a large harbour. Design a Kalman filter based tracking system for this task. The radar makes measurements of the range to a ship and the bearing of a ship every 4 seconds. Range is measured in metres to an accuracy of 4 metres r.m.s. and bearing is measured in degrees to an accuracy 1 degree r.m.s. The ships may be assumed to travel at constant velocity subject to small random accelerations due to the tide and the weather. Assume that these accelerations are zero mean and white with an r.m.s value of 1 m/s/s in each of two orthogonal directions. [**Hint** This problem is not an exact application of the Kalman filter in that the measurements are not linearly related to the states of the system. The usual approach is to invent pseudo-measurements which are linearly related to the states. The design of a Kalman filter based system is a matter of identifying the state matrices which define the motion of a ship and the measurement or pseudo-measurement system.]

Chapter 10
ADAPTIVE FILTER DESIGNS

10.1 INTRODUCTION

The design of optimal filters or estimators such as the Wiener FIR filter of chapter 8 or the Kalman filter of chapter 9 requires explicit knowledge of the environment in the form of correlation functions, state space models or possibly even probability density functions. In many situations such functions are unknown and/or time-varying. An adaptive filter [Honig & Messerschmitt, Widrow & Stearns, Haykin, Mulgrew & Cowan] is a means of realising an optimal estimator in these situations. The 'explicit knowledge' is replaced with a requirement for a second input sequence, known as a training or desired input (Figure 10.1). The training signal is in some sense close to or it approximates the output of an optimal filter. Such an input is available in many practical situations (e.g. echo-cancellation, channel equalisation and speech coding) [Cowan & Grant]. The impulse response of the adaptive filter is then altered as more of the input and training sequence become available, so that the output y more closely approximates (usually in a mean-square error (MSE) sense) the training sequence and hence the output of the optimal filter. The strategy by which the impulse response of the adaptive filter is altered is the adaptive filter algorithm. An adaptive filter is thus a time varying filter whose impulse response at a particular time is dependent on the input sequence, the training sequence and the adaptive filter algorithm. The time varying nature of an adaptive filter gives rise to the concept of convergence. In stationary environment the convergence performance is a measure of how many data samples are required for the impulse response of the adaptive filter to come within a specified distance of the optimal filter. In a non-stationary environment the convergence performance is also a measure of how closely the impulse response of the adaptive filter follows the now time varying impulse response of the optimal filter. Adaptive filters may be both infinite impulse response (IIR) or finite impulse response (FIR) in nature. In this chapter only adaptive FIR filters will be considered.

A general block diagram of an adaptive FIR filter is shown in Figure 10.2. An input data sequence, $\{y(n)\}$, is convolved with a time-varying FIR sequence, $\{h_i(n)\}$ The output of this filter is $\{\hat{x}(n)\}$.

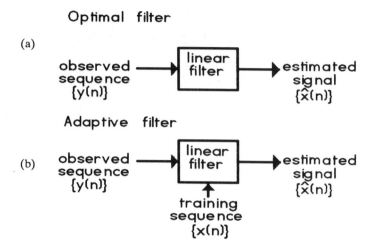

Figure 10.1   A linear filter or estimator: (a) optimal; (b) adaptive.

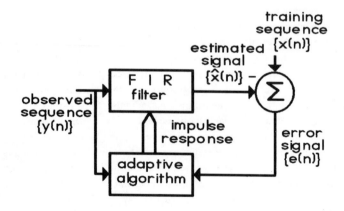

Figure 10.2   General adaptive filter sub-system.

$$\hat{x}(n) = \sum_{i=0}^{N-1} h_i(n) \, y(n-i)$$

This can also be written as a vector inner product.

$$\hat{x}(n) = \underline{h}^T(n) \, \underline{y}(n) = \underline{y}^T(n) \, \underline{h}(n)$$

$$\underline{y}(n) = [\, y(n) \; y(n-1) \; .... \; y(n-N+1) \,]^T$$

$$\underline{h}(n) = [\, h_0(n) \; h_1(n) \; .... \; h_{N-1}(n) \,]^T$$

The filter output, $\hat{x}(n)$, is used as the estimate of the training signal, $x(n)$, and is subtracted from this signal to yield a scalar error signal, $e(n)$.

$$e(n) = x(n) - \hat{x}(n)$$

The error is used in conjunction with the input signal vector, $\underline{y}(n)$, to determine the next set of filter weight values, $\underline{h}(n)$. The eventual objective of the adaptive algorithm is to estimate the optimum impulse response. Usually 'optimum' is defined in a MSE sense in which case the optimum filter in a stationary environment is the Wiener FIR filter of chapter 8.

$$\underline{h}_{opt} = \underline{\phi}_{yy}^{-1} \, \underline{\phi}_{yx} \qquad (10.1)$$

There are basically three modes of operation of an adaptive filter and these are illustrated in Figure 10.3.

(i) Inverse system modelling (Figure 10.3(a)) which is what is normally implied in the communications channel equalisation application.

(ii) Direct system modelling (Figure 10.3(b)) which is typified by the application to echo cancellation.

(iii) Prediction (Figure 10.3(c)), for instance as used in autoregressive spectral analysis (chapter 13) and in the linear predictive coding (LPC) of speech (chapter 16).

In this chapter three classes of adaptive filter algorithm are described. These are: recursive least squares (RLS), stochastic gradient (SG) and self-orthogonalising (SO) algorithms. Their relative convergence performance and computational complexity will also be discussed.

10.2 RECURSIVE LEAST SQUARES

In order to design the Wiener FIR filter of chapter 8, both the autocorrelation matrix, $\underline{\phi}_{yy}$, and the cross correlation vector, $\underline{\phi}_{yx}$, must be known. The Wiener filter being obtained by minimising the MSE cost function, ξ, which is defined using the expectation operator, $E[.]$. Ensemble averages such as $\underline{\phi}_{yy}$ and $\underline{\phi}_{yx}$ are rarely accessible in practice. Rather, what is available, are portions of the data sequences themselves. One method of defining the impulse

(a)

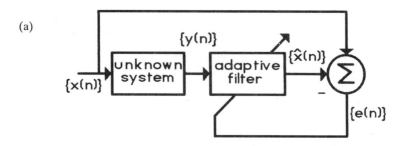

(b)

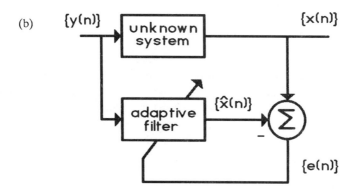

(c)

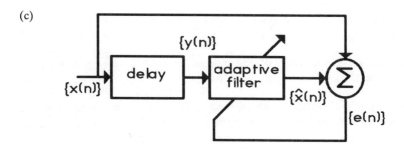

Figure 10.3   Modes of operation: (a) inverse system modelling; (b) direct system modelling; (c) linear prediction.

response of an adaptive filter is to choose the coefficients to minimise a sum of squared errors cost function.

$$\sum_{k=0}^{n} (x(k) - \hat{x}(k))^2 \tag{10.2}$$

Minimisation of this cost function with respect to the impulse response vector, $\underline{h}$, associated with the estimate, $\hat{x}(n)$, leads to a least squares (LS) estimate. The impulse response vector, $\underline{h}(n)$, which minimises the sum of squared errors cost function is now a function of the available data rather than ensemble averages. While an expression for $\underline{h}(n)$ could be derived by a similar method to that employed to derive the Wiener filter, a more elegant approach is to note that the two optimisation problems are similar and obtain the solution by analogy. Since the sum of squared error cost function, (10.2), was obtained from the MSE cost function by replacing expectation with summation, the impulse response vector, $\underline{h}(n)$ can be obtained from (10.1) by replacing expectation with summation. Thus

$$\underline{r}_{yy}(n) \, \underline{h}(n) = \underline{r}_{yx}(n) \tag{10.3}$$

where

$$\underline{r}_{yy}(n) = \sum_{k=0}^{n} \underline{y}(k) \, \underline{y}^T(k) \tag{10.4}$$

and

$$\underline{r}_{yx}(n) = \sum_{k=0}^{n} \underline{y}(k) \, x(k) . \tag{10.5}$$

There is a requirement in many applications of adaptive filters that the impulse response be modified or updated as new data samples appear. The most direct method of meeting this requirement is to increment the upper limits of the summations of equations (10.2), (10.4), and (10.5) and completely resolve equation (10.3). However a computationally more efficient method is to derive a time recursion for $\underline{h}(n)$ in terms of the previous least squares solution $\underline{h}(n-1)$ and the new data, $\underline{y}(n)$ and $x(n)$. The first step is to obtain recursions for $\underline{r}_{yy}(n)$ and $\underline{r}_{yx}(n)$. This is straightforward as they are both defined as summations, equation (10.4) and (10.5).

$$\underline{r}_{yy}(n) = \underline{r}_{yy}(n-1) + \underline{y}(n) \, \underline{y}^T(n) \tag{10.6}$$

$$\underline{r}_{yx}(n) = \underline{r}_{yx}(n-1) + \underline{y}(n) \, x(n) \tag{10.7}$$

Substitute for $\underline{r}_{xy}$ in equation (10.7) using equation (10.3).

$$\underline{r}_{yy}(n) \, \underline{h}(n) = \underline{r}_{yy}(n-1) \, \underline{h}(n-1) + \underline{y}(n) \, x(n)$$

Then use equation (10.6) to replace $r_{yy}(n-1)$.

$$L_{yy}(n) \, \underline{h}(n) = \left(L_{yy}(n) - \underline{y}(n) \, \underline{y}^T(n) \right) \underline{h}(n-1) + \underline{y}(n) \, x(n)$$

After rearrangement this yields

$$\underline{h}(n) = \underline{h}(n-1) + L_{yy}^{-1}(n) \, \underline{y}(n) \, e(n) \tag{10.8}$$

where

$$e(n) = x(n) - \underline{h}^T(n-1) \, \underline{y}(n) . \tag{10.9}$$

A recursion for $L_{yy}^{-1}(n)$ may be obtained by application of the Sherman-Morrison identity [Broyden 1975] to (10.6).

$$L_{yy}^{-1}(n) = L_{yy}^{-1}(n-1) - \frac{L_{yy}^{-1}(n-1) \, \underline{y}(n) \, \underline{y}^T(n) \, L_{yy}^{-1}(n-1)}{\left(1 + \underline{y}^T(n) \, L_{yy}^{-1}(n-1) \, \underline{y}(n) \right)} \tag{10.10}$$

Together equations (10.8), (10.9), and (10.10) are known as the recursive least squares (RLS) algorithm.

The LS approach that has just been described involves all the available data in forming the estimate $\hat{x}(n)$. In many applications where the underlying processes are nonstationary, it is often more appropriate to forget old data by reducing or removing its contribution to the squared error cost function. This is akin to assuming that the processes are stationary over short data records. A convenient technique for providing a forgetting mechanism is to replace the cost function of (10.2) with an exponentially weighted cost function.

$$\sum_{n=0}^{k} (x(n) - \hat{x}(n))^2 \, \alpha^{k-n} \tag{10.11}$$

The parameter, α, is a positive constant which is less than or equal to unity. It is often known as the forgetting factor as it controls the effective length of the memory of the algorithm. As α is reduced in size the memory of the algorithm is reduced. One of the major attractions of using the exponentially weighted cost function of (10.11) is that the resultant RLS algorithm is similar in form and hence complexity to the standard RLS form of equations (10.8), (10.9) and (10.10). The only difference is that equation (10.10) is replaced with

$$L_{yy}^{-1}(n) = \frac{1}{\alpha} \left(L_{yy}^{-1}(n-1) - \frac{L_{yy}^{-1}(n-1) \, \underline{y}(n) \, \underline{y}^T(n) \, L_{yy}^{-1}(n-1)}{\left(\alpha + \underline{y}^T(n) \, L_{yy}^{-1}(n-1) \, \underline{y}(n) \right)} \right) . \tag{10.12}$$

10.3 STOCHASTIC GRADIENT METHODS

One of the attractions of the MMSE definitions of optimality is that for a FIR filter there is one unique solution and that solution is provided by the Wiener equation, (10.1). Many other optimisation problems are less tractable in that direct solutions do not exist and iterative search techniques must be applied. One of the most important iterative techniques is the method of steepest descent. The importance of this method in adaptive filtering is that it provides the basis from which the stochastic gradient (SG) algorithms may be developed. Further an understanding of the method can give insight into the operation of the stochastic gradient algorithms.

The operation of the method of steepest descent is illustrated in Figure 10.4, which shows the contours of constant MSE for a 2 coefficient FIR filtering problem. Note in particular the elliptical nature of the contours. In Figure 10.4, the optimum Wiener solution is clearly identified. In applying the method of steepest descent an initial guess such as $\underline{h}_i$ is made. The gradient vector, $\underline{\nabla}_i$, of the MSE surface at $\underline{h}_i$ is then calculated.

$$\underline{\nabla}_i = \left[\frac{\partial \xi}{\partial h_0} \frac{\partial \xi}{\partial h_1} \cdot \cdot \frac{\partial \xi}{\partial h_{N-1}} \right]^T_{h \,=\, h_i}$$

$$= 2 \, \underline{\phi}_{yy} \, \underline{h}_i - 2 \, \underline{\phi}_{yx} \tag{10.13}$$

Since the gradient vector is in the direction of the greatest rate of increase of the MSE cost function, the initial guess may be improved by moving in the opposite direction, the direction of steepest descent. Such a move may be facilitated by subtracting a scaled version of the gradient, from the initial guess to give a new guess $\underline{h}_{i+1}$.

$$\underline{h}_{i+1} = \underline{h}_i - \mu \, \underline{\nabla}_i \tag{10.14}$$

The small positive constant μ is known as the step size. The optimum solution may be obtained by repeated application of equations (10.13) and (10.14) if the step size lies within a range specified by the largest eigenvalue, λ_{max}, associated with the autocorrelation matrix, $\underline{\phi}_{yy}$.

$$0 < \mu < \frac{1}{\lambda_{max}} \tag{10.15}$$

Such a process is known as convergence (Figure 10.4).

In order to calculate the gradient of equation (10.13) the autocorrelation matrix and cross correlation vector are still required. Thus the method of steepest descent is not an adaptive filter algorithm but is an indirect method of solving the linear equations summarised by equation (10.1). In order to obtain the least mean squares (LMS) stochastic gradient algorithm, the gradient of equation (10.13) is replaced by a noisy estimate of the gradient, $\hat{\underline{\nabla}}$, based on the data and the iterative step of equation (10.14) replaced with a time recursion to give

$$\underline{h}(n+1) = \underline{h}(n) - \mu\ \hat{\underline{V}}(n) \ . \tag{10.16}$$

The vector $\underline{h}(n)$ is an estimate of the Wiener impulse response at time sample n and the vector $\hat{\underline{V}}(n)$ is an associated estimate of the gradient. An exact expression for the gradient vector, $\underline{V}(n)$, in terms of the impulse response vector, $\underline{h}(n)$, can be obtained from equation (8.7).

$$\underline{V}(n) = -2\ E[\ \underline{y}(k)\ (\ x(k) - \underline{h}^T(n)\ \underline{y}(k)\ )\ ] \ .$$

$$\qquad = -2\ E[\ \underline{y}(k)\ e(k)\ ] \tag{10.17}$$

The error, $e(k)$, is the error at data sample k of a filter with impulse response $\underline{h}(n)$.

$$e(k) = x(k) - \underline{h}^T(n)\ \underline{y}(k)$$

An estimate, $\hat{\underline{V}}(n)$, of the gradient, $\underline{V}(n)$, could be formed by replacing the ensemble average of (10.17) by a time average. This would involve holding the filter impulse response constant at $\underline{h}(n)$ and processing data with the filter. However if the impulse response of the data changes at every sample point as suggested by equation (10.16), the time average reduces to a single multiplication at $k = n+1$. This leads to simple expressions for the estimated gradient and the associated error.

$$\hat{\underline{V}}(n) = -2\ \underline{y}(n+1)\ e(n+1) \tag{10.18}$$

$$e(n+1) = x(n+1) - \underline{h}^T(n)\ \underline{y}(n+1) \tag{10.19}$$

Substitution of (10.18) into (10.16) yields the LMS algorithm [Widrow & Stearns].

$$\underline{h}(n+1) = \underline{h}(n) + 2\ \mu\ \underline{y}(n+1)\ e(n+1) \tag{10.20}$$

Other stochastic gradient techniques are available such as the block least mean squares (BLMS) algorithm, where the impulse response of the adaptive filter is held constant for several data samples during which time an improved estimate of the gradient may be obtained. The BLMS algorithm has the further advantage that both the filtering operation and the calculation of the gradient estimate may be implement efficiently using the fast Fourier transform (FFT) (discussed in chapters 11 and 12). An adaptive FIR filter and LMS algorithm are illustrated in Figure 10.5.

The theoretical analysis of the convergence of adaptive filter algorithms is an area of current research and demands a considerable degree of mathematical sophistication. The simplest form of analysis is to consider the evolution of the mean of the impulse response vector of the adaptive filter and attempt to show that as the time index n increases the mean will tend to the impulse response of the Wiener filter. This technique was first suggested by Widrow for the LMS algorithm and while not being strictly rigorous does highlight some of the factors which affect the convergence rate of SG algorithms. The first step involves taking the ensemble average of both sides of equation (10.20).

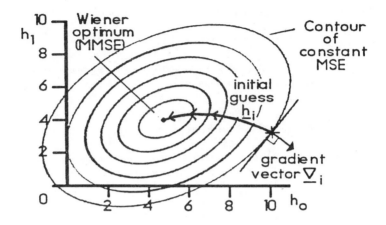

Figure 10.4 The method of steepest descent.

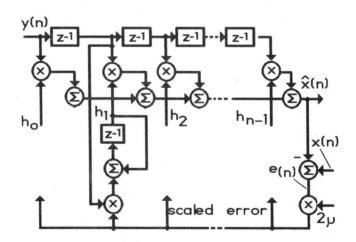

Figure 10.5 The least mean squares (LMS) algorithm.

$$E[\,\underline{h}(n+1)\,] = E[\,(\,I_N - 2\,\mu\,\underline{y}(n+1)\,\underline{y}^T(n+1)\,)\,\underline{h}(n)\,]$$

$$+ 2\,\mu\,E[\,\underline{y}(n+1)\,y(n+1)\,]\,.$$

I_N is an $(N \times N)$ identity matrix. If $\underline{y}(n+1)$ and $\underline{h}(n)$ are assumed to be uncorrelated, which they are not in general, then this equation reduces to a difference equation in terms of the mean of the impulse response.

$$E[\,\underline{h}(n+1)\,] = (\,I_N - 2\,\mu\,\underline{\phi}_{yy}\,)\,E[\,\underline{h}(n)\,] + 2\,\mu\,\underline{\phi}_{yx} \tag{10.21}$$

Equations such as (10.21) are common in many linear systems problems, where their convergence characteristics are usually ascertained by what is called modal or eigenvalue analysis.

It is convenient to define an error vector $\bar{\underline{h}}(n)$ which is the difference between the optimum and estimated impulse responses.

$$\bar{\underline{h}}(n) = \underline{h}(n) - \underline{h}_{opt}$$

Equation (10.21) is then rewritten in terms of the error vector to yield a simpler difference equation with no input or driving function.

$$E[\,\bar{\underline{h}}(n+1)\,] = (\,I_N - 2\,\mu\,\underline{\phi}_{yy}\,)\,E[\,\bar{\underline{h}}(n)\,]\,.$$

If $E[\,\bar{\underline{h}}(n)\,]$ converges to the zero vector as $n \to \infty$, then $E[\,\underline{h}(n)\,]$ will converge to $\underline{h}_{opt}$. It is usually possible to factorise the autocorrelation matrix in terms of a diagonal matrix Λ and a matrix V which contain the eigenvalues and the eigenvectors of $\underline{\phi}_{yy}$ respectively i.e.

$$\underline{\phi}_{yy} = V\,\Lambda\,V^T\,,$$

where

$$\Lambda = diagonal\,[\,\lambda_0\,\lambda_1\,\cdots\,\lambda_{N-1}\,]\,.$$

If the difference vector $\bar{\underline{h}}(n)$ is multiplied or transformed by the matrix of eigenvectors V^T to give a vector $\bar{H}(n)$ where,

$$\bar{H}(n) = V^T\,\bar{\underline{h}}(n)\,.$$

the resultant vector, $\bar{H}(n)$, evolves according to a difference equation

$$E[\,\bar{H}(n+1)\,] = (\,I_N - 2\,\mu\,\Lambda\,)\,E[\,\bar{H}(n)\,]$$

which is defined completely by a diagonal matrix, $(I - 2\mu\Lambda)$. Because this matrix is diagonal, a separate recursion for each element, $\bar{H}_j(n)$, of $\bar{H}(n)$ can be written down.

$$E[\,\tilde{H}_j(n+1)\,] = (\,1 - 2\mu\lambda_j\,)\,E[\,\tilde{H}_j(n)\,], \quad j = 0, 1, ..., N-1$$

Each components or mode, $\tilde{H}_j(n)$, evolve in time independently of the others and each of these modes decays exponentially to zero provided

$$|\,1 - 2\mu\lambda_j\,| < 1.$$

Hence convergence of all the elements of $\tilde{\underline{H}}(n)$ to zero is assured if

$$o < \mu < \frac{1}{\lambda_{max}}, \tag{10.22}$$

which is identical to the condition for convergence for the method of steepest descent, (10.15). Convergence of $\tilde{\underline{H}}(n)$ to the zero vector is equivalent to convergence of $\underline{\tilde{h}}(n)$ to the zero vector.

A time constant, τ_j, can be defined for each mode and is given approximately as

$$\tau_j \approx \frac{1}{2\mu\lambda_j}.$$

The largest time constant, τ_{max}, is due to the smallest eigenvalue, λ_{min}.

$$\tau_{max} \approx \frac{1}{2\mu\lambda_{min}} \tag{10.23}$$

Combining (10.22) with (10.23) gives,

$$\tau_{max} > \frac{\lambda_{max}}{2\lambda_{min}} \tag{10.24}$$

which suggests that the larger the eigenvalue ratio (EVR) or condition number, $\dfrac{\lambda_{max}}{\lambda_{min}}$, of $\underline{\phi}_{yy}$ the longer the LMS algorithm will take to converge.

10.4 SELF-ORTHOGONALISING ALGORITHMS

Other more rigorous analyses of the SG algorithms than that outlined in section 10.3 also indicate that the time taken for these algorithms to converge is highly dependent on the condition number and eigenvalues of the autocorrelation matrix. Although the relationship may not be quite as simple as that indicated by (10.24), the conclusion is the same i.e. the greater the condition number the longer the algorithm will take to converge. This dependency can be removed by first applying a linear transformation defined in terms of a $(N \times N)$ matrix P, to the input vector, $\underline{y}(n)$, to form a second vector,

$$\underline{z}(n) = P\,\underline{y}(n). \tag{10.25}$$

The matrix P is specially chosen such that

$$\phi_{zz} = E[\, z(n)\, z^T(n)\,] = I_N \,, \tag{10.26}$$

where I_N is an $(N \times N)$ identity matrix. The vector $z(n)$ is then used as the input to the LMS algorithm instead of $y(n)$. Because the eigenvalues of ϕ_{zz} are all identical and equal to unity, the convergence performance of the resultant adaptive filter algorithm will be improved. The output of the adaptive filter, $\hat{x}(n)$, is a linear combination of the elements of the vector, $z(n)$, and is defined by a vector of time varying coefficients, w.

$$\hat{x}(n) = w^T(n-1)\, z(n) \tag{10.27}$$

This structure is illustrated in Figure 10.6(a). The vector, w, is updated using the LMS algorithm of equation (10.20) and (10.19).

$$w(n) = w(n-1) + 2\,\mu\, z(n)\, e(n) \tag{10.28}$$

$$e(n) = x(n) - \hat{x}(n) \tag{10.29}$$

Equations (10.25), (10.27), (10.28) and (10.29) summarise the explicit form of a self-orthogonalising (SO) adaptive filter algorithm.

Provided that ϕ_{yy} is a positive definite matrix then a matrix P can always be found such that

$$\phi_{zz} = P\,\phi_{yy}\, P^T = I_N. \tag{10.30}$$

Equation (10.30) is a square root factorisation of the autocorrelation matrix.

$$\phi_{yy} = P^{-1}(\,P^{-1}\,)^T \tag{10.31}$$

Since such a factorisation is not unique, there may be several transforms such as P which exhibit the useful property of equation (10.30).

The algorithm described above evolves in term of the weight vector $w(n)$. For system identification tasks it is necessary to derive a relationship between $w(n)$ and the overall impulse response vector $h(n)$. This relationship can be obtained from equation (10.27).

$$\hat{x}(n) = z^T(n)\, w(n-1)$$

$$= \left(P\, y(n)\,\right)^T w(n-1)$$

$$= y^T(n)\, P^T\, w(n-1)$$

$$= y^T(n)\, \left(P^T\, w(n-1)\,\right)$$

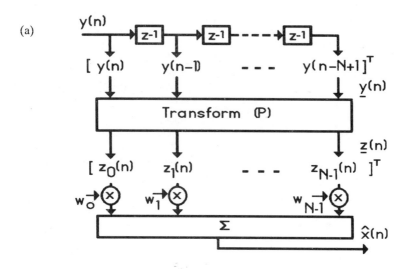

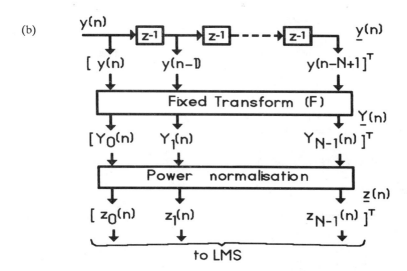

Figure 10.6   Self-orthogonalising structure: (a) theoretical; (b) practical.

$$= \underline{y}^T(n)\,\underline{h}(n-1)$$

Hence

$$\underline{h}(n) = P^T\,\underline{w}(n) \tag{10.32}$$

and

$$\underline{w}(n) = (P^T)^{-1}\,\underline{h}(n) \tag{10.33}$$

It is then possible to reformulate the SO algorithm in terms of the impulse response vector $\underline{h}(n)$. Multiplying both sides of equation (10.28)) by P^T. and substituting for $\underline{z}(n)$ using equation (10.25) gives

$$\underline{h}(n) = \underline{h}(n-1) + 2\,\mu\,P^T\,\underline{z}(n)\,e(n)$$

$$= \underline{h}(n-1) + 2\,\mu\,P^T\,P\,\underline{y}(n)\,e(n)\ .$$

The P matrices can then be replaced by the autocorrelation matrix $\underline{\phi}_{yy}$ using the definition of equation (10.31) to yield the implicit form of a SO algorithm.

$$\underline{h}(n) = \underline{h}(n-1) + 2\,\mu\,\underline{\phi}_{yy}^{-1}\,\underline{y}(n)\,e(n)$$

Neither of the explicit or implicit formulations of SO algorithm discussed so far are truly adaptive filter algorithms since the autocorrelation matrix $\underline{\phi}_{yy}$ or its square root P is required to construct the algorithms. In practice either $\underline{\phi}_{yy}$ or P must be estimated from the data. The usual approach, typified by the sliding discrete Fourier transform (DFT) adaptive filter, is to estimate P using a two stage process. The input signal vector $\underline{y}(n)$ is first multiplied by a constant matrix F to form a second vector $\underline{Y}(n)$.

$$\underline{Y}(n) = [\ Y_0(n)\ Y_1(n)\ .....\ Y_{N-1}(n)\ ]^T$$

$$= F\,\underline{y}(n)$$

For the sliding DFT adaptive filter the element in row l column n of F is a complex exponential term.

$$F[l,m] = \exp\left(-\sqrt{(-1)}\ \frac{2\pi lm}{N}\right)$$

The function of the matrix F is to approximately orthogonalise the input signal.

$$E[\ Y_i(n)\ Y_j(n)\ ] = 0 \qquad i \neq j$$

Therefore the autocorrelation matrix $\underline{\phi}_{YY}$ associated with the vector $\underline{Y}(n)$ is approximately diagonal.

$$\underline{\phi}_{YY} = E[\underline{Y}(n) \underline{Y}^T(n)]$$

$$= diagonal \left[E[Y_0^2(n)] E[Y_1^2(n)] \,.....\, E[Y_{N-1}^2(n)] \right]$$

$$= diagonal [D_0 D_1 \,....\, D_{N-1}]$$

$$= D$$

An approximation to $\underline{z}(n)$ can the be obtained by dividing each element of $\underline{Y}(n)$ by the square root of the appropriate element of D.

$$z_i(n) = \frac{Y_i(n)}{\sqrt{D_i}}$$

The elements of the diagonal matrix D can be estimated directly from the data. A typical structure is illustrated in Figure 10.6(b).

10.5 A COMPARISON OF ALGORITHMS

In this section, simulation results are used to show the performance differences between the three algorithm types that have been described in the previous sections. The structure used to highlight these differences is illustrated in Figure 10.7. This is an example of a system modelling mode of operation. The noise shaping filter is a convenient mechanism for conditioning the input signal to the unknown system and the adaptive filter and hence to control the eigenvalue ratio. The error vector norm defined as

$$\rho(n) = E[(\underline{h}(n) - \underline{h}_{opt})^T (\underline{h}(n) - \underline{h}_{opt})]$$

was chosen as a measure of performance in preference to the output MSE. This is because the convergence plots can then be used to demonstrate the behaviour of the algorithm below the output noise floor which is determined by the additive noise on the training signal. Three sets of results for a 16-coefficient adaptive FIR filter are illustrated in Figure 10.8. For all simulations the additive noise was set at −60 dB.

The first point to consider is the relative performance of the various algorithms above the noise floor of −60 dB. When the input signal is white, Figure 10.8(a), the condition number or eigenvalue ratio of the input autocorrelation matrix is unity. The RLS algorithm converges to the noise floor in approximately 30 data samples or iterations. The SO and LMS algorithms are identical in performance and reach the noise floor within 400 iterations. If the eigenvalue ratio of the input signal is increased to 11 by altering the frequency response of the noise shaping filter, the performance of the RLS algorithm depicted in Figure 10.8(b) is hardly

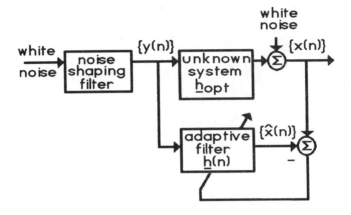

Figure 10.7   System identification simulation.

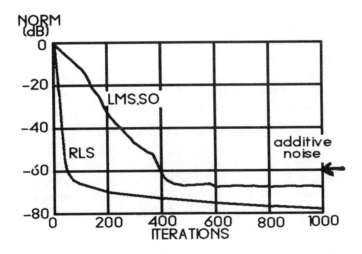

Figure 10.8(a)   Simulation results for 16-tap system identification (EVR = 1).

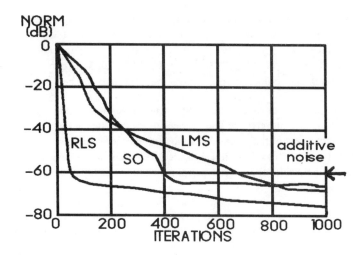

Figure 10.8(b)   Simulation results for 16-tap system identification (EVR = 11).

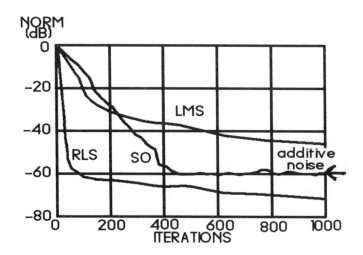

Figure 10.8(c)   Simulation results for 16-tap system identification (EVR = 68).

altered. Also the performance of the SO algorithm in Figure 10.8(b) is almost identical to that of Figure 10.8(a). On the other hand, the performance of the LMS algorithm in Figure 10.8(b) is significantly degraded, taking 700 iterations to reach the noise floor. Finally in Figure 10.8(c) the eigenvalue ratio is 68 which would be considered to be severe conditions. The RLS reaches the noise floor in 70 iterations the LMS in 2000 iterations and the SO in 400.

Taking the noise floor as a performance goal the results can be summarised. The RLS provides consistent fast convergence independent of the eigenvalue ratio. The SO algorithm is also robust to the effects of the eigenvalue ratio but does not achieve as fast convergence as the RLS. Rather its performance is identical to the LMS under white input conditions. The LMS on the other hand provides the poorest performance being highly dependent on the eigenvalue ratio.

The second point of interest is the performance of the algorithms below the noise floor. For instance in all three examples the convergence rate of the RLS algorithm decreases dramatically after it reaches the noise floor. The LMS and SO algorithms converge to a constant level on or just below the noise floor. This is a consequence of the choice of step-size, μ, that was employed. The step size for all simulations was set at $1/(6N)$ in order to assure convergence over the wide range of input conditions. The final value of the norm achieved by the LMS and SO algorithms could have been improved if a smaller step size was used but this would have resulted in a slowing down of the initial rate of convergence.

· The selection of an adaptive algorithm for a particular application involves an assessment of the computational complexity as well as the convergence performance. Considerable research effort has been applied to the development of computationally efficient implementations of all three classes of adaptive filter algorithm. Some of these are summarised in Table 10.1, where their complexity is compared in terms of computational operations. For further details on the lattice filter implementation see chapter 16.

Class	Implementation	Computational Load		
		mult	add/sub	div
Recursive Least Squares	fast Kalman	$10N+1$	$9N+1$	2
	lattice	$8N$	$8N$	$6N$
Stochastic Gradient	LMS	$2N$	$2N$	-
	BLMS (FFT)	$10\log(N)+8$	$15\log(N)+30$	-
Self-Orthogonalising	Sliding DFT	$8N+16$	$6N+9$	N

Table 10.1 Complexity Comparison of N-point Adaptive FIR Filter Algorithms.

10.6 SUMMARY

Adaptive filters provide a mechanism for implementing optimal filters when there is not enough a priori information with which to design these optimal filters. The necessary information is extracted from the data by the adaptive algorithm through the use of an additional input known as the training signal. At first glance the requirement for a training signal may appear to beg the question. However in many practical applications particularly in communications systems a training signal is readily available. A further advantage of adaptive filters lies in their ability to operate in non-stationary or time-varying environments.

TUTORIAL Adaptive Filter Designs

1. The following input sequence, $\{ y(n) \}$, is applied to an unknown 2-coefficient FIR filter.

$$y(1) = 1.0, \, y(2) = 1.0, \, y(3) = -1.0, \, y(4) = -1.0, \, y(5) = 1.0$$

The associated output sequence is $\{ x(n) \}$ where

$$x(1) = 0.898, \, x(2) = 1.346, \, x(3) = -0.415, \, x(4) = -1.236, \, x(5) = 0.467.$$

Use the LMS algorithm to estimate the impulse response of the FIR filter. For the purposes of this calculation use a step size of 0.25 and assume $y(0) = 0.0$. *[0.852, 0.385]*

2. An electronic diagnosis system is proposed to monitor patient health in an intensive care unit of a busy hospital. Three symptoms are recorded every hour. At the nth hour these are: the pulse rate $y_0(n)$; the temperature $y_1(n)$; the blood pressure $y_2(n)$. A linear estimate, $\hat{x}(n)$, of the patient health, $x(n)$, is formed using a set of coefficients h_0, h_1 and h_2.

$$\hat{x}(n) = h_0 \, y_0(n) + h_1 \, y_1(n) + h_2 \, y_2(n)$$

Show from first principles that the estimate will be optimal in a MSE sense if the following conditions apply.

$$E[\, y_0 \, e(n) \,] = 0$$

$$E[\, y_1 \, e(n) \,] = 0$$

$$E[\, y_2 \, e(n) \,] = 0$$

The error, $e(n)$, is the difference between the actual patient health and the estimate.

$$e(n) = x(n) - \hat{x}(n)$$

In order to implement the system a senior medical doctor makes himself available as the expert and provides the training signal for the first couple of days. The coefficients are calculated using the LMS algorithm during the training period. Draw a diagram showing how the individual symptoms are combined to form the estimate and how the error signal is generated. Write down equations to show explicitly how the coefficient, h_0, at the n th hour is calculated from the coefficients at the previous hour.

Chapter 11

DISCRETE
AND
FAST FOURIER TRANSFORMS

11.1 INTRODUCTION

In this chapter we study discrete and fast Fourier transforms, the fast Fourier transform (FFT) being a rapid way of computing the discrete Fourier transform (DFT). First we consider the question why transform? Transformations are often computationally intensive and thus must be justified. Then the continuous Fourier transform is considered and the DFT derived from it. Some analogies for the DFT are given and finally, the FFT is studied in detail by deriving the general N-point case and considering the 8-point case as an example.

11.2 COMMON TRANSFORMATION TYPES

Figure 11.1 illustrates four common transforms. The Fourier transform (F) is usually thought of as operating on a time-domain signal to transform it into the frequency domain while the inverse Fourier transform (F^{-1}) performs the inverse mapping back to the time domain. The other three transforms depicted in Figure 11.1 are : (1) The z-transform (Z) which transforms a sampled data signal from the time domain to the z domain and its inverse Z^{-1} which performs the inverse mapping. (2) The Laplace transform (L) which transforms a continuous time domain signal into the s domain and its inverse transformation (L^{-1}). (3) The Walsh transform (W) which transforms a continuous time domain signal to the 'Walsh' domain and its inverse (W^{-1}).

11.3 MOTIVATION FOR TRANSFORMATION

The main reason for performing a transform is to improve the detectability of some aspect of a signal which is not easily detected in its domain of origin.

Application example: improving detectability. Figure 11.2 illustrates one application of the DFT, the measurement of harmonic distortion in the output of an oscillator or amplifier. A

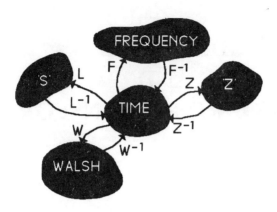

Figure 11.1   Four common transforms and their inverses.

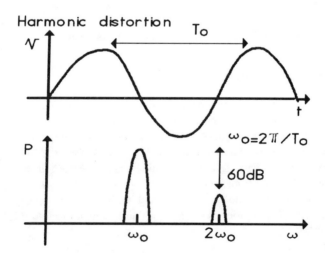

Figure 11.2   Frequency domain detection of harmonic distortion in oscillators.

The harmonic distortion is normally undetectable in the time domain by visual inspection on an oscilloscope but when transformed into the frequency domain using a DFT, or equivalently an FFT, the harmonic distortion becomes clearly visible. In this example there is second harmonic distortion (i.e. at $2\omega_0$) at a level of -60 dB with respect to the fundamental component.

11.4 REVISION OF FOURIER THEORY

The equations which define the continuous Fourier transform are :

the (forward) Fourier transform

$$F(\omega) = \int_{-\infty}^{\infty} f(t) \, e^{-j\omega t} \, dt \tag{11.1}$$

the inverse Fourier transform

$$f(t) = \frac{1}{2\pi} \int_{-\infty}^{\infty} F(\omega) \, e^{j\omega t} \, d\omega \tag{11.2}$$

Equation (11.1) holds for any deterministic waveform, periodic or non-periodic, and is the starting point for the derivation of the DFT. Firstly, if the waveform being transformed is periodic, then the integral in (11.2) degenerates into a summation of harmonically related components. In this case the Fourier transform pair become :

the (forward) Fourier transform

$$F(k\omega_0) = \int_{-\infty}^{\infty} f(t) \, e^{-jk\omega_0 t} \, dt \tag{11.3}$$

the inverse Fourier transform

$$f(t) = \sum_{k=-\infty}^{\infty} F(k\omega_0) \, e^{jk\omega_0 t} \tag{11.4}$$

Here the Fourier transform which was previously continuous (in (11.1)) is now discrete and can be written as a (Fourier) series comprising a fundamental component and a set of higher harmonics. The fundamental component is at ω_0 rad/s (where $\omega_0 = 1/T_0$ and T_0 is the fundamental period of the waveform) and the higher harmonics are at integer multiples of ω_0. A further important observation for the case of a periodic waveform is that the span of the integration may be reduced to any integer multiple of the fundamental period while still obtaining a valid transform. Equation (11.5) is the case where integration is over the fundamental period (the Fourier series of chapter 2).

$$F(k\omega_0) = \int_{-T_0/2}^{T_0/2} f(t)\, e^{-jk\omega_0 t}\, dt \tag{11.5}$$

In addition to going from a continuous to a discrete function of frequency, a discrete function of time (sampled input data) may be employed. The transform is now referred to as the discrete Fourier transform. It is appropriate at this point to revise some sampled data concepts.

11.5 REVIEW OF SAMPLED DATA CONCEPTS

In Figure 11.3 a function of time, $f(t)$, is being sampled every T seconds to give a corresponding sampled data function $f(nT)$. The sampling waveform is modelled as a train of impulses which may be described mathmaticaly as a summation of time-shifted Dirac delta functions, the Dirac delta function being denoted by $\delta(t-nT)$. The sampling operation may be modelled as the multiplication of $f(t)$ by the impulse train, the product being $f(nT)$. To obtain the Fourier transform of $f(nT)$ we replace $f(t)$ in equation (11.5) by $f(t)\sum_{n}\delta(t-nT)$ as shown in equation (11.6).

$$F(k\omega_0) = \int_{-T_0/2}^{T_0/2} f(t)\, \sum_{n=-\infty}^{\infty} \delta(t-nT)\, e^{-jk\omega_0 t}\, dt \tag{11.6}$$

11.6 DERIVATION OF THE DISCRETE FOURIER TRANSFORM

Due to the presence of the Dirac delta function in equation (11.6) the continuous integral degenerates into a discrete summation. This is because the Dirac delta function is zero unless $t = nT$ when it becomes unity. Finally taking N samples over a single fundamental period of the input waveform, $f(t)$, the N-point DFT is obtained:

$$F(k\omega_0) = \sum_{n=0}^{N-1} f(nT)\, e^{-j\frac{2\pi nk}{N}} \tag{11.7}$$

Dropping the ω_0 and T we have:

$$F(k) = \sum_{n=0}^{N-1} f(n)\, e^{-j\frac{2\pi nk}{N}} \tag{11.8}$$

Conventionally the shorthand notation $W_N = \exp(-j2\pi/N)$ is adopted where W_N is the fundamental Nth root of unity (the smallest of the N, Nth roots). For example the eight eighth roots of unity are illustrated in Figure 11.4.

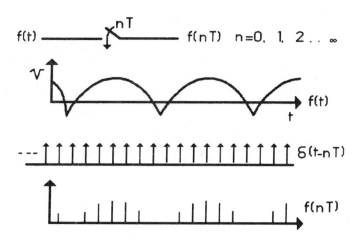

Figure 11.3   Review of sampled data concepts.

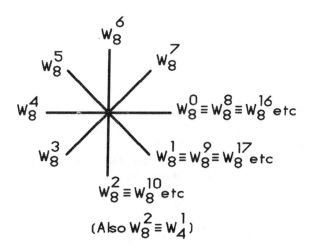

Figure 11.4   Phasor diagram illustrating the 8, 8th roots of unity.

11.7 MATRIX FORMULATION OF THE DFT

Equation (11.8) represents the kth component of the frequency domain expression for $f(nT)$. This equation may be expanded horizontally as a function of sample number n for $n = 0$ to $N-1$ and vertically as a function of k for $k = 0$ to $N-1$ giving the set of equations below (equations (11.9)).

$$
\begin{aligned}
F(0) &= f(0) + f(1) + \ldots + f(N-1) \\
F(1) &= f(0) + f(1)\,W_N^1 + \ldots + f(N-1)\,W_N^{N-1} \\
F(2) &= f(0) + f(1)\,W_N^2 + \ldots + f(N-1)\,W_N^{N-2} \\
&\ \ \vdots \\
F(N-1) &= f(0) + f(1)\,W_N^{N-1} + \ldots + f(N-1)\,W_N^1
\end{aligned}
\tag{11.9}
$$

When referring to the DFT it is more usual to use x_i to denote the ith time domain sample and X_i to denote the ith frequency domain sample. Thus we make the following substitution:

$$
\begin{aligned}
x_i &= f(i) \\
X_i &= F(i)
\end{aligned}
\tag{11.10}
$$

Equation (11.9) can then be expressed in vector/matrix form as illustrated in equation (11.11).

$$
\begin{bmatrix} X_0 \\ X_1 \\ X_2 \\ \vdots \\ X_{N-1} \end{bmatrix}
=
\begin{bmatrix}
1 & 1 & 1 & \cdots & 1 \\
1 & W_N^1 & W_N^2 & \cdots & W_N^{N-1} \\
1 & W_N^2 & W_N^4 & \cdots & W_N^{N-2} \\
\vdots & \vdots & \vdots & & \vdots \\
1 & W_N^{N-1} & W_N^{N-2} & \cdots & W_N^1
\end{bmatrix}
\begin{bmatrix} x_0 \\ x_1 \\ x_2 \\ \vdots \\ x_{N-1} \end{bmatrix}
\tag{11.11}
$$

The elements of the above DFT matrix form the set of N, N th roots of unity. Each row of the matrix represents a sampled complex sinusoid (or phasor). The top row is at zero frequency. The second row consists of samples from a phasor at one cycle per N samples, while the third row represents a phasor at two cycles per N samples (or block length) etc. Commonly only the powers of the W_N terms are included in the matrix as shown in equation (11.12) below.

$$
\begin{bmatrix} X_0 \\ X_1 \\ X_2 \\ \vdots \\ X_{N-1} \end{bmatrix}
=
\begin{bmatrix}
0 & 1 & 1 & \cdots & 1 \\
0 & 1 & 2 & \cdots & N-1 \\
0 & 2 & 4 & \cdots & N-2 \\
\vdots & \vdots & \vdots & & \vdots \\
0 & N-1 & N-2 & \cdots & 1
\end{bmatrix}
\begin{bmatrix} x_0 \\ x_1 \\ x_2 \\ \vdots \\ x_{N-1} \end{bmatrix}
\tag{11.12}
$$

A clearer picture of the contents of the DFT matrix may frequently be obtained if the elements of equation (11.12) are replaced with their pictorial representations as phasors as shown in Figure 11.5.

The DFT is defined in the complex domain and the vector of time domain samples, $[\,x_0\,x_1\,\cdots\,x_{N-1}\,]^T$, is also complex which is often the case when the signal is coming from a radar or communications receiver with 'I' and 'Q' (or 'real' and 'imaginary' channels). Alternatively if the signal is coming from a baseband source (e.g. from a microphone), then it is 'real' and its 'imaginary' component is zero. In this case the input array holding the imaginary input components must be set to zero if a valid transform is to be obtained.

11.8 EXAMPLE USING AN 8-POINT DFT

The 8-point DFT is a good example as it is the smallest non-degenerate transform which is a power of two. As will be shown later, transforms of size N, where $N = 2^M$, lead to the simplest FFT algorithms but if $N = 2$ or 4 then the DFT can be performed without recourse to any complex multiplies. Hence the term degenerate has been applied to these two sizes.

The elements of the 8-point DFT matrix are the eight, 8th roots of unity as shown in Figure 11.4. Recall that an 8th root of unity is a complex number which when raised to the power 8 equals unity. Progressing round the roots in increasing order implies clockwise rotation round Figure 11.4. An input signal phasor, on the other hand, rotates in an anti-clockwise direction in the complex plane (cosine leads sine by $\pi/2$ radians). Each phasor in the DFT matrix will seek to derotate a component in the input signal at its own frequency. The resulting stationary component will build up through the transform and appear in the corresponding frequency output. This will be further explained later in this section. For an N-point transform, the first root encountered when rotating in a clockwise direction from the real axis in the complex plane may be regarded as the primitive root of a related number system having elements which are the N, Nth roots of unity. This primitive root may be used to generate all the other (higher order) roots by, in this case, raising it to the appropriate integer power. The integer powers 0 to $N-1$ produce distinct roots in the primary region (0 to 2π). Integer powers of N and above do not produce more roots, they reproduce one of the existing roots by an "aliasing" like effect. Thus the powers (or exponents) of W_N which appear in Figure 11.5 are reduced modulo-N (modulo-8 in this example) and although the exponent of W_N at the intersection of the ith row and jth column is the product ij, this is taken modulo-8, or in general, modulo-N.

Multiplication of the N element time domain input vector by the DFT matrix produces a corresponding N element frequency domain output vector. The first row of the DFT matrix (row zero) finds the d.c. component in the signal. The second row finds the component at one cycle per block length etc. Each successive frequency domain output is referred to as residing in a frequency "bin". For an N-point transform there are N equally spaced bins from d.c. to the sample rate, but not including the sample rate which aliases to D.C.

The above may be illustrated by applying a simple input signal to the 8-point DFT. The simplest complex signal which may be considered is the complex sinusoid,

$$e^{j\theta} = cos(\theta) + j\ sin(\theta) \tag{11.13}$$

This signal is shown in Figure 11.6. We take 8 equally spaced (complex) samples, x_0 to x_7, from this signal. These samples are shown in phasor form in Figure 11.6. The starting phase has been chosen to be zero and the frequency has been chosen to be one cycle per block length. These assumptions are very restrictive and the problem is hence a very artificial one but they do allow the mechanism of the transformation to be seen more clearly and we will remove both restrictions in turn, explaining the consequences at each step. The term by term multiplication of this input vector with the second row of the DFT matrix is also illustrated in Figure 11.6. Recall that this row is "seeking" a component at one cycle per block length (which is the only component in this particular input signal). Since, in this case, each element of this row of the DFT matrix is multiplying its complex conjugate then the result of each multiplication is real and all eight vectors add co-linearly to give a large output in the second frequency bin, indicating a large component at one cycle per block length. In order to conserve power through the transform all outputs should be divided by the transform size. When this signal is multiplied by the third row of the DFT matrix the resultant is zero. Recall that the input phasor here is rotating once anticlockwise per transform block while the phasor in this third row of the DFT matrix is rotating twice in a clockwise direction. Regarding the term by term multiplication as a mixing operation will reveal that the resultant will rotate once in a clockwise direction. This is illustrated in Figure 11.7. Repetition of the above for each of the other rows of the DFT matrix reveals zero output from each of them. The resultant output vector is $X^T = [0,1,0,0,0,0,0,0]$. The initial assumption of zero starting phase will now be removed.

The case of an arbitrary starting phase θ is depicted in Figure 11.8(a). The terms of X_1 build up linearly as before indicating a component at one cycle per block length. The magnitude of the resultant is the same as previously but the phase component now has a value θ, previously zero. Thus phase information is not lost in performing a DFT and upon performing the inverse DFT the signal will be recovered with the correct starting phase. Since many people are only interested in signal power as a function of frequency they take the squared magnitude of each complex frequency component and in the process they "throw away" the phase information. It is interesting to note that if the inverse DFT is performed on the resulting power spectrum an estimate of the autocorrelation function of the original signal is obtained (chapter 13). The autocorrelation function of a signal is independent of the starting phase of the signal.

The assumption of an integer number of cycles of the input signal per block length will now be removed. Recall that the continuous Fourier transform was valid if the integration was performed over the interval $-\infty$ to $+\infty$ or over an integer number of cycles of the waveform. If we now attempt to perform a DFT over a non-integer number of cycles of the input signal we would expect to in some way invalidate the transform. This indeed happens and the problems

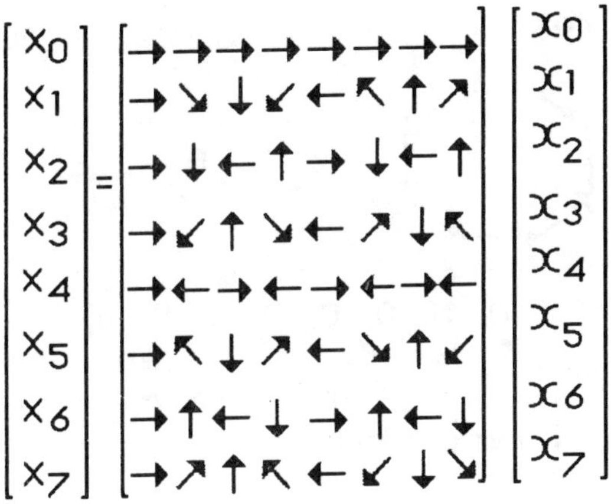

$$
\begin{bmatrix} X_0 \\ X_1 \\ X_2 \\ X_3 \\ X_4 \\ X_5 \\ X_6 \\ X_7 \end{bmatrix} =
\begin{bmatrix}
\rightarrow & \rightarrow & \rightarrow & \rightarrow & \rightarrow & \rightarrow & \rightarrow & \rightarrow \\
\rightarrow & \searrow & \downarrow & \swarrow & \leftarrow & \nwarrow & \uparrow & \nearrow \\
\rightarrow & \downarrow & \leftarrow & \uparrow & \rightarrow & \downarrow & \leftarrow & \uparrow \\
\rightarrow & \swarrow & \uparrow & \searrow & \leftarrow & \nearrow & \downarrow & \nwarrow \\
\rightarrow & \leftarrow & \rightarrow & \leftarrow & \rightarrow & \leftarrow & \rightarrow & \leftarrow \\
\rightarrow & \nwarrow & \downarrow & \nearrow & \leftarrow & \searrow & \uparrow & \swarrow \\
\rightarrow & \uparrow & \leftarrow & \downarrow & \rightarrow & \uparrow & \leftarrow & \downarrow \\
\rightarrow & \nearrow & \uparrow & \nwarrow & \leftarrow & \swarrow & \downarrow & \searrow
\end{bmatrix}
\begin{bmatrix} x_0 \\ x_1 \\ x_2 \\ x_3 \\ x_4 \\ x_5 \\ x_6 \\ x_7 \end{bmatrix}
$$

Figure 11.5   The 8-point DFT matrix in phasor form.

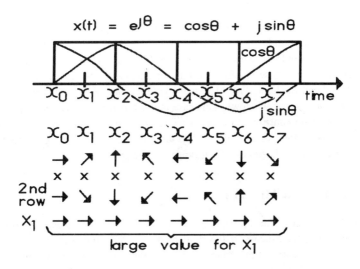

Figure 11.6   Calculation of the component at 1 cycle per block length.

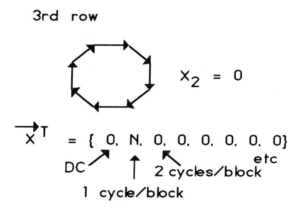

3rd row

$X_2 = 0$

$X^T = \{ \ 0, \ N, \ 0, \ 0, \ 0, \ 0, \ 0, \ 0 \}$

DC

2 cycles/block

etc

1 cycle/block

Figure 11.7   Calculation of the component at 2 cycles per block length.

manifest themselves in the form of "leakage" of energy from any given bin into all the other bins, particularly the surrounding bins. This leakage and its control is of major importance in DFT theory. Tapered windows (such as those considered in chapters 7 and 12) are used to control leakage and to minimise its effect on the dynamic range of the transform output. This will be studied in detail in chapter 12. The worst case leakage occurs when there are $n + 1/2$ cycles in the block length (or window). This case is illustrated in Figure 11.8(b) where $n = 1$ for clarity. The resultant contributing to X_1 is not now stationary but is rotating at 1/2 a cycle per block length. As a result X_1 is diminished in amplitude and the missing energy is found in the other bins. Figure 11.9 illustrates this "leakage" of energy.

11.9 ANALOGIES FOR THE DFT

The filter bank analogy for a DFT is illustrated in Figure 11.10. Again an 8-point case is chosen for clarity. Here the 8-point DFT is thought of as being equivalent to a contiguous bank of band-pass filters with each output from the DFT being considered equivalent to the output of the corresponding filter. Such a contiguous bank of band-pass filters have an equivalent realisation at baseband through the use of mixers followed by low-pass filters, the well established baseband analyser approach to spectral analysis. Thus we have a second analogy for the DFT as being equivalent to a baseband analyser. This is illustrated in Figure 11.11.

$$x_0 = 0$$
$$x_1 =$$
$$x_2 = 0$$
$$etc = 0$$

Figure 11.8(a)   Component at 1 cycle per block (arbitrary starting phase).

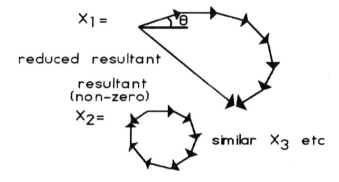

$$x_1 =$$

reduced resultant

resultant
(non–zero)
$$x_2 =$$

                                                       similar x_3 etc

Figure 11.8(b)   Components at 1 and 2 cycles per block (non-integer cycles per block).

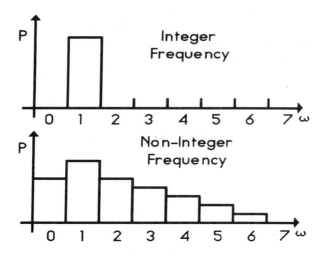

Figure 11.9   Illustration of leakage of power from a frequency bin into surrounding bins for a non-integer number of cycles per block.

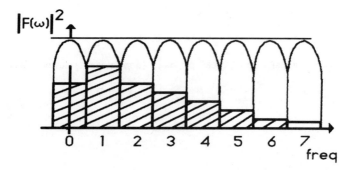

Figure 11.10   Filter bank analogy for an 8-point DFT.

Figure 11.12 shows how this might be implemented in hardware. The oscillators in the section determining the d.c. component are "oscillating" at zero Hz and therefore are redundant. Both of the above analogies employ filtering before delivering each output. Equations (11.14) and (11.15) show how the DFT performs the filtering operation.

$$X_k = \sum_{n=0}^{N-1} x_n \, e^{-j\frac{2\pi nk}{N}} \tag{11.14}$$

$$= \sum_{n=0}^{N-1} x_n \left\{ cos\left(\frac{2\pi nk}{N}\right) + j \, sin\left(\frac{2\pi nk}{N}\right) \right\} \tag{11.15}$$

The filtering operation is performed in the DFT by summing over N samples which is inherent in the vector/matrix multiplication.

The problem with direct implementations such as filters or the DFT is that they effectively perform a convolution operation involving order N^2 multiplications for an N-point transform. This is computationally intensive by one dimensional signal processing standards and was the main cause of the delay in the widespread adoption of computer based frequency domain techniques. This situation changed dramatically with the discovery of the FFT algorithm for rapid computation of the DFT.

11.10 THE FAST FOURIER TRANSFORM

The FFT was discovered by Cooley and Tukey [Cooley & Tukey] on the observation that there were many symmetries in the DFT matrix and that many multiplications were being needlessly repeated or could be performed in stages. In its simplest form the FFT reduces the number of complex multiplies from N^2 to $(N/2)\log_2(N)$ for an N-point transform. The major drawback of the FFT over the DFT is the control overhead required for its implementation. This is the price which must be paid for the increased computational efficiency and in some applications where (for example) hardware multipliers are available and time permits, then a simple DFT implementation may be preferable.

We will now derive the FFT from the DFT. Recall the equation for the kth frequency domain output from the DFT. It is conventional at this point to denote the nth element of the time domain (input) vector as $x(n)$.

$$X_k = \sum_{n=0}^{N-1} x(n) \, W_N^{nk} \tag{11.16}$$

This is the algebraic equivalent of the vector multiplication (dot or inner product) of the kth row of the N-point DFT matrix with the input vector. Derivation of the FFT begins by splitting the single summation over N samples into two summations, each over $N/2$ samples as shown in equation (11.17).

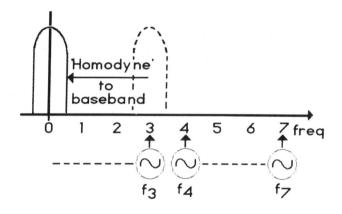

Figure 11.11   Baseband analyser analogy for an 8-point DFT.

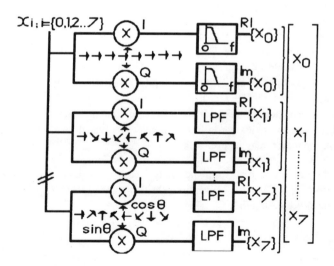

Figure 11.12   Possible realisation of the baseband analyser illustrating correspondence between oscillator frequency and rows of the DFT matrix.

$$X_k = \sum_{\substack{n=0 \\ n \text{ even}}}^{N-1} x(n) \, W_N^{nk} + \sum_{\substack{n=0 \\ n \text{ odd}}}^{N-1} x(n) \, W_N^{nk} \tag{11.17}$$

The division here is into a summation over the even samples and a summation over the odd samples. Now make the substitution of variable shown in equation (11.18).

$$\text{substitute } m = \begin{cases} \dfrac{n}{2}, & n \text{ even} \\[2mm] \dfrac{n-1}{2}, & n \text{ odd} \end{cases} \tag{11.18}$$

We now have two summations, each over the range $N/2$.

$$X_k = \sum_{m=0}^{\frac{N}{2}-1} x(2m) \, W_N^{2mk} + \sum_{m=0}^{\frac{N}{2}-1} x(2m+1) \, W_N^{(2m+1)k} \tag{11.19}$$

This is the first step towards expressing the single N-point DFT as two $N/2$ point DFT's. Reference to Figure (11.4) will show that $W_N^2 = W_{N/2}$. Also the even data are denoted by the sub-sequence $x_1(m)$ and the odd data by the sub-sequence $x_2(m)$ (i.e. $x_1(m)$ is the m th sample from the even sequence). These substitutions are made into equation (11.19) giving equation (11.20).

$$\begin{aligned} X_k &= \sum_{m=0}^{\frac{N}{2}-1} x_1(m) \, W_{N/2}^{mk} + W_N^k \sum_{m=0}^{\frac{N}{2}-1} x_2(m) \, W_{N/2}^{mk} \\ X_k &= X_1(k) + W_N^k \, X_2(k) \end{aligned} \tag{11.20}$$

In equation (11.20) we can identify two transforms, $X_1(k)$ and $X_2(k)$, each of size $N/2$. In the case of the second transform the component W_N^k has been taken outside the summation (it is a constant with respect to the variable m). This component is referred to in the literature as a "twiddle factor" and is a rotational operator in that it is complex, has unit magnitude and thus rotates the vector representation of any complex number which it multiplies. Thus the outputs of the N-point transform (X_k, $k = 0$ to $N-1$) may be obtained by suitable combination (using twiddle factors) of the outputs of two $N/2$ point transforms, one on the odd input data and one on the even input data. This is illustrated in Figure 11.13(a) for the 8-point case. Assuming N is highly composite and a power of 2, we can repeat the above process on the two $N/2$ point transforms, breaking them down to $N/4$ point transforms etc. until we come down to 2-point transforms. Figure 11.13(b) also shows the the flowgraph for the 2-point transform which is the basic building block for the radix-2 FFT. This is actually a 2-point transform in flowgraph form and shows two inputs x_0 and x_1 which are respectively added and subtracted to provide the two outputs X_0 and X_1. This flowgraph can also be expressed in matrix form as shown again in Figure 11.13(b). The basic add/subtract operation is referred to as a "butterfly" operation. The complete radix-2 representation of the 8-point transform is shown in

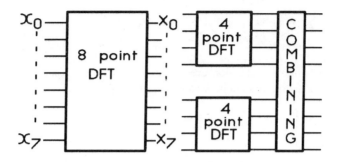

Figure 11.13(a) 8-point DFT realisation as two 4-point DFT's with post combining.

$$X_0 = x_0 + x_1$$

$$X_1 = x_0 - x_1$$

$$\equiv \begin{bmatrix} X_0 \\ X_1 \end{bmatrix} = \begin{bmatrix} 1 & 1 \\ 1 & -1 \end{bmatrix} \begin{bmatrix} x_0 \\ x_1 \end{bmatrix}$$

Figure 11.13(b) Basic 2-point transform (butterfly) in flowgraph and matrix form.

Figure 11.14. The term "pass" is used to refer to the complete cycle wereby all the data flows through the arithmetic unit once. In the case of the 8-point transform this occurs 3 times in the radix-2 implementation and in general occurs $\log_2(N)$ times for an N-point transform. Figure 11.15 is the normal full flowgraph representation of the 8-point transform. Thus the N-point transform can be expressed as repeated applications of 2-point transforms, the outputs of which are combined with rotational operators to produce the N-point result.

The above algorithm is referred to as the Cooley-Tukey, radix-2, in-place, decimation-in-time (DIT) algorithm. The term in-place refers to the facility to take two data numbers from RAM, modify them by addition and subtraction, and return the two resultant numbers to the same two RAM locations. This minimises the RAM requirement which was an important feature of the algorithm when first developed in the mid 1960's. Now RAM is cheap and dense and for some applications the in-place algorithm has been superceded by algorithms with other advantages which are more relevant to modern technology (i.e. the constant geometry algorithm discussed in chapter 12). The term decimation-in-time comes from the successive splitting (decimation) of the time domain (input) data into even and odd subsequences until we have $N/2$ pairs of numbers on which to perform 2-point transforms. This process is illustrated in Figure 11.16. This particular "shuffle" of the input data leads to the time domain data appearing in "bit reversed" order on the flowgraph in Figure 11.15. If the binary addresses of the input locations 0 to 7 are reflected "mirror" fashion with the MSB being regarded as the LSB etc., then the resulting number indicates which data sample should be stored in any given location. For example location 1 (address 001_2) would hold data sample 4 (sample 100_2).

If the data are divided into two sub-sequences comprising respectively the first $N/2$ data points and the last $N/2$ data points etc., then the algorithm which results is referred to as the decimation-in-frequency (DIF) algorithm. The resulting flowgraph for the DIF algorithm is shown in Figure 11.17. In this case the inputs are in natural order and the outputs are in bit-reversed order. In the DIF flowgraph the weights (or twiddle factors) which appear explicitly on the first pass are W_N^0, W_N^1, W_N^2, etc. to $W_N^{(N/2-1)}$. The Nth roots of unity from $W^{N/2}$ to W^{N-1} appear implicitly in the lower output from each butterfly as $-W_N^0$, $-W_N^1$, etc. Thus on the first pass all N, Nth roots of unity appear. On the second pass every second Nth root appears (W_N^0, W_N^2, W_N^4, ...), again either explicitly or implicitly. These should, however, be regarded as all the order $N/2$ roots of unity. Similarly on the third pass all the $N/4$ th roots of unity appear etc. until on the last pass the 2, 2nd roots appear (1, -1). Thus on the last pass of a DIF algorithm there are no actual complex multiplies to be performed. With the DIT algorithm, on the otherhand, the twiddles are redundant on the first pass and grow to include all the Nth roots of unity on the last pass.

Figure 11.18 summarises the fundamental difference between the DIT and DIF algorithms. With the DIT algorithm the twiddle appears on both outputs from the butterfly operation while with the DIF algorithm it only appears in one output. This is the way to distinguish between DIT and DIF and not on the ordering of the inputs or outputs as the options for radix-2, in-place algorithms depicted in Figure 11.19 show.

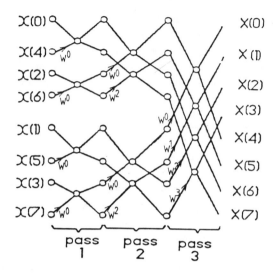

Figure 11.14   8-point transform as successive applications of 2-point transforms.

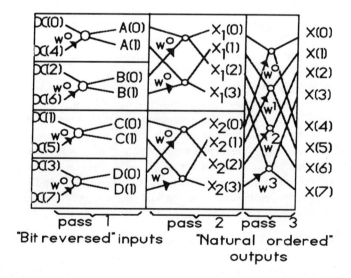

Figure 11.15   Flowgraph of radix-2, in-place, DIT FFT algorithm for computing the 8-point DFT.

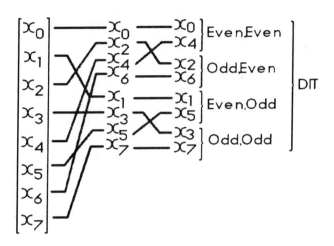

Figure 11.16   DIT shuffles on the input data to the flowgraph in Figure 11.15.

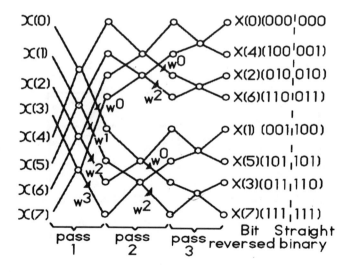

Figure 11.17   Flowgraph of radix-2, in-place, DIF FFT algorithm for computing the 8-point transform.

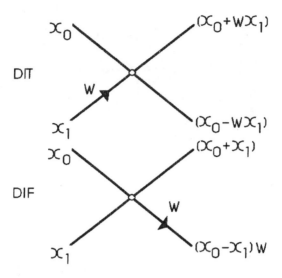

Figure 11.18   DIT and DIF butterfly operations.

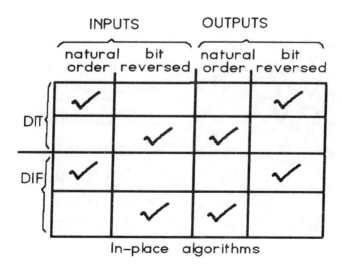

Figure 11.19   Summary of radix-2 FFT algorithms.

11.9 SUMMARY

In this chapter various reasons for performing transforms have been explored and the need to justify the computational burden has been recognised. Starting with the continuous Fourier transform, the DFT was derived and then the FFT was derived from the DFT. After deriving the FFT in its DIT form, the DIF form was introduced and the corresponding butterfly operations were compared.

Chapter 12
FAST FOURIER TRANSFORMS
AND
HARDWARE

12.1 INTRODUCTION

This is the second DFT/FFT chapter. The understanding of several parts of this chapter depends on prior study of chapter 11 where the Cooley-Tukey, radix-2, in-place DIT and DIF algorithms were derived. These were the original forms in which the FFT algorithm was developed in the mid 60's, when RAM was expensive and the in-place algorithm minimised the amount of RAM required. In this chapter some further algorithms are introduced such as the constant geometry algorithm, the radix-4 and mixed radix algorithms. The attributes of zero padding will be considered and, finally, some dedicated hardware and windows will be studied.

12.2 THE CONSTANT GEOMETRY ALGORITHM

Figure 12.1(a) is a flowgraph for the 4-point case of the in-place algorithm derived in its general N-point form in chapter 11. Figure 12.1(b) shows the flowgraph for the corresponding 4-point constant geometry algorithm. In the 4-point case we have 2 passes, radix-2. In the case of the in-place algorithm these passes have different addressing regimes but in the case of the constant geometry algorithm the addressing regimes are the same on each pass. This leads to simplified RAM address generation. Unfortunately though, with the constant geometry algorithm, we are not working in-place and this leads to a requirement for twice as much RAM. We now require separate source RAM and sink RAM (as seen by the arithmetic unit). This doubling of the RAM requirement is not a problem, since RAM is now dense and cheap.

Figure 12.2 depicts an 8-point, radix-2, constant geometry algorithm with naturally ordered inputs and bit-reversed outputs. Data points are selected in pairs from the source RAM on each pass. These pairs are spaced by $N/2$ points for an N-point transform. After being "twiddled" and operated on by the radix-2 "butterfly" (2-point transform) they are placed in the sink RAM in adjacent locations. This addressing strategy is the same for each pass, hence the term constant geometry.

In place 4-point

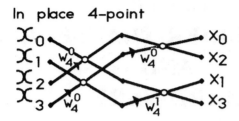

Figure 12.1(a) In place, radix-2, 4-point FFT.

Constant geometry 4-point

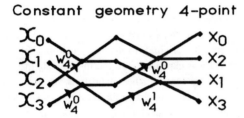

Figure 12.1(b) Constant geometry, radix-2, 4-point FFT.

12.3 RADIX-4 IMPLEMENTATIONS

Figure 12.3 shows the operations performed in the basic arithmetic computational unit (AU), radix-2 (the 2-point DFT or "butterfly") and the basic AU radix-4 (the 4-point DFT). The advantage shared by both these arithmetic units is that neither of them require a complex multiplier. In the case of the radix-2 "butterfly" multiplication is by $+1$ or -1 as illustrated by the 2-point DFT matrix shown in this figure. In the radix-4 case, multiplication is $+1$, -1 or $+j$, $-j$. Multiplication of a complex number $\pm j$ may be simply achieved by interchanging real and imaginary parts and changing the sign of the real or imaginary parts of the resultant respectively. A radix-4 implementation is normally twice as fast as a radix-2 implementation given the same hardware. This is because in a radix-4 implementation there are only half the number of RAM accesses that there are radix-2 since the radix-4 transform is achieved in half the number of passes ($\log_4(N)$ passes as opposed to $\log_2(N)$ passes). Unfortunately, only transform sizes which are powers of 4 can be accommodated. If, for instance, an 8-point or 32-point transform size is required then a radix-2 or a mixed radix solution must be employed.

12.4 MIXED RADIX IMPLEMENTATIONS

A simple mixed-radix implementation is illustrated in Figure 12.4 with an example. Here the first pass is implemented radix-4 and the second pass is implemented radix-2. A more general example is $N = 60$. This transform size may be implemented in mixed radix as a radix-2 pass followed by another radix-2 pass, a radix-3 pass and, finally, a radix-5 pass. As always, all these constituent radicies are prime. In the case of a 60-point transform there is an alternative to using this mixed-radix decomposition. The data may be zero-padded to 64 points and a standard radix-2 transform (6 passes) or a radix-4 transform (3 passes) employed. This is quite legitimate and avoids having to resort to mixed radix implementations. If a substantial amount of zero-padding is employed then an interprolation effect is obtained.

12.5 INTERPOLATION THROUGH ZERO-PADDING

Figure 12.5 illustrates zero-padding. Here 8 data points have been zero-padded by factor of 3, out to 32 points. The result is a decrease in quantisation in the frequency domain, but the resolution afforded by the transform is unaltered. Within the context of the DFT, it is only possible to increase resolution by lengthening the duration of "look" at the signal (taking a longer sample in time). It is not possible to increase resolution by zero-padding although some apparent increase is often achieved which invariably reflects suboptimum frequency domain peak detection in the unpadded case. Some appropriate hardware techniques will now be considered. Most of these are not confined to FFT hardware, but are most generally applicable to high-speed signal processing implementations.

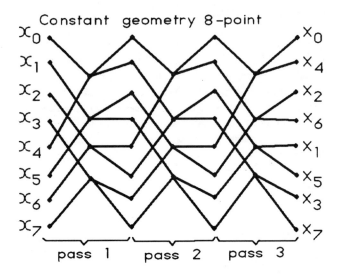

Figure 12.2   Constant geometry, radix-2, 8-point FFT.

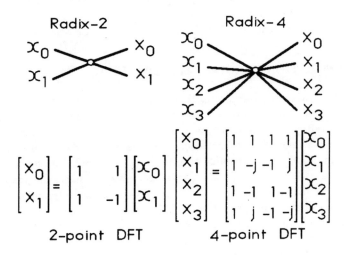

Figure 12.3   2-point and 4-point transform flowgraphs and corresponding matrices.

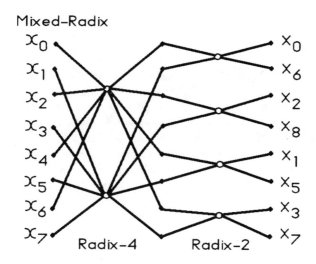

Figure 12.4   Mixed radix 8-point transform.

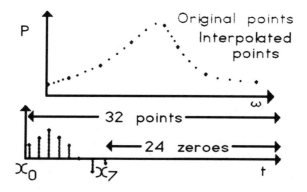

Figure 12.5   Zero-padding to achieve interpolation.

12.6 HARDWARE FOR HIGH SPEED IMPLEMENTATIONS

Pipelining

The technique of pipelining, which is illustrated in Figure 12.6 is generally applicable in high speed real-time arithmetic processor design. In this illustration a source RAM is supplying data to a multiplier which, in turn, is multipling that data by complex weights from a "twiddles" PROM. The multiplier output is passed to an arithmetic unit (AU) which would typically perform 2-point or 4-point DFT's and finally, the output from the AU is passed to a sink RAM. In order to permit concurrent processing all of these stages are separated by latches. The whole structure is referred to as a pipeline. This pipeline has 4 stages. The source RAM may be addressing the next data while the multiplier is multipling previous data held in the first latch. Simultaneously, the AU is adding and subtracting number pairs held in its input latch while the sink RAM is storing the previous data from the AU. Pipelining facilitates high-speed arithmetic in real-time applications.

Swinging Buffers

If there is a requirement to block process data in real time with contiguous blocks then provision must be made to input data through the analogue-to-digital converter (ADC) while concurrently performing the FFT and, again, concurrently outputting previous transformed data to a post-processor. Figure 12.7 illustrates the swinging buffer solution to this problem. Here four RAM's are being used. Recall that in the original form in which the FFT was derived (the in-place algorithm) only one RAM was required. The constant geometry algorithm reduces the address generation problem at the expense of requiring second RAM. Now, if concurrent processing in real-time with swinging buffers is employed, the RAM requirement is again doubled leading to a requirement for four RAM's. These are shown in Figure 12.7 as RAM 0,1,2 and 3. At the top of figure 12.7 RAM 0 is depicted filling from the ADC. Concurrently, on the right of the dotted line, RAM's 1 and 2 are involved in performing the transform in conjunction with the AU (a three pass case, is shown). The transform starts with the time domain data in RAM 1 passing through the AU into RAM 2. When all the data in RAM 1 is exhausted the first pass is complete. RAM 2 then becomes the source RAM and RAM 1 becomes the sink RAM and the data flows through the AU again until the end of the second pass and similarly for the third pass. While this process is continuing, RAM 3 is outputting to a post processor. The outputting process and the transform process must finish and flag that they are finished before the input RAM (servicing the ADC) is filled so that the moment this happens all RAM's can swing around and an empty RAM may be placed at the disposal of the ADC without loss of data. The bottom half of Figure 12.7 shows the disposition of RAM's during the next transform. RAM 1 is filling from the ADC, RAM's 0 and 3 are involved in the next transform and RAM 2, which now holds the previously transformed data, is outputting to a post processor and so the cycle continues. Choosing an example with an even number of passes would reveal a control cycle of 4 transforms in that case. It is useful to consider how this swinging buffer arrangement might be implemented.

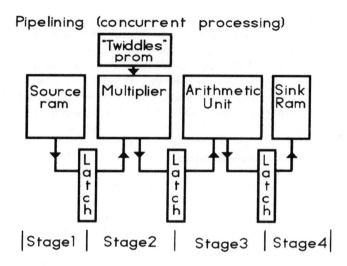

Figure 12.6 Radix-2 FFT processor configured as a 4-stage pipeline.

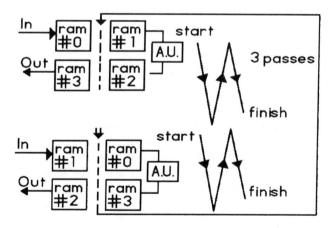

Figure 12.7 FFT processor configured for continuous processing using 4 swinging buffers.

Figure 12.8 depicts one possible implementation based on data buses and tri-state buffers (TSB's). The 4 RAM's are shown labelled as before. Also shown are 4 address busses carrying the appropriate addressing for each RAM depending on its function at the particular instant of time. (i.e. inputing from the ADC, outputting to the post-processor, sourcing data to the AU or sinking data from the AU) The input from the ADC is fed via a tristate buffer (TSB) to data bus 1 where it is time-division-multiplexed (TDM) with the data from the AU. Data bus 2, meanwhile, carries TDM data from RAM's to the AU input and the processor output (via output buffers).

Address Generation for Hardware Processors

As a specific example of address generation assume a 256 point, constant geometry, radix-2, DIT algorithm with naturally ordered inputs and bit-reversed outputs. Figure 12.9 shows the address buses involved in this case. Three 8-bit straight binary counters (SBC's), which will generate numbers from 0 to 255 are required. Each counter produces 8 address lines on an address bus. The input RAM (sourcing from the ADC) and the RAM which is sinking data from the AU both employ a straight binary count, thus no manipulation on these address bus is required. The outputs from the other 2 counters are modified. The counter generating the source RAM address sequence requires to address sequentially, data which are spaced in the RAM by half the transform size (Figure 12.1(b)). This is achieved by taking the least significant bit (LSB) of the counter and making it the most significant bit in the source RAM address. The other bits are brought down in significance to make way for the least significant bit. Finally, at the bottom of the Figure 12.9 we see the counter output being completely twisted so that the LSB becomes MSB and the MSB becomes the LSB etc. Thus modified, it can address the output RAM in bit reversed sequence.

Complex Multiplier Hardware

Consider the multiplication of the two complex numbers:-

$$(a + j\,b)(c + j\,d) = (a\,c - b\,d) + j\,(a\,d + b\,c) \qquad (12.1)$$

For fastest implementation this requires 4 multipliers as shown in Figure 12.10. Notice that these multipliers have latches at their inputs and outputs. Thus they are well suited to pipeline operations. The inputs here are 16 bit with 16 bit rounded outputs from the multipliers possibly growing to 17 bits at the output from the add/subtract units. This leads to a requirement to round back to 16 bits before storage in the sink RAM. Experience shows that 16 bit fixed-point arithmetic is sufficient for most signal processing applications, except some, such as Kalman filtering (chapter 9), where floating point is necessary. In fact the full dynamic range potential of a 16 bit fixed-point processor (some 96 dB) will only be exploitable if a suitable data window is used on the rectangular block of time domain input samples. The following section addresses this very important subject.

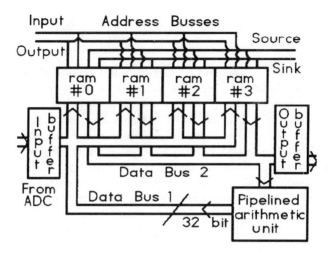

Figure 12.8   Two bus implementation of the processor of Figure 12.7.

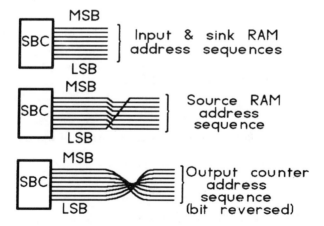

Figure 12.9   Address generation for a 256-point, constant geometry, radix-2 DIT FFT with naturally ordered inputs and bit reversed outputs.

12.7 DATA WINDOWS

The Rectangular Window

Implicitly, every DFT is windowed, since a finite time-series is obtained by effectively multiplying an infinite duration time-series by a rectangular (sampling) window. But, multiplication in the time domain is equivalent to convolution in the frequency domain. For the case of the rectangular window the DFT obtained is the convolution of the DFT of the signal itself, with the DFT of a rectangle. The result is set of $sinc$ $(sin(x)/x)$ functions, each raised on the corresponding unwindowed frequency domain signal component. The spreading associated with the sidelobes of the sinc function is termed "leakage". The problem of leakage and its control is illustrated with a carefully chosen test signal comprising two tones as shown in Figure 12.11 Here, a large sinewave of amplitude 1 is shown in bin 10 (this sinewave has a normalised frequency of 10 cycles per block length). Signal 2 is in bin 16 and has an amplitude of 0.01. Thus both of these signals have an integer number of cycles over a block length and will exhibit no leakage. Any apparent width in Figure 12.11 is due to the graphics plotting routine. By contrast, Figure 12.12 shows what happens if the frequency of the large signal is moved by half a bin. A worse case leakage problem results as explained in chapter 11. Leakage from this signal has spread through the complete transform, and has masked the small signal, which is now well below leakage from the large signal. Thus, the dynamic range is severly reduced, particularly close in to large signals. This is unacceptable since we have an ultimate dynamic range limitation of some 96 dB due to the 16 bit fixed-point arithmetic (6 dB per bit). The problem is that the leakage here follows the envelope of the peaks of the $sinc^2$ ($(sin(x)/x)^2$) function shown in Figure 12.13. As with all the similar plots, Figure 12.12 was calculated by plotting the squared magnitude of a highly zero-padded FFT of the time domain window shape. The zero padding creates an interpolation effect which allows plotting of the fine detailed structure of the sidelobes. This leakage may be reduced by use of a "tapered" window. Almost any tapered window [Harris] will be better than the rectangular window. The main families of tapered windows will now be considered.

Cosine Windows

Figure 12.14 shows the most important member of a family of windows called the cos^α family given by the equation:

$$sin^\alpha(\frac{n\pi}{N}), \qquad 0 < n \le N-1 \tag{12.2}$$

This member of the family ($\alpha=2.0$) is known as the sine squared window. It is also commonly referred to as the Hanning window or the raised cosine window since it may be regarded as a cosine on a pedestal of height 0.5.

$$sin^2(\frac{n\pi}{N}) = 0.5 [1.0 - cos(\frac{2n\pi}{N})] \tag{12.3}$$

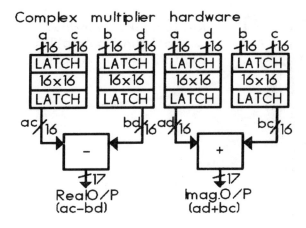

Figure 12.10   Complex multiplier using 4, 16-bit multipliers.

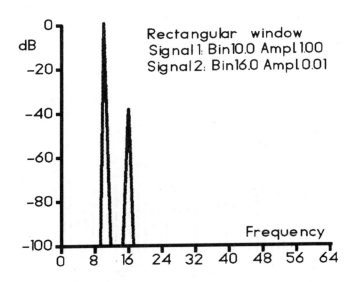

Figure 12.11   Test signal composed of two integer frequency sinewaves.

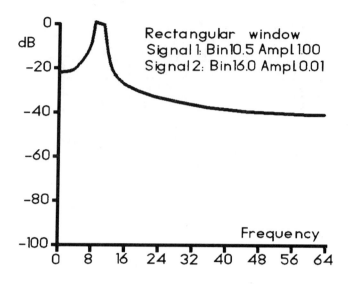

Figure 12.12   Large sinusoid of Figure 12.11 shifted by half a bin to produce worst case leakage.

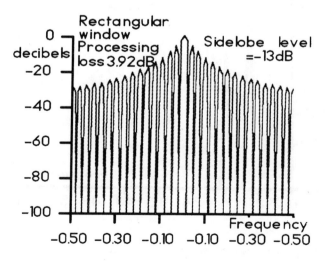

Figure 12.13   Power spectrum from zero-padded FFT of a rectangular window.

Figure 12.15 shows the transform of this window. The highest sidelobe level is -32 dB and it rolls-off rapidly to give very good visibility well away from the mainlobe.

$$W(n) = 0.5 - 0.5 \cos(\frac{2\pi n}{N}) \qquad\qquad (12.4)$$

Figure 12.16 illustrates the effect of this window on the test signal for the case of the large signal in bin 10.5 and the small signal in bin 16. The leakage is well controlled in comparison with the rectangular window, with the small signal being just visible on the side of the leakage from the large signal.

The Hamming Window

The Hamming Window is a slight modification of the raised cosine window and is given by the formula:

$$W(n) = 0.54 - 0.46 \cos(\frac{2\pi n}{N}) \qquad\qquad (12.5)$$

The Hamming Window which is shown in Figure 12.17, differs from the raised cosine window in that the height of the pedestal has been increased from 0.5 to 0.54. This sounds like quite a small modification but it has a significant effect on the side lobe performance of the window shown in Figure 12.18. Compare this with Figure 12.15. This Hamming window has a maximum sidelobe level of -43 dB, which is 11 dB lower than the corresponding maximum of the Hanning window, but the trade-off here is that far away from the main lobe the sidelobes do not decrease as rapidly, as with the Hanning window. They "bottom out" at about 50 dB below the main lobe. What this means is that by symmetry, leakage from a signal in the position of the main lobe will come through in bins which are far away from that bin with an attenuation of 50 dB and will mask smaller signals that may lie in those bins. Figure 12.19 shows the effect of this Hamming window on the test signal. The small signal is again visible with this tapered window.

Another important family of windows in the Dolph-Chebychev family given by the formula:

$$W(n) = \frac{(-1)^n \cos[N \cos^{-1}[\beta \cos(\frac{n\pi}{N})]]}{\cosh[N \cosh^{-1}(\beta)]}, \qquad 0 \le |n| \le N-1 \qquad (12.6)$$

where

$$\beta = \cosh[\frac{1}{N} \cosh^{-1}(10^\alpha)]$$

and

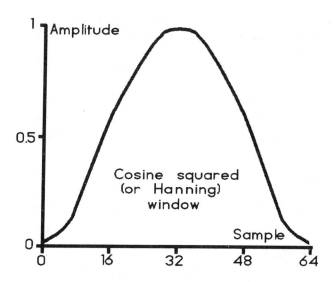

Figure 12.14   64-point cosine squared (also referred to as raised cosine or Hanning) window.

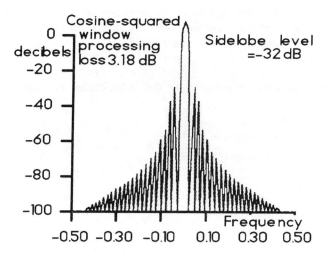

Figure 12.15   Squared magnitude of the Fourier transform of the Hanning window.

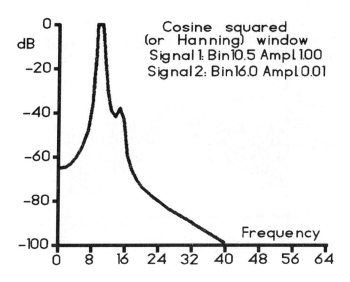

Figure 12.16   Hanning windowed test signal of Figure 12.12.

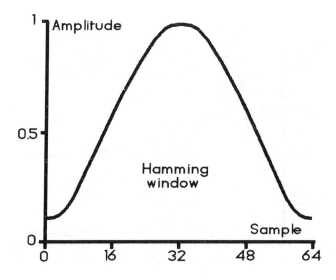

Figure 12.17   64-point Hamming window.

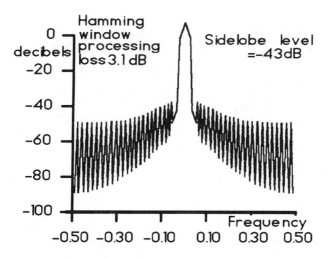

Figure 12.18   Squared magnitude of the Fourier transform of the Hamming window.

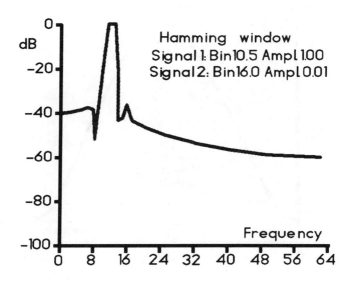

Figure 12.19   Hamming windowed test signal of Figure 12.12.

$$
\cos^{-1}(x) = \begin{cases} \dfrac{\pi}{2} - \tan^{-1}\left(\dfrac{x}{\sqrt{1.0 - x^2}}\right) & |x| \le 1.0 \\[3mm] \ln\left(x + \sqrt{x^2 - 1.0}\right) & |x| \ge 1.0 \end{cases}
$$

The parameter α governs the degree of taper (or severity) of the window. The leakage properties of 3 typical members of this family are shown in Figure 12.20 ($\alpha = 2.5$), Figure 12.21 ($\alpha = 3.0$) and Figure 12.22 ($\alpha = 3.5$). The striking feature of these windows is the fact that the background leakage from the main lobe is at a constant amplitude. This is the main attraction of this window family, particularly for small transforms because on a small transform there only are a small number of bins. This means that good visibility close to the mainlobe is important and thus the Dolph-Chebychev window is a good choice. The sidelobe levels for these 3 windows are −50 dB, −60 dB and −70 dB respectively. Obviously the lower the sidelobe level the better but what prevents making α very large and making the sidelobe level arbitrarily low? As the window becomes more strongly tapered, resolution is lost due to a progressive widening of the mainlobe. Hence visibility is achieved at the expense of resolution and it depends on the particular application where the optimum trade-off lies. The Dolph-Chebychev window does, however, provide the minimum mainlobe width for a given amount of sidelobe leakage. Figure 12.23 depicts the 60 dB Dolph Chebychev windowed FFT output in response to the test signal of Figure 12.12.

12.8 SUMMARY

The constant geometry algorithm was shown to make address generation easier at the expense of doubling the RAM requirement. The need was stressed for choosing the right degree of parallelism in transform design in order to have optimum hardware and the radix-4 and mixed radix transforms were considered in this context. Zero padding was investigated as a means of taking a number of points which was not a power of two to the nearest power of 2 in order to implement a radix-2 transform. The use of large amounts of zero padding in order to achieve interpolation in the frequency domain was outlined and it was stressed that there was no increase in resolution afforded by zero padding, merely a decrease in frequency domain quantisation. Then some dedicated hardware appropriate for real time FFT processing was introduced, such as swinging buffer memories, complex multipliers and bus orientated architectures. Finally the important topic of windows was studied. It is very seldom that a FFT or DFT can be performed without the application of a tapered window because of the enormous amount of leakage associated with the rectangular window. Several window families were considered and a trade-off was demonstrated between resolution (or mainlobe width) and visibility (or dynamic range) against background leakage. For small transforms the Dolph-Chebychev window was recommended as optimum and for large transforms the Hamming or Hanning windows were advocated.

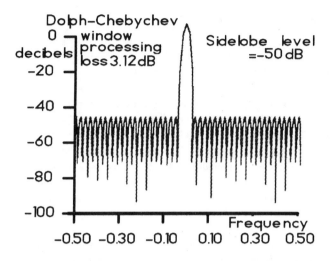

Figure 12.20   Squared magnitude of a 50 dB Dolph-Chebychev window.

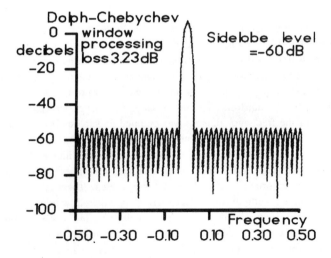

Figure 12.21   Squared magnitude of a 60 dB Dolph-Chebychev window.

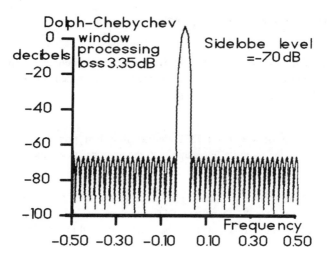

Figure 12.22   Squared Magnitude of a 70 dB Dolph-Chebychev window.

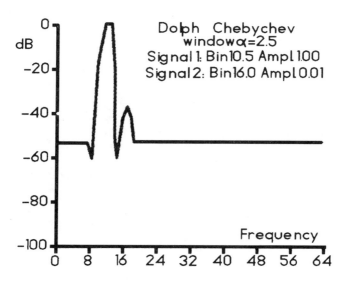

Figure 12.23   Effect of windowing the test signal of Figure 12.12 with a 60 dB Dolph-Chebychev window.

TUTORIAL Discrete and Fast Fourier Transforms

1. Work out by hand $X(0)$ and $X(1)$, the 1st two frequency bin outputs for an 8 point DFT assuming the complex input to be a unit amplitude phasor which rotates 1 cycle during the transform length and has zero starting phase.

2. From the definition of a 4 point DFT derive from first principles the radix-2 DIT algorithm and show the requisite flowgraph with the appropriate weights.

3. Derive the FFT decimation in time algorithm from the definition of the DFT for the specific case where $N = 8$. Draw the DIT flowchart for the 8 point transform and indicate the twiddle values as complex number pairs expressed to 6 decimal digits.

4. Repeat question 3 for the decimation in frequency case.

5. Rearrange the flowgraph of question 3 for constant geometry implementation. What are the advantages of in-place and constant geometry implementation respectively?

Chapter 13
MODERN SPECTRAL ANALYSIS

13.1 INTRODUCTION

In its simplest form spectral analysis involves estimating the amplitude of the harmonics of a periodic signal from a finite set of data samples i.e. making an estimate of the energy in each Fourier component. Since practical signals are rarely periodic it is more useful to replace the Fourier series with the Fourier transform and resort to energy density rather than energy as a measure of the frequency content of a signal. Finally if the signal is to some degree random and thus of infinite energy a more appropriate measure is power. Thus in order to deal with the widest class of signal, which would include periodic, non-periodic and stochastic processes, spectral analysis is most often defined as an estimate of the power spectral density (PSD).

At an intuitive level spectral analysis can be visualised as a bank of contiguous band pass filters (BPF) as in Figure 13.1. If the bandwidth of each filter is extremely narrow then an estimate of the PSD at a particular frequency can be formed by squaring the output of a filter and averaging it over M samples. This visualisation can also be used to highlight the important concepts of spectral resolution and quality. Spectral resolution cannot be defined in a rigorous quantitative manner nevertheless qualitatively it can be though of as a measure of how closely spaced in frequency two sinusoids can become before they merge into one. Thus in Figure 13.1 the resolution is directly related to the bandwidth of the BPF's. The narrower the bandwidth of the BPF's the better the spectral resolution will be. Spectral quality on the other hand is a measure of how good the spectral estimate is in a statistical sense e.g. in terms of its mean and variance. In order to improve the quality of a spectral estimate at a particular frequency, the number of samples, M, over which the time average is performed could be increased.

However both the quality and resolution of a spectral estimate cannot be improved simultaneously for a given number of data samples, M. If in attempt to improve resolution the bandwidth of the BPF's is reduced then the impulse response of these filters will become longer and consequently it will take longer for the output of a filter to reach a steady state. The time-averaging processor can only form an unbiased estimate of the spectral density if the signal at the output of a BPF is stationary. Thus in an attempt to improve resolution two alternatives are open either (i) average over all M time samples and accept a spectral estimate which becomes increasingly biased as the resolution improves or (ii) allow enough time for the natural response of the BPF to decay to zero and average over the remaining data samples with the result that the variance of the spectral estimate becomes larger with increasing resolution.

Spectral analysis is a large and much researched subject. A very readable account is available in [Marple]. The key techniques are summarised and related in Figure 13.2. They can be roughly classified into classical and modern. The classical techniques are considered briefly in subsection 13.2. The modern techniques have evolved in an attempt to improve on the resolution limitations of the classical techniques. Two important sub-classes can be identified: parametric and non-parametric. Parametric spectral analysis is discussed in general terms in subsection 13.3. The most frequently used form of parametric spectral analysis is the autoregressive (AR) form which is described in detail in subsection 13.4. Many techniques are available with which to estimate the parameters or AR coefficients which define the PSD. The most notable of these are least squares (LS) algorithm and the Burg algorithm [Marple], which are closely related to the adaptive filter concepts considered in chapter 10. Finally the minimum variance spectral estimator is described as an example of a modern non-parametric technique. Before discussing spectral estimation, power spectral density must be defined.

For a wide sense stationary random process, $\{x(n)\}$, the power spectral density, $S_{xx}(\omega)$, is defined as the discrete Fourier transform (DFT) of the autocorrelation sequence, $\{\phi_{xx}(m)\}$.

$$\phi_{xx}(m) = E[x(n)x(n+m)] \tag{13.1}$$

$$S_{xx}(\omega) = \sum_{m=-\infty}^{\infty} \phi_{xx}(m)\, e^{-j\omega mT} \tag{13.2}$$

The autocorrelation function can be obtained from the spectral density, which is a periodic function of ω, by evaluating the Fourier coefficients of the density function.

$$\phi_{xx}(m) = \frac{T}{2\pi} \int_{0}^{2\pi/T} S_{xx}(\omega)\, e^{j\omega mT}\, d\omega \tag{13.3}$$

13.2 CLASSICAL SPECTRAL ANALYSIS

Calculation of the spectral density using equation (13.2) requires an infinite set of autocorrelation coefficients, $\{\phi_{xx}(m)\}$. All that is available in the practical situation is a finite set of M signal samples e.g.

$$x(0)\, x(1)\ \cdots\ x(n)\ \cdots\ x(M-1) \tag{13.4}$$

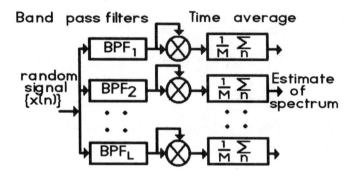

Figure 13.1   Frequency content of a stationary random signal.

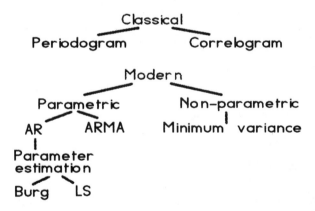

Figure 13.2   Overview of spectral analysis.

This provides a definition of spectral analysis i.e. from a finite set of data samples such as (13.4) form an estimate of the power spectral density.

The oldest and most popular approach is to form an M-point DFT of the finite sequence.

$$X_M(\omega) = \sum_{n=0}^{M-1} x(n) e^{-j\omega nT}$$

An estimate of the spectral density is then formed by dividing the energy at each frequency by the number of data samples.

$$\hat{S}_{xx}(\omega) = \frac{|X_M(\omega)|^2}{M} \qquad (13.5)$$

This technique is the simplest form of what is known as a periodogram, the structure of which is illustrated in Figure 13.3. The popularity of this method lies in the availability of the fast Fourier transform (FFT) to perform the DFT step.

An alternative approach relies on the transform relationship of equation (13.3). Since the process $\{x(n)\}$ is stationary the expectation operator of equation (13.1) can be replaced with a time average.

$$\phi_{xx}(m) = E[x(n) x(n+m)]$$

$$= \lim_{M \to \infty} \frac{1}{M} \sum_{n=0}^{M-1} x(n) x(n+m)$$

This infinite summation can be approximated by a finite summation over the available data to form an estimate, $\hat{\phi}_{xx}(m)$, of the autocorrelation coefficient, $\phi_{xx}(m)$.

$$\hat{\phi}_{xx}(m) = \frac{1}{M} \sum_{n=0}^{M-1} x(n) x(n+m) \qquad (13.6)$$

A DFT of the set of estimated autocorrelation coefficients provides an estimate of the PSD, $\hat{S}_{xx}(\omega)$.

$$\hat{S}_{xx}(\omega) = \sum_{m} \hat{\phi}_{xx}(m) e^{-j\omega mT} \qquad (13.7)$$

The limits on the size of the DFT have not been specified because it is often zero padded to produce more spectral detail. This form of spectral estimate is known as a correlogram. The structure is illustrated in Figure 13.4.

Classical techniques for spectral analysis are based on either the correlogram or periodogram or hybrids of the two. They tend to be robust in that their performance is not usually affected by the signal environment. They have the additional advantages that they are well understood because of their age and can be made computationally efficient through the use

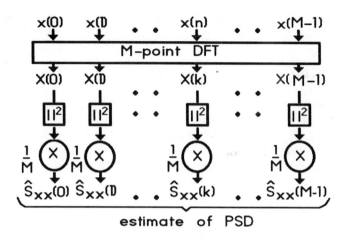

Figure 13.3   Periodogram PSD estimator.

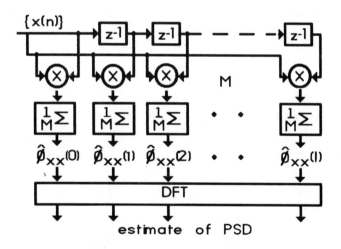

Figure 13.4   Correlogram PSD estimator.

of FFT techniques. On the negative side they usually provide a poor compromise between spectral resolution and quality.

13.3 PARAMETRIC SPECTRAL ANALYSIS

Parametric spectral analysis relies on the assumption that the PSD of the observed signal is the result of filtering a white noise sequence. This has great intuitive appeal. The flat PSD of the white noise may be coloured or shaped by the filter to provide a PSD of a desired shape. The theoretical foundation to this model is provided by the Wiener-Kintchine equation which relates the PSD, $S_{xx}(\omega)$, at the output of a digital filter with transfer function, $H(z)$, to the PSD at the input, $S_{uu}(\omega)$.

$$S_{xx}(\omega) = |H(e^{-j\omega T})|^2 S_{uu}(\omega)$$

If the input signal is white, i.e. $S_{uu}(\omega) = \sigma_u$, then

$$S_{xx}(\omega) = |H(e^{-j\omega T})|^2 \sigma_u$$

in which case the PSD is completely characterised by the amplitude response of the filter and the variance of the white noise. If the filter can be defined by a finite set of parameters the the PSD is also defined by these parameters.

Since the hypothetical process with PSD $S_{uu}(\omega)$ is inaccessible, the filter $H(z)$ can not be identified. However an alternative approach is possible. If an inverse filter $H^{-1}(z)$ can be found which whitens the process $x(n)$ then by the Wiener Kintchine relationship it will also completely parameterise the PSD of the signal.

$$S_{ee}(\omega) = \sigma_e$$

$$= |H^{-1}(e^{-j\omega T})|^2 S_{xx}(\omega)$$

$$S_{xx}(\omega) = \frac{\sigma_e}{|H^{-1}(e^{-jn\omega T})|^2} \tag{13.8}$$

Parametric spectral analysis is thus a 2-stage process

(i)   Estimate the coefficients of the whitening filter, $H^{-1}(z)$, and the noise variance, σ_e.

(ii) Form an estimate of the PSD based on equation (13.8).

The complete signal modelling and analysis structure is illustrated in Figure 13.5.

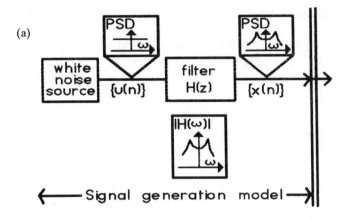

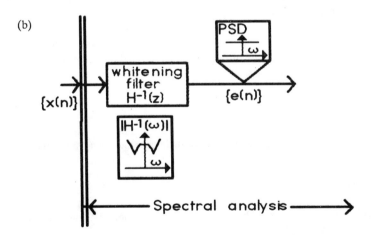

Figure 13.5   Parametric spectral analysis: (a) signal generation model; (b) analysis.

13.4 AUTOREGRESSIVE SPECTRAL ANALYSIS

The most straightforward approach to parametric spectral estimation is to assume that the signal generating filter, $H(z)$, is autoregressive (AR) in nature i.e.

$$x(n) = u(n) + \sum_{i=1}^{P} a_i \, x(n-i)$$

$$H(z) = \cfrac{1}{1 - \sum\limits_{i=1}^{P} a_i \, z^{-1}}$$

Given an order P generation model, the whitening filter, $H^{-1}(z)$, is an order P moving average (MA) filter.

$$H^{-1}(z) = 1 - \sum_{i=1}^{P} a_i \, z^{-1} \tag{13.9}$$

The order P AR filter and the corresponding MA whitening filter are illustrated in Figure 13.6. The AR filter might seem an unlikely first choice signal generation model. The attractiveness of this approach lies in the fact that the whitening filter is FIR and hence the coefficients, a_i, may be estimated from a finite data set by techniques similar to those discussed in the lecture on adaptive filters.

The MA structure of Figure 13.6 is a linear predictor or forward prediction error filter as discussed in chapter 16. An estimate or prediction, $\hat{x}(n)$, of the current signal sample, $x(n)$, is formed using the P previous samples, $x(n-1)\, x(n-2) \, \cdots \, x(n-P)$.

$$\hat{x}(n) = \sum_{i=1}^{P} a_i \, x(n-i)$$

The output, $e(n)$, of the whitening filter is the difference between the current signal sample and the prediction.

$$e(n) = x(n) - \hat{x}(n)$$

This linear estimation problem may be solved using the Wiener FIR filter i.e. the coefficients are chosen to minimise the MSE

$$\xi = E[\, e^2(n) \,].$$

Using the results obtained in chapter 8 for the Wiener FIR filter, the optimum tap vector $\underline{a}$ is given by

$$\underline{\phi}_{yy} \, \underline{a} = \underline{\phi}_{yx} \tag{13.10}$$

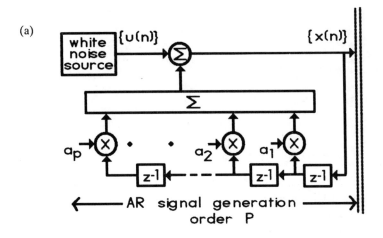

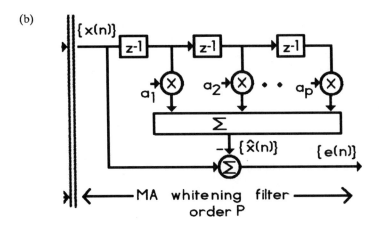

Figure 13.6   Auto-regressive spectral analysis: (a) AR signal generation (order P); (b) MA whitening filter (order P).

where

$$\underline{\phi}_{yy} = E[\, \underline{x}(n-1)\, \underline{x}^T(n-1)\,]$$

$$\underline{\phi}_{yx} = E[\, x(n)\, \underline{x}(n-1)\,]$$

$$\underline{a} = [\, a_1\, a_2\, \cdots\, a_P\,]^T$$

and

$$\underline{x}(n-1) = [\, x(n-1)\, x(n-2)\, \cdots\, x(n-P)\,]^T$$

The structure is illustrated in Figure 13.7. The input to the P-tap FIR filter, formerly $\{\, y(n)\,\}$, is replaced with a delayed version, $\{\, x(n-1)\,\}$, of the signal sequence, $\{\, x(n)\,\}$. The optimum filter, $\underline{a}$, of equation (13.10) is obtained by simply relacing $y(n)$ of equation (8.8) with $x(n-1)$. The minimum MSE, σ_e, is given by

$$\min \xi = \sigma_e = E[\, x^2(n)\,] - \underline{a}^T\, \underline{\phi}_{yx} \tag{13.11}$$

The Wiener equation (13.10) provides a mechanism for calculating P AR coefficients from the $(P+1)$ autocorrelation coefficients $\phi_{xx}(m)$, used to construct $\underline{\phi}_{yy}$ and $\underline{\phi}_{yx}$. In common with the adaptive filter techniques of chapter 10 and the classical methods of spectral analysis discussed above, AR analysis is usually performed on data such as (13.4) rather than on autocorrelation coefficients which are generally unknown. Again in common with adaptive filtering one method to circumvent this problem is to replace the MSE cost function with a sum of squared error cost function.

$$\rho = \sum_n (\, x(n) - \underline{a}^T\, \underline{x}(n-1)\,)^2 \tag{13.12}$$

By analogy with the MSE problem, the vector $\underline{a}$ which minimises this cost function and provides the least squares solution is provided by the deterministic form of the Wiener equation.

$$\underline{r}_{yy}\, \underline{a} = \underline{r}_{yx} \tag{13.13}$$

where

$$\underline{r}_{yy} = \sum_n \underline{x}(n-1)\, \underline{x}^T(n-1)$$

and

$$\underline{r}_{yx} = \sum_n \underline{x}(n-1)\, x(n)\,.$$

When equation (13.13) is substituted in (13.12) the minimum value of the cost function is obtained.

$$\rho = \sum_n x^2(n) - \underline{r}_{yx}^T \underline{a} \qquad (13.14)$$

The range of the summation over which the cost function is evaluated has been omitted deliberately. Choosing limits on this summation leads to implicit assumptions about the signal before the first signal sample $x(0)$ and after the last signal sample $x(M-1)$. These windowing assumptions directly affect the accuracy of both the estimate of the AR coefficients provided by equation (13.13) and the spectral estimate itself. To illustrate this relationship assume the summation begins at $n = 0$. Hence an error associated with this signal sample must be computed.

$$e(0) = x(0) - \underline{a}^T \underline{x}(-1)$$

Since all the elements of $\underline{x}(-1)$ lie outside the window of available data, an assumption must be made about its contents. The usual assumption is that it contains all zero elements in which case.

$$e(0) = x(0)$$

Thus the error $e(0)$ provides no information about the AR coefficients. Yet it is weighted equally with errors from the middle of the sequence when forming an estimate of the AR coefficients. In a similar manner the error at $n = 1$ can be considered

$$e(1) = x(1) - \underline{a}^T \underline{x}(0)$$

$$= x(1) - a_1 x(0)$$

Thus this error only contains information about one AR coefficient. It is only when the error $e(P)$ is considered that no implicit assumptions about the data have to be made.

$$e(P) = x(P) - \underline{a}^T \underline{x}(P-1)$$

$$= x(P) - a_1 x(P-1) - \ldots - a_{P-1} x(1) - a_P x(0)$$

Similar arguments hold for the other end of the data block. In fact there are 4 possible variations which lead to 4 possible LS estimates of the AR coefficients. These variations are summarised in Table 13.1.

The autocorrelation form has been popular in speech coding because it ensures that the LS matrix $\underline{r}_{yy}$ is Toeplitz. This allow the use of the Levinson recursion to solve equation (13.13) at a lower cost in computation than Gaussian elimination. Further the Toeplitz property also ensures that the AR filter has all its poles within the unit circle in the z-plane and is thus stable. This is important in linear predictive coding (LPC) of speech where the AR filter must be constructed in order to regenerate the speech in the receiver (c.f. chapter

lower limit	upper limit $\sum\limits^{M+P}$	$\sum\limits^{M-1}$
$\sum\limits_{n=0}$	autocorrelation	prewindowed
$\sum\limits_{n=P}$	postwindowed	covariance

Table 13.1 Least squares windows

16). However since the autocorrelation form embodies assumptions about the data at both ends of the data block it provides the poorest spectral estimates. In the other forms the LS matrix is not Toeplitz but rather the product of 2 Toeplitz matrices. This near to Toeplitz property has facilitated the development of efficient fast algorithms for the calculation of the AR parameters. The covariance form is at the other extreme from the autocorrelation form embodying no assumptions about the data outside those samples that are available. Thus it is to be preferred as it produces the best spectral estimates of the 4 variants. Finally the minimum of the sum of squared error cost function ρ provides a mechanism for estimating the minimum MSE σ_e. Taking the covariance form as an example, an estimate, $\hat{\sigma}_e$, of the minimum MSE can be formed by dividing the minimum of the sum of squared errors, ρ, by the number of errors, $M-1-P$.

$$\hat{\sigma}_e = \frac{\sum\limits_{n=P}^{M-1} x^2(n) - \underline{r}_{yx}^T \underline{a}}{(M-1-P)} \qquad (13.15)$$

The final covariance-form order-P AR spectral estimate is given by:

$$\hat{S}_{xx}(\omega) = \frac{\hat{\sigma}_e}{\mid 1 - \sum\limits_{i=1}^{P} a_i \, e^{-ji\omega T} \mid^2} \qquad (13.16)$$

A significant problem in AR spectral analysis is the selection of the model order, P. The intuitive approach is to increase the order until the MSE drops below a specified threshold. Figure 16.7 illustrates how the spectral whitening progressively improves with increasing order. However the MSE decreases monotonically with increasing order and a clear decision point is not usually evident. Several order selection criteria have been suggested. They are all functions of the number of data points, the order and the MSE. The order which minimises a particular criteria is the one that is chosen. Three of the most well known order selection criteria are summarised below [Marple].

final prediction error (FPE)

$$FPE(P) = \hat{\sigma}_e \left(\frac{M + P + 1}{M - P - 1} \right)$$

Akaike information criteria (AIC)

$$AIC(P) = M \ ln(\hat{\sigma}_e) + 2P$$

criterion autoregressive transfer (CAT)

$$CAT(P) = \left\{ \frac{1}{M} \sum_{j=1}^{P} \frac{1}{\hat{\sigma}_{ej}} \right\} - \frac{1}{\hat{\sigma}_e}$$

The use of any of these techniques presumes that a range of MSE values for various filter orders is available. This will of course add to the computational complexity. The above criteria can give satisfactory order estimates when the signal is truly AR, but experiment indicates that they tend to be less than satisfactory when the signal is not AR. Their value is in giving an initial estimate of the model order.

13.5 MINIMUM VARIANCE SPECTRAL ESTIMATION

Minimum variance spectral estimation is an example of a modern non-parametric technique. Thus there are no underlying assumptions about how the data was generated. Conceptually the estimate takes the form of a bank of FIR filters, one filter for each frequency of interest. The coefficients that define a particular filter are chosen to minimise the output variance of the filter while constraining the frequency response at the frequency of interest to be unity. The net effect is that the filter will tend to reject other frequencies. A measure of the strength of the signal at a particular frequency is the value of the minimum variance.

A typical FIR filter is illustrated in Figure 13.8. The signal sequence, $\{x(n)\}$, is the input this filter and the output sequence is $\{v(n)\}$. As in chapter 8 it is convenient to describe the convolution operation performed by the filter as a vector inner product.

$$v(n) = \underline{h}^T \underline{x}(n)$$

where the vector $\underline{h}$ contains the $P+1$ elements of the impulse response sequence,

$$\underline{h} = [\ h_0 \ h_1 \ \cdots \ h_P\ ]^T$$

and the vector $\underline{x}(n)$ the last $P+1$ signal samples.

$$\underline{x}(n) = [\ x(n) \ x(n-1) \ \cdots \ x(n-P)\ ]^T$$

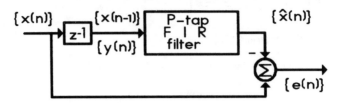

Figure 13.7   AR parameter estimation.

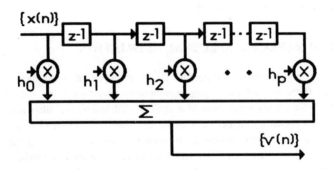

Figure 13.8   Minimum variance FIR filter.

The mean-square value or variance of the output sequence is given by

$$E[\,v^2(n)\,] = E[\,\underline{h}^T\,\underline{x}(n)\,\{\,\underline{h}^T\,\underline{x}(n)\,\}^T\,]$$

$$= \underline{h}^T\,E[\,\underline{x}(n)\,\underline{x}^T(n)\,]\,\underline{h}$$

$$= \underline{h}^T\,\underline{\phi}_{xx}\,\underline{h} \tag{13.17}$$

where $\underline{\phi}_{xx}$ is a $(P+1)\times(P+1)$ autocorrelation matrix.

$$\underline{\phi}_{xx} = E[\,\underline{x}(n)\,\underline{x}^T(n)\,]$$

This variance is then minimised with respect to the impulse response vector, $\underline{h}$, and subject to the constraint that the frequency response, $H(e^{j\omega})$, at the frequency of interest, ω, is unity.

$$H(e^{j\omega}) = \sum_{i=0}^{P} h_i\,e^{-ji\omega T}$$

$$= 1 \tag{13.18}$$

Again it is more convenient to express equation (13.18) as a vector inner product of the impulse response, $\underline{h}$, and the $(P+1)\times 1$ frequency vector $\underline{e}(\omega)$. Thus

$$\underline{h}^T\,\underline{e}(\omega) = 1 \tag{13.19}$$

where

$$\underline{e}(\omega) = [\,1\ e^{-j\omega T}\ e^{-j2\omega T}\ \cdots\ e^{-jP\omega T}\,]^T\ .$$

The solution to this constrained minimisation problem is the impulse response vector, $\underline{h}_{MV}$.

$$\underline{h}_{MV} = \frac{\underline{\phi}_{xx}^{-1}\,\underline{e}(\omega)}{\underline{e}^H(\omega)\,\underline{\phi}_{xx}^{-1}\,\underline{e}(\omega)} \tag{13.20}$$

The superscript H denotes the conjugate transpose operation. Substitution of (13.20) in (13.17) yields a value for the constrained minimum variance which is a spectral estimate of the signal at frequency ω.

$$\hat{S}_{xx}(\omega) = \frac{1}{\underline{e}^H(\omega)\,\underline{\phi}_{xx}^{-1}\,\underline{e}(\omega)} \tag{13.21}$$

As with the AR techniques described in section 13.4, the autocorrelation matrix is not usually known but can be estimated from the data using the LS matrices summarised in Table 13.1.

13.6 A COMPARISON OF TECHNIQUES

To illustrate the relative performance achieved by these algorithms a simple example is considered. The theoretical PSD of the test signal is shown in Figure 13.9(a). It consists of 3 sinusoids with relative power levels of 0dB, −33dB and −33dB in additive noise. The noise is white with a PSD of −50dB. From this signal 64 samples were used to generate the spectral estimates which are summarised in Figure 13.9(b)-(d). The frequency spacing of the sinusoids in the test signal was chosen so that it would be difficult to resolve them with classical techniques. Figure 13.9(b) illustrates the results obtained with a DFT which has been zero-padded to 512 points to provide more spectral detail. Clearly the 3 sinusoids cannot be distinguished. The results for a minimum variance spectral estimate are shown in Figure 13.9(c). There is a peak visible at each of the sinusoids and the noise provides a flat background level. The conceptual FIR filters used to produce this estimate contained 16 coefficients i.e. order 15. Finally the results for an order 15 AR spectral estimate are shown in Figure 13.9(d). This provides the best resolution as the 3 sinusoids can be clearly identified. However the quality of the spectral estimate is not as good as the minimum variance. There are spurious peaks due to the background noise and the height of the two peaks associated with the sinusoids at −33dB are significantly different.

13.7 SUMMARY

The motivation for most modern techniques for spectral analysis has been the desire to improve upon the resolution of the classical techniques without a significant loss in quality. The most notable of these modern techniques is AR spectral analysis, which is parametric in that the observed signal is assumed to have been generated by passing white noise through an AR filter. While AR analysis can provide excellent results when the underlying process is exactly or approximately AR (e.g. speech), the results can be less than satisfactory when the process is not AR or the order is chosen incorrectly. The non-parametric techniques, on other hand, do not involve an inherent modelling assumption. However they do still demand a selection of order (e.g. the order of the minimum variance FIR filters). The improved performance that can be achieved with the modern techniques usually involves a significant increase in computational complexity.

TUTORIAL   Modern Spectral Analysis.

1.   The first three autocorrelation coefficients of a stationary random sequence are $\phi(0) = 1.03$, $\phi(1) = 0.31$ and $\phi(2) = -0.81$. Using (a) a second order autoregressive estimate and (b) a second order minimum variance estimate calculate spectral estimates of the signal at 6 equally spaced frequencies starting at 0 Hz and finishing at half the sampling frequency. Sketch your results. *(a) [-14.6 -11.8 16.7 -13.4 -18.6 -20.0 dB] (b) [-14.8 -12.3 -2.9 -13.8 -18.7 -20.0 dB]*

2.   The following set of samples is all that is available from a sequence $\{ x(n) \}$.

$$3.0, \ 2.0, \ -0.5, \ 1.5, \ -1.0$$

A third order autoregressive spectral estimate is required and it is proposed that the LS technique should be used to calculate the AR coefficients. Calculate the 4 forms of the LS matrix $\underline{r}_{xx}$ that are possible.

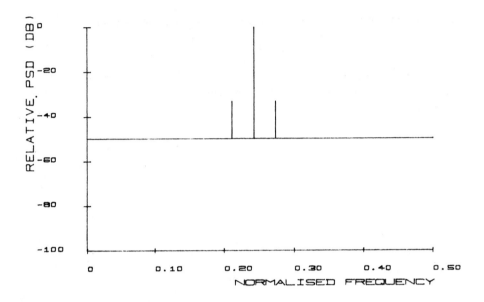

Figure 13.9(a)   Comparison of spectral estimates: theoretical PSD of 64-point test signal.

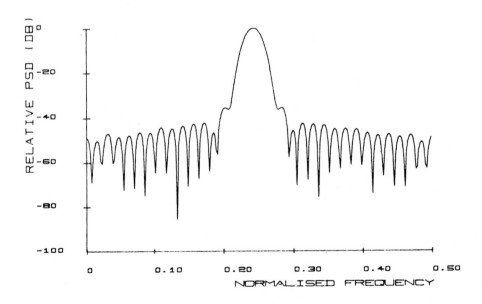

Figure 13.9(b)   Comparison of spectral estimates: DFT with Hamming window.

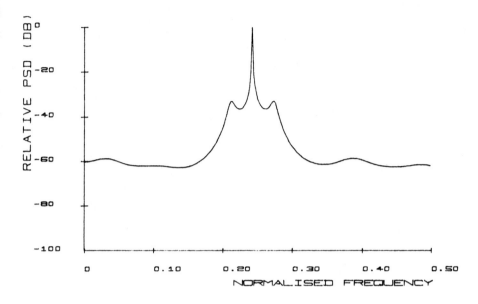

Figure 13.9(c) Comparison of spectral estimates: minimum variance (16 coefficient FIR filter).

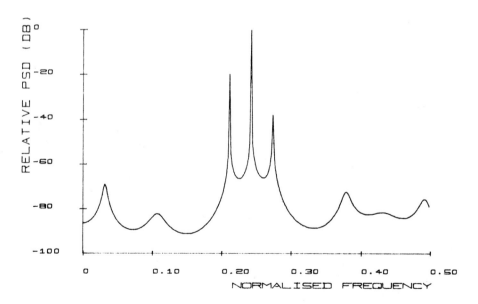

Figure 13.9(d) Comparison of spectral estimates: covariance-form AR spectral estimate (order = 15).

Chapter 14
BLOCK CODES FOR ERROR DETECTION AND CORRECTION

14.1 INTRODUCTION

This is the first of two chapters on forward error correcting coding (FECC), which is also referred to as channel coding. FECC should not be confused with source coding which removes redundancy from certain sources, such as pictures. The chapter begins with a discussion of error rate control in digital communications and five methods of error rate control are discussed. Some typical applications of FECC are outlined and the threshold problem, which is similar to the threshold problem in wide-band frequency modulation (FM), is highlighted. The concept of party checks, both single and multiple, and the representation of these in matrix form is introduced and the probability of having more than R errors in an N-digit codeword is calculated. Group codes are introduced as the most important block codes. The concept of Hamming distance, the minimum Hamming distance for a code and nearest neighbour or maximum likelihood decoding is discussed and, finally, the Hamming bound for the performance of a block code is derived.

14.2 ERROR RATE CONTROL

The terms bit error rate (BER) and probability of error (Pe) can be used interchangeably. Pe is simply the probability of any given transmitted digit being in error. The BER is the average rate at which errors occur and is given by the product $Pe\ R$, where R is the transmission rate in the channel. If the BER is unacceptable then what can be done to make it acceptable? The first and most obvious solution is to increase transmitter power, but this may not always be desirable, for example in man-portable systems where the extra weight may be unacceptable.

The second possible solution is to use diversity. There are three main types of diversity: (1) space diversity, (2) frequency diversity and (3) time diversity. In space diversity two or more antennae are used, each connected to a receiver. These antennae are sited sufficiently far apart to decorrelate fading at the outputs of the corresponding receivers. Frequency diversity is a technique whereby two different frequencies are used to transmit the same information. Frequency diversity can be in-band or out-band depending upon the distance between the carriers. In time diversity the same message is transmitted more than once. The most common case is dual diversity (two antennae, two frequencies or two transmissions of the information). Over a wide range of applications a 3 dB signal-to-noise-ratio (SNR) improvement is achieved by use of dual diversity. A 3 dB SNR improvement implies an increase in performance equivalent to doubling the transmitter power for a given additive noise situation.

The third possible solution to the problem of unacceptable BER is to introduce full duplex transmission. Here when a transmitter sends information to a receiver, the information is "echoed" back to the transmitter on a separate feedback channel. This requires twice the bandwidth of single direction (simplex) transmission which may be unacceptable in terms of spectrum utilisation. It is normally more effective to use FECC in conjunction with a multi-level (phase) modulation system. Furthermore, the feedback channel betrays the position of the receiver which may be unacceptable in certain military applications.

The fourth technique for coping with unacceptable BER is automatic request repeat (ARQ). Here an error detecting block code is used and if an error is detected in a given block then a request is sent via a feedback channel requesting that the block be retransmitted. This is a very effective technique except on long links with very fast transmission rates, such as space and satellite links, where ARQ can be very difficult to implement. Consequently space and satellite communications provided the motivation for the introduction of FECC.

Finally, the fifth technique for coping with unacceptable BER is to employ FECC. The widespread adoption of this approach was delayed through its complexity and cost of implementation relative to the other possible solutions but complexity is now less of a problem following the introduction of VLSI custom coder/decoder chips.

14.3 APPLICATIONS OF FECC

Compact disc players is a growing application area for FECC. In this application the very powerful Reed-Solomon code is used as it works at a symbol level rather than at a bit level and is very effective against burst errors, particularly when combined with interleaving to randomise the bursts. The Reed-Solomon code is also used in computers for data storage and retrieval. Cosmic particles create, on average, 1 error every 2 to 3 days in a 4 M byte memory, although small geometries are helping to reduce this probability. Another application for FECC is in simplex communications as there is no feedback channel and therefore errors must be corrected at the receiver. Space communications and, particularly, deep-space planet photography is another classic application for FECC. In the later, a pixel from a photograph of a planet may be digested and each digit coded and expanded into a PN (pseudo-noise) code. The PN code is then detected in a correlation receiver giving the SNR improvement required to lift the signal out of the noise. This is then followed by error correction in a FECC decoder. The use of ARQ via a feedback channel is obviously not a possibility in this application since the round trip delay could be of the order of one hour. Finally, digital audio and video are also good application areas for FECC. Combining the regenerative repeater action of a digital decision making device with FECC preserves the quality of a digital master recording.

14.4 THRESHOLD PHENOMENON

Figure 14.1 illustrates this phenomenon with an uncoded system where the Pe increases gradually as the SNR decreases. With a coded system, on the otherhand, the SNR curve is more vertical. If the SNR is above the threshold, which is here around 6 dB, the error rate will be virtually zero. Below this threshold SNR system performance degrades rapidly and the coded system is actually poorer than the corresponding uncoded system. The reason for this is that in the region below threshold, in attempting to correct errors, the decoder actually approximately doubles the number of errors in a given incorrectly decoded codeword. This behaviour is analogous to the threshold phenomenon in wide band frequency modulation. The wide band FM improvement suddenly collapses due to capture of the received process by noise at about 10 dB SNR. There are two types of codes, block codes and convolutional codes. Convolutional codes will be studied in chapter 15.

14.5 (N,K) BLOCK CODES

Figure 14.2 illustrates a block coder with K information digits going into the coder and N digits coming out in response. The N digit codeword is made up of K information digits and $(N-K)$ parity check digits. The rate for this code (R) is K/N, the ratio of information digits to the total number of digits in the codeword. This is an example of a systematic code in that the information digits are explicitly transmitted together with party check digits. In a non-systematic code the N digit codeword may not contain any of the information digits explicitly. There are two definitions of systematic codes in the literature. The more strict of the two definitions assume that for the code to be systematic the K information digits must be transmitted contiguously as a block with the party check digits as another contiguous block making up the codeword. The less strict of the two definitions merely stipulates that the information digits must be included in the codeword but not necessarily in a contiguous block. The latter definition is the one which is adopted here. Consider the example of a single party check code.

14.6 SINGLE PARITY CHECK CODE

This example will be familiar to many as an option in ASCII coded data transmission, Figure 14.3. Consider the data sequence 1101000, to which will be added a single party check (P). Assuming even parity, then for this data sequence P will be 1. Assuming odd parity, P will be 0. Since the seven information digits in this example contain three 1's, another 1 is added giving an even number of 1's for even party, or a zero is added, ensuring an odd number of 1's for odd parity. The rate (R/N) is seven-eighths. This is a very low level of redundancy and this scheme can only detect odd numbers of errors. It cannot detect an even

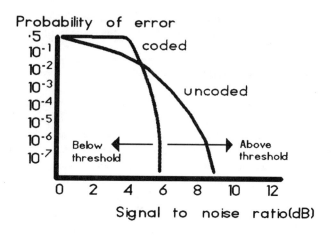

Figure 14.1   The threshold phenomenon in FECC systems.

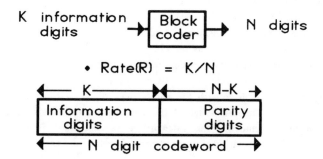

Figure 14.2 (N, K) systematic block code.

number of errors because an even number of errors will not upset the party check. The single error case is illustrated in Figure 14.4.

In the English language there is quite a high level of redundancy. This is the means whereby we can correct spelling mistakes and decode abbreviations. There is, in fact, an approximate correspondence between words in the English language and code words, although in the English languages contextual information goes beyond isolated words. In a block code each codeword is decoded in isolation. For error correction capabilities more redundancy is needed and therefore more parity check digits must be introduced.

14.7 (7,4) BLOCK CODE EXAMPLE

Figure 14.5 illustrates a seven digit codeword with four information digits (I_1 to I_4) and three party check digits (P_1 to P_3), commonly referred to as a (7,4) block code. Even party is assumed and encoding of P_1, P_2 and P_3 is achieved by using a cascade of 2-input exclusive OR gates. In this example P_1 is the modulo-2 sum of I_1, I_3 and I_4. P_2 is the modulo-2 sum of I_1, I_2 and I_4 etc. Figure 14.6 shows how the party check equations for P_1, P_2 and P_3 may be written and reduced to matrix form in the party check matrix (H). The coefficients of the information digits I_1, I_2, I_3 and I_4 are to the left of the dotted partition in the party check matrix. The top row of the matrix contains the information about party check 1, the second row about party check 2 and third row about party check 3. Consider the top left hand corner of the matrix (1011). This corresponds to the coefficients 1011 of the information digits I_1, I_2, I_3 and I_4 in the equation for P_1. Similarly, the second row is 1101 to the left of the partition because I_3 is not involved in parity check 2 and the corresponding part of the bottom row is 1110 because I_4 is not involved in the parity check 3. To the right of the dotted partition we have a 3 by 3 diagonal matrix of 1's. Each column in this diagonal matrix corresponds to a party check. The first column (100) indicates party check 1. The second column indicates parity check 2 and the third column parity check 3.

14.8 PROBABILITY OF ≥R ERRORS FOR N-DIGITS

Consider the problem of performance prediction and the question: What is the probability of having more than R errors in N digits? This problem is now considered in the form a worked example. Assume that Pe is 0.01, that R is 3 and N is 10. i.e. determine the probability of having more than 3 errors in a block of 10 digits:

$$recall: \quad Pr\{>3\ errors\} = 1 - Pr\{\leq 3\ errors\} \tag{14.1}$$

This is because total probability must sum to 1. We also assume that errors are independent. The above equation may be expanded as:

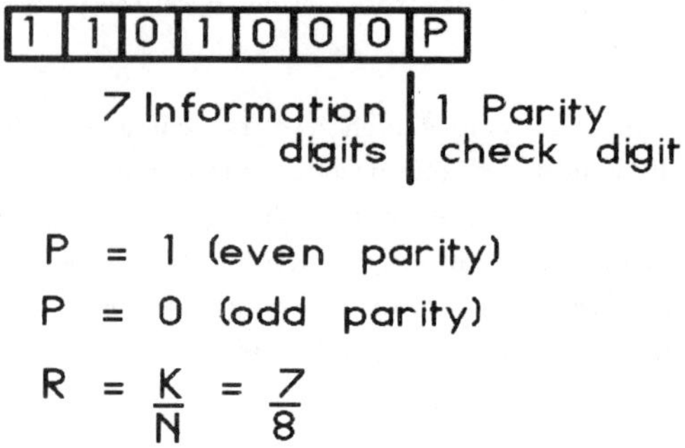

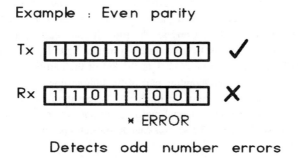

$$\boxed{1}\,\boxed{1}\,\boxed{0}\,\boxed{1}\,\boxed{0}\,\boxed{0}\,\boxed{0}\,\boxed{P}$$

7 Information | 1 Parity
       digits | check digit

P = 1 (even parity)

P = 0 (odd parity)

$$R = \frac{K}{N} = \frac{7}{8}$$

Figure 14.3   Single parity check error detecting block code.

Example : Even parity

Tx $\boxed{1}\,\boxed{1}\,\boxed{0}\,\boxed{1}\,\boxed{0}\,\boxed{0}\,\boxed{0}\,\boxed{1}$ ✓

Rx $\boxed{1}\,\boxed{1}\,\boxed{0}\,\boxed{1}\,\boxed{1}\,\boxed{0}\,\boxed{0}\,\boxed{1}$ ✗

* ERROR

Detects odd number errors

Figure 14.4   A single error in the code of Figure 14.3.

Example: (7,4) Block Code

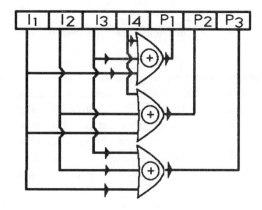

Figure 14.5   A (7,4) block code illustrating generation of the three parity check digits with modulo-2 summers.

$$P_1 = 1 \cdot I_1 \oplus 0 \cdot I_2 \oplus 1 \cdot I_3 \oplus 1 \cdot I_4$$

$$P_2 = 1 \cdot I_1 \oplus 1 \cdot I_2 \oplus 0 \cdot I_3 \oplus 1 \cdot I_4$$

$$P_3 = 1 \cdot I_1 \oplus 1 \cdot I_2 \oplus 1 \cdot I_3 \oplus 0 \cdot I_4$$

$$[H] = \begin{bmatrix} 1 & 0 & 1 & 1 & 1 & 0 & 0 \\ 1 & 1 & 0 & 1 & 0 & 1 & 0 \\ 1 & 1 & 1 & 0 & 0 & 0 & 1 \end{bmatrix}$$

Figure 14.6   Representation of the code of Figure 14.5 by parity check equations and by the [H] matrix.

$$Pr\{>3\ errors\} = 1 - [\ Pr\{0\ errors\} + Pr\{1\ error\} + Pr\{2\ errors\} + Pr\{3\ errors\}\ ]$$

$$(14.2)$$

These probabilities will be calculated individually starting with the probability of no errors, Figure 14.7.

Consider the probability of having no errors, the case at the top of Figure 14.7 . A block representing the codeword is divided it into bins labelled 1 to 10. Each bin corresponds to a digit in the 10 digit codeword and is labelled with the probability of the event in question. Here the assumption is that there are no errors so that each digit is received correctly. The probability of error is 0.01 and hence the probability of correct reception is 0.99. If all events (receptions) are independent then probability of having no errors is $(0.99)^{10}$. Now consider the probability of 1 error. Initially assume that the error is in the first position. Its probability is 0.01. All other digits are received correctly, so their probabilities are 0.99 and there are 9 of them. There are 10 ways of having a single error in 10 digits and therefore the overall probability of 1 error is:

$$Pr\{1\ error\} = (0.01)^1\ (0.99)^9\ {}^{10}C_1 \tag{14.3}$$

where $^{10}C_1$, is the number of combinations of 1 object from 10 objects. We can similarly calculate the probability of 2 errors as:

$$Pr\{2\ errors\} = (0.01)^2\ (0.99)^8\ {}^{10}C_2 \tag{14.4}$$

Now consider the general case of J errors in N digits with a probability of error per digit of Pe:

$$Pr\{J\ errors\} = (Pe)^J\ (1-Pe)^{N-J}\ {}^N C_J \tag{14.5}$$

where

$${}^N C_J = \frac{N!}{J!\ (N-J)!}$$

This is the probability of J errors in an N-digit codeword, but what we are interested in is the probability of having more than R errors. We can write this as:

$$Pr\{>R\ errors\} = 1 - \sum_{J=0}^{R} P\{J\} \tag{14.6}$$

Now, finally, on the subject of Pe and the need for long blocks (large N). For large N we have statistical stability in the sense that the fraction of errors in a given block will tend to product $Pe\ N$. Also, the fraction of blocks containing a number of errors that deviates significantly from this value tends to zero. The above statistical stability gained from long blocks is very important in the design of an effective code. Statistical stability may be illustrated with a coin tossing analogy.

14.9 COIN TOSSING ANALOGY ILLUSTRATING STATISTICAL STABILITY

Figure 14.8 depicts the outcome of a number of trials of tossing a coin. An analogy is being drawn between the outcome of a coin tossing being a "head" and having an error and the outcome being a "tail" not having an error. As the process of tossing the coin continues what is known as statistical convergence occurs and after a large number of tosses a good estimate of the probability of having a head may be obtained. The situation is analogous to having long block codes. A long block embodies a large number of trials as to whether an error will occur and the number of times where an error will occur comes very close to $Pe\ N$. Choosing a code that can correct $Pe\ N$ errors in a codeword will ensure that there are very few cases where the coding system will fail. This is the reason for the desirability of long block codes. The attraction of block codes is that they are amenable to precise performance analysis and by far the most important and most amenable set of block codes are the group codes.

14.10 GROUP CODES

The codewords in a group code have a one-to-one correspondence with the elements of a mathematical group. Group codes contain the all 0's codeword and have the property referred to as closure. That is, taking any two codewords C_i and C_j then $C_i \oplus C_j = C_k$. Thus adding modulo-2 corresponding pairs of digits in each of the two codewords produces another code word C_k. The presence of the all-zeros codeword and the closure property together contribute to the ease of performance calculation with group codes, as will be seen in a later section. Figure 14.9 illustrates a simple example of a group code which will be used at various points in this chapter. It is first used to illustrate the property of closure. Figure 14.9 depicts a source alphabet with 4 members: a, b, c and d (i.e. the number of information digits, $K = 2$). Each symbol is coded into an N-digit codeword (where $N = 5$) as shown. By the less strict definition, this is a systematic code where the information digits are in columns 2 and 4. Consider the codewords corresponding to c and b. Modulo-2 summing c and b gives the codeword d.

14.11 MEMBERS OF THE GROUP CODE FAMILY

Group codes can be divided into 2 types: (1) those which are "polynomial generated" in simple feedback shift registers and (2) others, Figure 14.10. The simplicity of the former have rendered the rest irrelevant. The polynomial generated codes can be further divided into subgroups, the main ones being BCH and Reed-Solomon. The others are of lesser importance. The Reed-Solomon codes are used extensively in compact disc players and computer memories as outlined in section 14.3.

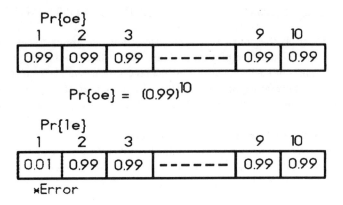

Figure 14.7   Diagram to aid calculation of the probability of R errors in an N digit codeword (showing no error and one error cases).

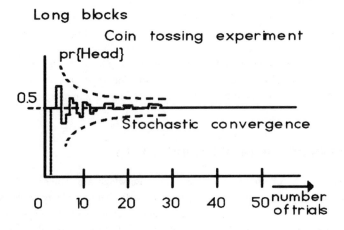

Figure 14.8   Illustration of stochastic convergence using a coin tossing analogy.

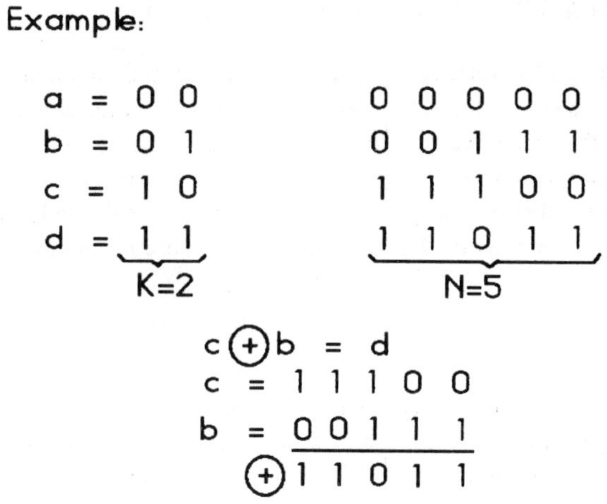

Example:

$$a = 0\ 0 \qquad\qquad 0\ 0\ 0\ 0\ 0$$
$$b = 0\ 1 \qquad\qquad 0\ 0\ 1\ 1\ 1$$
$$c = 1\ 0 \qquad\qquad 1\ 1\ 1\ 0\ 0$$
$$d = \underbrace{1\ 1}_{K=2} \qquad\qquad \underbrace{1\ 1\ 0\ 1\ 1}_{N=5}$$

$$c \oplus b = d$$
$$c = 1\ 1\ 1\ 0\ 0$$
$$b = \underline{0\ 0\ 1\ 1\ 1}$$
$$\oplus\ 1\ 1\ 0\ 1\ 1$$

Figure 14.9 Illustration of the closure property of a group code.

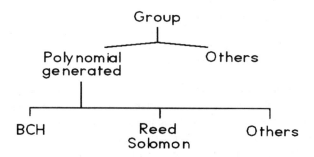

Figure 14.10 Group code family tree showing main types.

14.12 PERFORMANCE PREDICTION IN GROUP CODES

Normally all possible codeword pairs would have to be considered in determining the performance of a block code, but for the case of group codes consideration of the all 0's codeword is sufficient. This is one advantage of using group codes and one reason why group codes are so important in relation to other possible block codes. Analysis for large N becomes much simpler, since the number of combinations of code words which would otherwise have to be searched is very large. Two important preliminary concepts are Hamming distance and code weight structure.

Hamming Distance

This concept is illustrated in Figure 14.11a by taking 2 codewords from the previous example. The Hamming distance between these two codewords is just the number of places in which they differ. These 2 codewords have a Hamming distance of 3. The important aspect as far as code performance prediction is concerned is the minimum Hamming distance between any pair of code words in the code. Inspection of Figure 14.11b will reveal a minimum Hamming distance of $3 (D_{\min} = 3)$.

Code Weight Structure

The concepts of codeword weight and code weight structure are explained with the aid of Figure 14.12. The weight of a codeword is simply the number of 1's which it contains and in this example, 110011, the weight is 4. The weight structure of a group code is just a list of the weights of all the codewords in the code. Consider the previous example with 4 codewords, the weights of these being 0,3,3 and 4 as shown. Ignoring the all 0's word (we are only interested in distances from the all 0's codeword), we see that the minimum weight in the weight structure (3) is equal to $D_{\min}$, the minimum Hamming distance for the code.

Consider the probability of the ith codeword (C_i) being misinterpreted as the jth codeword (C_j). This probability depends on the distance between these two codewords (D_{ij}). Since this is a group code, this distance D_{ij} is equal to the weight of a third codeword C_k which is actually the module-2 sum of C_i and C_j. Furthermore, the probability of C_k being mistaken for the all 0's codeword (C_0) is equal to the probability of C_0 being misinterpreted as C_k (by symmetry). The probability of C_0 being misinterpreted as C_k in turn, depends on the weight of C_k. This emphasises the importance of the weight structure in this reasoning. Thus the performance of a group code can be determined completely by consideration of C_0, and the code weight structure.

The error correcting power of a code is stated as its ability to correct all patterns of t or less errors where t is given by:

Hamming distance

Example: 1 1 1 0 0
                  1 1 0 1 1
                  —————————
                      x x x

Hamming distance = 3

Minimum Hamming distance

Example: 0 0 0 0 0
             0 0 1 1 1
             1 1 1 0 0
             1 1 0 1 1
             —————————
        D min = 3

Figure 14.11   Hamming distance between two codewords and minimum Hamming distance for a set of four codewords.

                 1 1 0 1 1

              weight = 4
     weight structure (group code)
                                wt.
             0 0 0 0 0   0
             0 0 1 1 1   3
             1 1 1 0 0   3
             1 1 0 1 1   4
          —————————————————
        Min. Wt. = D min = 3

Figure 14.12   Weight of a codeword and weight structure for a group code consisting of four codewords.

$$t = \lfloor \frac{D_{min} - 1}{2} \rfloor \tag{14.7}$$

$\lfloor \rfloor$ indicates "the integer part of". If we take the case where D_{min} is 3, such a code could correct all single error patterns. Alternatively, used as an error detection code, it could detect $D_{min} - 1$ errors (2 in this case) but it cannot work in both detection and correction modes simultaneously.

14.13 NEAREST NEIGHBOUR DECODING OF BLOCK CODES

Encoding is achieved by use of a feedback shift register and is relatively simple. The two most important concepts for decoding are nearest neighbour and maximum likelihood. The equivalence of these relies on the fact that the probability of t errors is much greater than that of $t+1$ errors etc. Therefore, using a decoding table which is based on nearest neighbours implies a maximum likelihood decoding strategy. This is illustrated with a simple example.

Figure 14.13 is a nearest neighbour decoding table for the previous four symbol example. The codewords are listed along the top of this table starting with the all 0's codeword on the top left hand corner. Below each codeword all possible receive sequences are listed which are at distance 1 from the particular codeword (in case of all 0's codeword the sequences 10000 to 00001). If this were a t error correcting code this list would continue with all the patterns of 2 errors, 3 errors etc up to all patterns of t errors. Below the table there are 8 patterns which are outside the table. These received sequences lie equidistant from 2 possible codewords, so the sequence lies on a decision boundary and consequently it is impossible to decide which of the 2 codewords it came from. These sequences are referred to as detectable error sequences.

14.14 HAMMING BOUND

This is an upper bound on the performance of block codes and is given by the equation:

$$2^K \leq 2^N / [1 + N + {}^N C_2 + {}^N C_3 + \cdots + {}^N C_t] \tag{14.8}$$

Consider the possibility of a code with codewords of length N, comprising K information digits and having error correcting power t. Insertion of these values of N, K and t into equation (14.8) reveals the possibility of such a code if the equation is satisfied. If, on the other hand, the left hand side of the equation is greater than the right hand side then no such code exists and we must either increase N, decrease K or decrease t until (14.8) is satisfied. The simplest way to derive (14.8) is to inspect the nearest neighbour decoding table for an (N, K), t error correcting code, Figure 14.14.

Figure 14.14 depicts the general case of a t error correcting code with 2^K codewords. Thus there are 2^K columns in the decoding table. Consider the left hand column. The all 0's codeword itself is obviously one possible received sequence. Also there are N single error patterns associated with that all 0's codeword. There are ${}^N C_2$ patterns of 2 errors etc. down to

Decoding table

00000	11100	00111	11011
10000	01100	10111	01011
01000	10100	01111	10011
00100	11000	00011	11111
00010	11110	00101	11001
00001	11101	00110	11010

10001	01101	10110	01010
10010	01110	10101	01001

Figure 14.13   Nearest neighbour decoding table for group code of Figure 14.9.

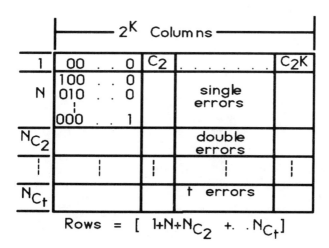

Figure 14.14   Decoding table for a t-error correcting (N,K) block code (used to derive the Hamming bound).

$^N C_t$ patterns of t errors. Totaling the number of entries in this column reveals the total number of rows in the table. Taking this total number of rows (given in square brackets under the table) and dividing into 2^N (which is the total number of possible received sequences), gives the maximum possible number of columns and hence the maximum number of codewords in the given code. If any of the possible received sequences lie on a decision boundary, these sequences would lie outside the table and hence we would have less than the maximum number of codewords.

14.15 SUMMARY

This chapter began by looking at different methods of achieving error rate control. The concept of a threshold analogous to the wide band FM threshold was discussed. Single parity checks and the multiple parity checks were considered and the probability of having more than R errors in a block of N digits was derived. Group codes were shown to be the most important block codes because of the ease of performance prediction (only transmission of the all 0's codeword need be considered). This involved the concept of Hamming distance between two codewords and the (minimum) Hamming distance for a complete code. Nearest neighbour decoding was introduced and its equivalence to maximum likelihood decoding was stressed following the strong inequality: the probability of t errors $<<$ probability of $t+1$ error etc. Finally the existence of block codes with given N, K and t was investigated and the Hamming bound was derived.

Chapter 15

BLOCK AND CONVOLUTIONAL FORWARD ERROR CORRECTING CODES

15.1 INTRODUCTION

This is the second of two chapters on error correcting coding. Study of the preceding chapter is a necessary prerequisite for understanding much of this material. The preceding chapter concentrated on block codes in general and group codes in particular. Here the study of block codes is continued and convolutional codes are introduced. Section 15.2 introduces the generator matrix $[G]$ and its close correspondence to the party check matrix $[H]$ is shown. Then the difficulty with decoding of block codes using the nearest neighbour decoding table is discussed. The syndrome decoding technique is described as a solution to this problem. Finally convolutional codes are discussed with particular emphasis on decoding. The Viterbi decoding algorithm is illustrated with a simple example.

15.2 THE GENERATOR MATRIX [G]

The generator matrix is a matrix of orthogonal basis vectors. The rows of the generator matrix $[G]$ are actual codewords. This is in contrast with the $[H]$ matrix, which does not contain any codewords. The generator matrix $[G]$ of an (N,K) block code can be used to generate the N digit codeword corresponding to any given K digit data sequence. Figure 15.1 illustrates the $[H]$ and corresponding $[G]$ matrices for an example (7,4) block code. Study of $[G]$ will show that on the left of the dotted partition there is in this example a 4×4 unit diagonal matrix and on the right of the partition there is a parity check section. This part of $[G]$ is the transpose of the left hand portion of $[H]$. The close linkage between $[H]$ and $[G]$ means that $[H]$ can be used to generate the syndrome decoding table. Continuing the (7,4) example, Figure 15.2 shows how $[G]$ can be used to construct a codeword. Assume the data sequence 1001. To generate the codeword associated with this data sequence multiply the data vector 1001 by $[G]$. The 4×4 unit diagonal matrix to the left of the partition results in the data sequence 1001 being repeated as the first four digits of the codeword and the right hand (parity check) portion results in the three party check digits P_1, P_2 and P_3 (in this case 001). It is now possible to see why the columns to the right of the partition in $[G]$ are the rows of

$$[H] = \begin{bmatrix} 1 & 0 & 1 & 1 & 1 & 0 & 0 \\ 1 & 1 & 0 & 1 & 0 & 1 & 0 \\ 1 & 1 & 1 & 0 & 0 & 0 & 1 \end{bmatrix}$$

$$\qquad\quad P^T \qquad\quad I_{N-K}$$

$$[G] = \begin{bmatrix} 1 & 0 & 0 & 0 & 1 & 1 & 1 \\ 0 & 1 & 0 & 0 & 0 & 1 & 1 \\ 0 & 0 & 1 & 0 & 1 & 0 & 1 \\ 0 & 0 & 0 & 1 & 1 & 1 & 0 \end{bmatrix}$$

$$\qquad\quad I_K \qquad\qquad P$$

Figure 15.1   [H] and corresponding [G] matricies for a typical (7,4) block code.

$$[1\ 0\ 0\ 1] \begin{bmatrix} 1 & 0 & 0 & 0 & 1 & 1 & 1 \\ 0 & 1 & 0 & 0 & 0 & 1 & 1 \\ 0 & 0 & 1 & 0 & 1 & 0 & 1 \\ 0 & 0 & 0 & 1 & 1 & 1 & 0 \end{bmatrix}$$

$$[G]$$

$$= [1\ 0\ 0\ 1\ 0\ 0\ 1]$$

Figure 15.2   Using the [G] matrix to generate a codeword from a data vector.

$[H]$ to the left of its dotted partition. Another viewpoint is the construction of a codeword as a weighted sum of the rows of $[G]$. The digits of the data sequence perform the weighting. With digits 1001 in this example, the top row of $[G]$ is weighted by 1, the second row by 0, the third row by 0 and the fourth row by 1. After weighting, corresponding digits from each row are added modulo-2 to obtain the required codeword.

15.3 SYNDROME DECODING

Recall the strong inequality that the probability of t errors is much greater than the probability of $t+1$ errors etc. This situation always holds above the threshold region where these systems normally operate. Thus nearest neighbour decoding is equivalent to maximum likelihood decoding. Unfortunately the nearest neighbour decoding table is normally too large for practical implementation and a different technique involving a smaller table is used instead. The table is referred to as the syndrome decoding table and is smaller than the nearest neighbour table by a factor equal to the number of codewords in the code (2^K). The syndrome table is smaller than the nearest neighbour table by this factor because the syndrome is independent of the transmitted codeword. It is only dependent on the error sequence as will be demonstrated below. As indicated previously for an (N,K) block code:

$$\vec{d} \ [G] = \vec{c} \tag{15.1}$$

where $\vec{d}$ is a message vector of K digits, $[G]$ is the $K \times N$ generator matrix and $\vec{c}$ is the N digit codeword corresponding to the message $\vec{d}$. Furthermore

$$[H] \ \vec{c} = \vec{0} \tag{15.2}$$

where $[H]$ is the parity check matrix corresponding to $[G]$ in (15.1) above and $\vec{c}$ is any codeword generated by $[G]$, also:

$$\vec{r} = \vec{c} \oplus \vec{e} \tag{15.3}$$

where $\vec{r}$ is the received sequence consequent on transmitting $\vec{c}$ and $\vec{e}$ is an error vector representing any errors which may lie in the received sequence $\vec{r}$. Consider the product $[H] \ \vec{r}$ referred to as the syndrome vector $\vec{s}$.

$$\vec{s} = [H] \ \vec{r} = [H] \ (\ \vec{c} \oplus \vec{e} \ ) \tag{15.4}$$

$$= [H] \ \vec{c} \oplus [H] \ \vec{e}$$

$$= \vec{0} \oplus [H] \ \vec{e}$$

$$= [H] \ \vec{e}$$

Thus $\vec{s}$ is easily calculated and $[H]$ is known so $\vec{e}$ may be determined and the errors corrected. A syndrome table is constructed by assuming transmission of the all zeros codeword and calculating the syndrome vector associated with each correctable error pattern. Figure (15.3) illustrates the case of no errors in the received sequence leading to the all zeros syndrome for a (6,3) code example. Figure (15.4) shows the completed syndrome table for this (6,3) code. In this case only single errors are correctable. If a double error occurs then it will normally give the same syndrome as some single error and since single errors are much more likely than double errors a single error will be assumed and the wrong codeword will be output from the decoder giving a "sequence" error. This syndrome decoding technique is still a nearest neighbour (maximum likelihood) decoding strategy.

As an example of the syndrome decoding technique, assume that the received vector ($\vec{r}$) = 100011. Figure 15.5 illustrates calculation of the corresponding syndrome (110). Reference to the syndrome table (Figure 15.4) reveals the corresponding error pattern (001000). Finally $\vec{c} = \vec{r} \oplus \vec{e}$ giving a transmitted codeword 101011.

15.4 ENCODING OF CONVOLUTIONAL CODES

Convolutional codes are generated by passing a data sequence through a filter structure similar to a transversal filter with binary taps, the outputs of which are combined at any given time in modulo-2 summers. Thus the coder output may be regarded as the convolution of the input sequence with the impulse response of the coder, hence the name convolutional code. Figure 15.6 illustrates this with a simple example.

Assume an input sequence 1101 to the three stage shift register which contains zeros prior to clocking through the above sequence. This example depicts a rate ½ coder (R=½) since there are two output digits for every one input digit. The coder is also non-systematic since the data digits are not explicitly present in the transmitted stream. The first output following a given input is obtained with the switch in its 1st position and the second output is achieved by switching to its 2nd position etc.

This encoder may be regarded as a finite state machine. The first stage of the shift register holds the next input and its contents may thus be regarded as determining the transition to the next state. The other two stages of the shift register hold past inputs with respect to the first stage and they may be regarded as determining the "memory" of the machine. In this example we have 2 "memory stages" and hence four possible states. In general an n-stage register would have $2^{(n-1)}$ states. Having been identified as a finite state machine, the convolutional encoder may be represented by a tree diagram.

15.5 TREE DIAGRAM REPRESENTATION

Figure 15.7 depicts the tree diagram corresponding to the example of Figure 15.6. Assume that the encoder is "flushed" with zeros prior to the first input of data and is in an

Example:

$$\begin{bmatrix} 1 & 0 & 1 & 1 & 0 & 0 \\ 0 & 1 & 1 & 0 & 1 & 0 \\ 1 & 1 & 0 & 0 & 0 & 1 \end{bmatrix} \begin{bmatrix} 0 \\ 0 \\ 0 \\ 0 \\ 0 \\ 0 \end{bmatrix} = [0\ 0\ 0]^T$$

[H] $-\vec{s}^T$

Figure 15.3   Constructing the syndrome table using the all zeros codeword.

$$[H]\vec{e}\ =\ \vec{s}$$

Error pattern	Syndrome
0 0 0 0 0 0	0 0 0
1 0 0 0 0 0	1 0 1
0 1 0 0 0 0	0 1 1
0 0 1 0 0 0	1 1 0
0 0 0 1 0 0	1 0 0
0 0 0 0 1 0	0 1 0
0 0 0 0 0 1	0 0 1

Figure 15.4   The complete syndrome table for the current example.

Example: $\vec{r}$ = 1 0 0 0 1 1

$\vec{s}$ = [H] $\vec{r}$ =

$$\begin{bmatrix} 1 & 0 & 1 & | & 1 & 0 & 0 \\ 0 & 1 & 1 & | & 0 & 1 & 0 \\ 1 & 1 & 0 & | & 0 & 0 & 1 \end{bmatrix} \begin{bmatrix} 1 \\ 0 \\ 0 \\ 0 \\ 1 \\ 1 \end{bmatrix} = \begin{bmatrix} 1 \\ 1 \\ 0 \end{bmatrix}$$

[H] $\vec{s}$

                                      $\vec{r}$

$\vec{r}$ = 1 0 0 0 1 1

$\vec{e}$ = 0 0 1 0 0 0

$\vec{c}$ ⊕ 1 0 1 0 1 1

Figure 15.5   Example of correcting a received vector $\vec{r}$ using the syndrome method.

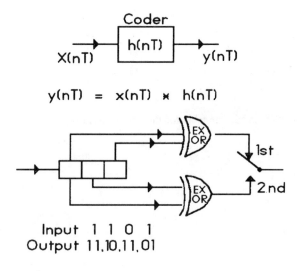

Input 1 1 0 1
Output 11,10,11,01

Figure 15.6   A simple example of a rate 1/2 convolutional encoder.

initial state which is labelled A on the tree diagram. Conventionally the tree diagram is drawn so that inputting a 0 results in exiting the present state by the upper path, while inputting a 1 causes exit by the lower path. Assuming a 0 is input the machine will move to state B and output 0,0. Outputs are shown on the corresponding branches of the diagram. Alternatively if the machine is in state A and a 1 is input then it proceeds to state C and 1,1 is output. Figure 15.7 depicts the first three stages of the tree diagram, after which there appears to be eight possible states. This is at variance with the previous statement that the machine in this example has only four states. There are, in fact, only four distinct states here, but each state appears twice giving the appearance of eight states. After the fourth stage each state would appear four times etc. Two states are identical if, on receiving the same input they respond with the same output. This exponential growth rate in the number of states can be contained by identifying identical states and overlaying them on top of each other. This leads to a trellis diagram.

15.6 THE TRELLIS DIAGRAM REPRESENTATION

Figure 15.8 shows the trellis diagram corresponding to the tree diagram of Figure 15.7. Here five stages are shown with the folding of corresponding tree diagram states being evident at the fourth and fifth stages (states $HIJK$,$LMNO$) by the presence of two entry paths to each state. There are still too many states here and inspection will show that H and L are equivalent etc. Thus four states may be identified. These are labelled a , b , c and d on this diagram. The final step in compacting the graphical representation of the convolutional encoder is to reduce this trellis diagram to a state transition diagram.

15.7 THE STATE TRANSITION DIAGRAM

Here the input to the encoder is shown on the appropriate branch and the corresponding outputs are shown in brackets beside the input, Figure 15.9. For example if the encoder is in state a , (the starting state) and a 0 is input then the transition is along the self-loop at state a . The corresponding output is 0,0 as shown. If, on the otherhand, a 1 is input while in state a , then 1,1 is output and the state transition is along the branch from a to b etc.

15.5 VITERBI DECODING OF CONVOLUTIONAL CODES

Since a message encoded by a convolutional code cannot be divided into blocks for decoding in the way that a block coded message can, then the decoding of convolutional codes is extremely difficult and quickly becomes unimplementable for long messages. The decoder memory requirements would grow exponentially with message length. Two steps are taken to solve this problem. Firstly, messages are broken down into blocks which are fed through the encoder after it has been "flushed" with zeros into state a . The block of data is followed with more zeros which bring the encoder back to state a at the end of the coding cycle. This simplifies decoding and "flushes" the encoder ready for the next block. The zeros do not, however, carry any information and the efficiency of the code is reduced to facilitate decoding.

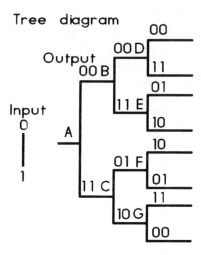

Figure 15.7   The tree diagram representation of the coder of Figure 15.6.

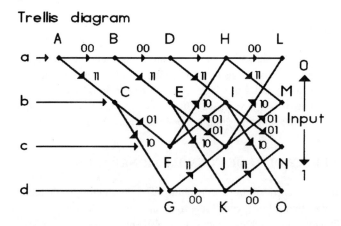

Figure 15.8   The trellis diagram representation of the coder of Figure 15.6.

Secondly, the Viterbi decoding algorithm is used at each stage of progression through the decoding trellis, retaining only the most likely path to a given node and rejecting the rest. This leads to a linear increase in storage requirement with block length as opposed to an exponential increase which is still important even when decoding with blocks rather than whole messages. The Viterbi decoding algorithm implements a nearest neighbour decoding strategy. It picks the path through the decoding trellis, which assumes the minimum number of errors (the probability of t errors being much greater than probability of $t+1$ errors etc). Conceptually a trellis is used for decoding. This decoding trellis is similar to the corresponding encoding trellis. The whole process is explained below in terms of a simple example.

Assume a received sequence 10101010. These eight binary digits correspond to four transmission digits. Also, assume that the first 2 of these digits are unknown data and the last 2 are flushing 0's and that the 3 stage encoder of Figure 15.6 has been used to encode the data transmitted. For reasons of efficiency the data sequence is normally much longer than the sequence shown here which is short for illustrative purposes. Decoding begins by building a decoding trellis corresponding to the encoding trellis starting at state A as shown in Figure 15.10. Decoding will start by assuming that the first input to the encoder was a zero. Reference to the encoding trellis would indicate that on entering a 0 with the encoder completely flushed 0,0 would be output, but 1,0 has just been received. This means that the received sequence is a Hamming distance 1 from the possible transmitted sequence. This distance is noted along the branch from A to B. The possibility that the input data may have been a 1 is now investigated. Again, reference to the encoding trellis will indicate that if a 1 is input to the encoder in state A, the encoder will output 1,1 and go onto state C. In fact, 1,0 was received, so again, the actual received sequence is at Hamming distance 1 from that possible transmitted sequence and that distance is noted as 1 along the branch from A to C. Now return to state B and assume that the input was 0 followed by another 0. If this were the case, the encoder would have gone from state B to state D and output 0,0 (Figure 15.11) but the third and fourth digits which were received were 1,0 and again there is a Hamming distance of 1 between the received sequence and this possible transmitted sequence. This distance is noted on the branch B,D and a similar operation is performed on branch B,E where the distance is 1. Next consider inputting 0 while in state C. This would create 0,1 and in fact 1,0 was received. The Hamming distance here is 2. This is noted on branch C,F and attention is tuned to branch C,G. Starting on state C and inputting a 1 would have output a 1,0, and in fact, 1,0 was received, so at last there is a reception which does not imply any errors. Figure 15.12 illustrates a problem. Decoding is now at stage 3 in the decoding trellis and the possibility of being in state H is being considered. From this stage on, each of the 4 states in this example have 2 inputs and 2 exits. The total cumulative Hamming distances are marked in square brackets above the states. Conventionally on reaching a state like H with two inputs, the cumulative Hamming distance of the upper route ($ABDH$) is shown first and the cumulative Hamming distance for the lower path ($ACFH$) is shown second in the number pair in square brackets over the state H. The real power of the Viterbi algorithm lies in its rejection of one of those two paths, retaining one path which is referred to as the "survivor". If the two paths had different Hamming distances then since this is a nearest neighbour decoding (maximum likelihood) strategy, the path with the larger Hamming distance would be rejected and the path

State transition diagram

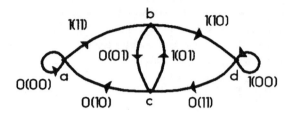

Figure 15.9   The state transition diagram representation of the coder of Figure 15.6.

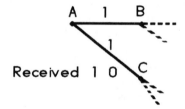

Figure 15.10   The first stage in building the decoding trellis for decoding a received sequence from the encoder of Figure 15.6.

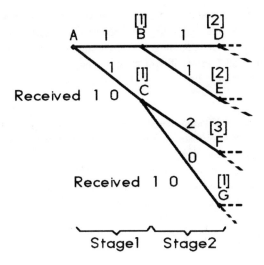

Figure 15.11   The second stage of the decoding trellis of Figure 15.10.

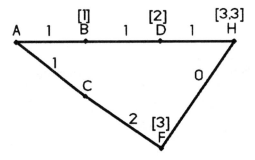

Figure 15.12   Illustration of a sequence containing a detectable but uncorrectable error pattern.

with the lower Hamming distance would be carried forward as the survivor. In the case illustrated in Figure 15.12 the decoder must flag an uncorrectable error sequence, if using incomplete decoding. If using complete decoding a random choice is made between the two paths bearing in mind there is a 50% probability of being wrong. Fortunately, this situation is rare in normal operation. The probability of error has been increased here for illustrative purposes.

There are two paths to state H of equal length [3,3] as just previously discussed. To state I there are two paths [3,5]. The path of distance 5 may be rejected as being less likely than the path of distance 3 etc. In the final stage in this example state L has been labelled as being the finish of the decoding process since in this example only two unknown data digits are being transmitted followed by 0,0 to flush the encoder and bring the decoder back to state a. Thus we need only choose the more likely of the two paths to state L. This is the lower path with a Hamming distance of two. Figure 15.13 shows the complete decoding trellis and the corresponding decoded sequence is shown (1100).

15.9 SUMMARY

In this chapter the generator matrix was introduced and its close relationship with the $[H]$ matrix was shown. Syndrome decoding was explained as a solution to the problem of the nearest neighbour decoding table being too large and finally convolutional coding and the Viterbi decoding algorithm were discussed.

TUTORIAL Block and Convolutional Codes

1.   For a (6,3) systematic linear block code, the three parity check digits are:

$$P_1 = 1.I_1 \oplus 1.I_2 \oplus 1.I_3$$

$$P_2 = 1.I_1 \oplus 1.I_2 \oplus 0.I_3$$

$$P_3 = 0.I_1 \oplus 1.I_2 \oplus 1.I_3$$

(a) construct the generator matrix $[G]$ for this code; (b) construct the code generated by this matrix; (c) determine the error-correcting capabilities for this code; (d) prepare a suitable decoding table; (e) decode the received words 101100, 000110 and 101010.

2.   Given a code with the parity check matrix shown:

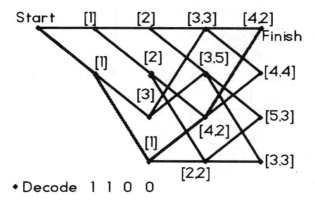

Figure 15.13   Complete decoding trellis for this simple example with the decoded sequence
1100.

$$\begin{bmatrix} 1 & 1 & 1 & 0 & & 1 & 0 & 0 \\ 1 & 1 & 0 & 1 & & 0 & 1 & 0 \\ 1 & 0 & 1 & 1 & & 0 & 0 & 1 \end{bmatrix}$$

(a) write down the generator matrix for this code showing clearly how you derive it from
the above matrix; (b) derive the complete weight structure for the above code and find its
minimum Hamming distance. How many errors can this code correct? How many errors
can this code detect? Can it be used in correction and detection modes simultaneously?
(c) Write down the syndrome table for this code showing how this may be derived by
consideration of the all-zeros codeword. Also comment on the absence of an all-zeros
column from the $[H]$ matrix. (d) Decode the received sequence 1 0 0 1 1 1 0 and
indicate the most likely error pattern associated with this sequence. Explain the statement
"most likely error pattern".

3.   What is the significance of the Hamming (or sphere packing) bound in the context of
block error correcting codes? Derive the Hamming bound from first principles with aid of
a nearest neighbour decoding table for a t error correcting (N,K) block code. Comment
on the feasibility of a (23,12) three error correcting code.

4.

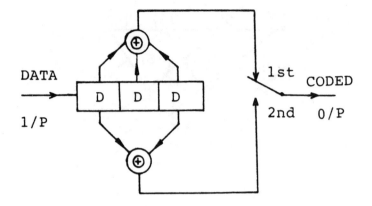

(a) Given the above encoder and assuming data is fed into the shift register one bit at a time, draw the following:

(1) the tree diagram for the encoder;

(2) the trellis diagram for the encoder;

(3) the state transition diagram for the encoder.

(b) Use the Viterbi decoding algorithm to decode the block of data, 10001000, from the above encoder. **Note** there may be errors in this received vector. Assume that the encoder starts in state *a* of the decoding trellis and, after inputting the unknown data digits, is driven back to state *a* with two "flushing" zeros.

Chapter 16
SPEECH CODING TECHNIQUES

16.1 INTRODUCTION

This survey of coding techniques for use in speech processing commences with a study of waveform coders including linear and companded pulse code modulation (PCM), adaptive differential PCM and delta modulation. It then examines two intermediate coder designs where spectral information is transmitted in place of time domain samples before briefly summarising the linear predictive and channel vocoders which, as source coders, implement full modelling of the speech production mechanism. All these techniques are compared in the context of typical transmission rates and speech quantity.

16.2 PULSE MODULATION

The most straightforward coding techniques are to sample the signal amplitude directly and transmit the samples either as pulse amplitude modulation (PAM), pulse position modulation (PPM) or pulse width modulation (PWM), Figure 16.1. The sampling rate must be chosen (chapter 4) to satisfy the Nyquist criterion, i.e. greater than 2 times highest frequency, and the PAM spectrum repeats at the sample frequency. Low pass filtering before Nyquist sampling ensures that no aliased errors will occur. Because the PAM signal contains amplitude information it requires a larger received signal to noise ratio (SNR) than PPM or PWM [Lathi].

In the PAM system the information bandwidth is equal to the original signal bandwidth, as the repeat spectrum at the sampling frequencies does not need to be transmitted, but in order to receive the short duration pulses and detect their amplitude a much wider bandwidth is often required. This deficiency can be overcome by stretching the pulses before transmission or else the gaps between the shorter pulses can be used to provide a signal multiplex capability.

16.3 WAVEFORM CODERS

Pulse Code Modulation

A further improvement is pulse code modulation (PCM) where the sampled signal is quantised into discrete levels and a binary code is allocated to each level. Figure 16.2 shows a 4-bit coded example. For a linear coded system, with a number of levels which are an integer power of two, then the bit rate of transmission is equal to the sample rate times the number of bits. In PCM this is normally 8 kHz × 8 bits = 64 kbit/s. PCM again uses constant amplitude transmission but it introduces quantisation noise when the input sample is converted to the nearest quantisation levels, and is typically 6 dB per bit of code, Figure 16.3. Thus for an 8 bit code SNR ≃ 48 dB. We have not considered the statistics of the signal or noise or whether the signal is a sinusoid or a random variable (such as speech) which typically reduces this approximate SNR by 6 - 9 dB.

In PCM the SNR thus increases in proportion to the number of quantisation levels while the bandwidth or bit rate increases in proportion to the logarithm of the number of quantisation levels. Thus bandwidth can be exchanged for SNR (as in FM) and it becomes more advantageous as the number of quantisation levels is increased. Close to threshold, Figure 16.3, PCM is superior to all other forms of pulse modulation and it is also marginally superior to FM at low SNR. All practical systems are an order of magnitude below the theoretical maximum. As PCM signals contain no amplitude information they can be regenerated at each repeater in a long haul system. This removes the accumulated noise of FM systems and gives a noise performance which is limited by the worst hop on a system. Signals can also be easily scaled for multiplex capability and coded for error detection and correction.

Companded PCM

PCM transmission rate is normally fixed at a maximum value of 64 kbit/s and in order to improve the performance, particularly at low signal levels, the linear PCM coder is replaced with a nonlinear design, Figure 16.4. Here the stepsizes are small at low amplitudes increasing to larger steps at large amplitudes. These graded stepsizes considerably improve the overall SNR. The scheme adopted in the USA is μ-law [Lathi].

$$F(x) = sign(x) \frac{\ln(1 + \mu \mid x \mid)}{\ln(1 + \mu)} \tag{16.1}$$

where

$$\mid x \mid = \frac{x}{V} = \frac{actual\ signal\ value}{full\ scale\ value}$$

The variable μ defines the curvature law with $\mu = 0$ giving a linear response, $\mu = 255$ is the commonly used value giving a companding noise improvement at low levels of 33.3 dB over a linear system operating at the same transmission rate. Companding is achieved with a 15 segment piecewise linear approximation where the slopes of the segments are related by powers

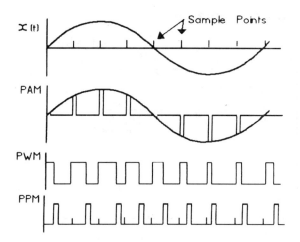

Figure 16.1   An illustration of pulse amplitude, width and position modulation signals.

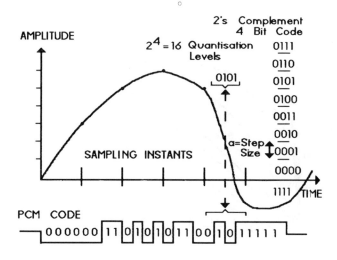

Figure 16.2   PCM example where transmitted bit rate = sample rate × no. of bits in code.

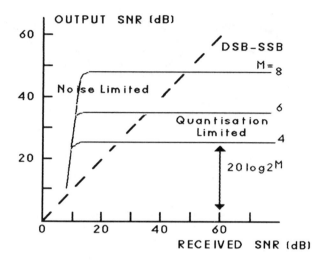

Figure 16.3   Input/output SNR for pulse code modulation.

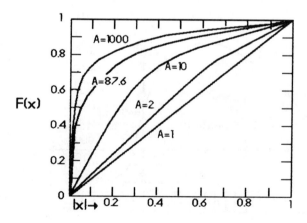

Figure 16.4 A -law companded PCM characteristics

of two. The μ = 255 coding has a performance which is equivalent to a 13 bit linear PCM coder.

The scheme preferred in Europe is A-law companding:-

$$
F(x) = \begin{cases} sign\,(x)\ \dfrac{1 + ln\,(A\ \lfloor x\ \rfloor)}{1 + \ln(A)}, & \dfrac{1}{A} < x < 1 \\[4mm] sign\,(x)\ \dfrac{A\ \lfloor x\ \rfloor}{1 + \ln(A)}, & 0 < x < \dfrac{1}{A} \end{cases}
\tag{16.2}
$$

Here A defines the curvature law with A = 1 being the linear response, Figure 16.4. The commonly adopted value is A = 87.6 giving a 24.1 dB improvement, over linear PCM, in noise at low levels. The A-law characteristic is achieved with a 13-segment piecewise linear approximation (in practice 16 where 4 near origin are colinear, Figure 16.5). In the 8 bit code; 1 bit gives polarity, 3 bits indicate segment and 4 bits the location on the segment. The slight performance reduction over μ-law is caused by the steps near the origin being twice the size in A-law.

These approaches are adopted for high (toll) quality transmission for long haul digital communications. If narrow bandwidth is more important then other coding techniques are employed.

Reduced Bandwidth PCM Techniques

One technique to reduce the bandwidth is to transmit information about the changes between samples rather than send a new value each sample. The simplest system is delta PCM which sends a correction from one sample to the next which requires fewer bits in the PCM coder. It is optimised for low frequency sinusoids and incurs a significant degradation when the signal approaches the Nyquist frequency.

Differential PCM (DPCM) sophisticates this system by employing a predictor [Gray & Markel] to process previous samples to predict the next sample value, Figure 16.6. The simplest predictor is the one sample predictor;-

$$
F(n, Ts) = AF([n-1], Ts)
\tag{16.3}
$$

where the previous sample is weighted by A to predict the next value. A more sophisticated version is the N-stage FIR based predictor, Figure 16.7, and the coder quantises the residual error, Figure 16.6. The fixed predictor coefficients are obtained by computing covariance matrices for several groups of input samples, the matrices are averaged and the simultaneous equations solved to yield the predictor coefficients. A further sophistication is adaptive DPCM (ADPCM) where the predictor coefficients are continuously updated to handle changing signal statistics. Other practical constraints are vector quantisation where the speech vectors are compared against a codebook and the address information is transmitted in place of the coefficient vector.

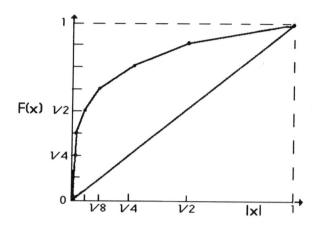

Figure 16.5   The 13 segment compression A-law realised by piecewise linear approximation.

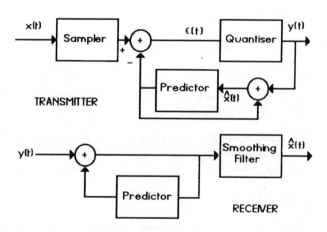

Figure 16.6   Transmitter and receiver for differential PCM.

Predictors, fall into a range of distinct designs. Figure 16.7 shows two designs of FIR adaptive predictors which utilise either forward or backwards adaptation. In adaptive predictors the internal coefficient values are updated to minimise the output error. These predictors, which are described earlier in chapter 13, are used in DPCM to perform a partial direct system modelling and output the error information for quantisation and transmission.

In adaptive predictor design two separate predictors are often used. A 3 coefficient term predictor with a pedestal delay extracts the pitch or vocal tract excitation information while a separate short delay predictor models the short term speech characteristic. These two separate predictors can be placed in either order. Predictors can also be realised either as FIR designs, Figure 16.7, or as an IIR design.

Backward adaptive predictors are usually preferred in ADPCM as they only rely on past samples of the sequence and hence the receiver can be realised more simply. Forward adaptation is less attractive as the receiver needs access to the predictor coefficients in the transmitter, reducing the available channel bandwidth for quantised error information. The length of the predictor is also important. Simple short predictors are less accurate requiring more quantisation accuracy in the transmitted error information. Long duration predictors overcome this deficiency but any error in the quantised information takes longer to propagate through the predictor extending the duration of the output error in the reconstructed speech.

A simplification on the prediction concept is delta modulation (DM) where only the sign information is transmitted. Here the prediction is based on history of past differences, rather than samples, and the predictors in the encoder and decoder can take the form of simple integrators, Figure 16.8. As only 1-bit quantisation is used the sample rate is higher than the 8 kHz of PCM.

Delta modulation suffers from slope overload distortion when the step size is small and idling (quantisation) noise at low frequencies which is dependent on the stepsize, Figure 16.9. The deficiencies are overcome in adaptive delta modulation (ADM) where the stepsize is varied. In one algorithm (SONG) the minimum stepsize is δ and the new stepsize equals the old stepsize $\pm \delta$. An alternative is the continuous variable slope delta modulation where the stepsize changes at a syllabic rate corresponding to the speech i.e. in a filter with $\simeq 100$ sec time constant.

These reduced bandwidth PCM based schemes reduce the transmission rate down as low as 16 kbit/s for ADM, Figure 16.10, with only a small penalty in the speech quality, reducing it from toll into communications quality. For radio systems the 16 kbit/s ADM allows digital speech to be transmitted directly over radio channels which are allocated on 25 kHz channel spacings.

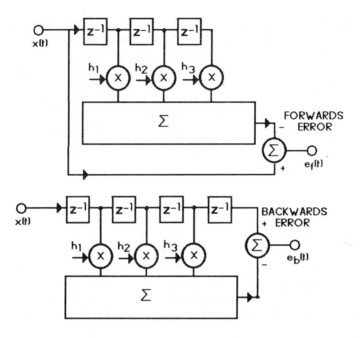

Figure 16.7   Third-order forwards and backwards prediction-error filters.

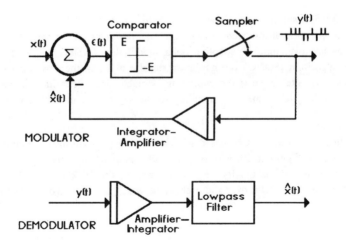

Figure 16.8   Transmitter and receiver for delta modulation.

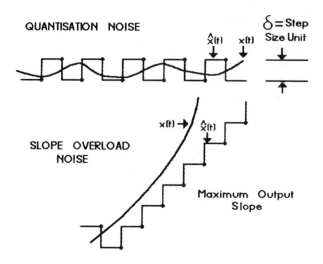

Figure 16.9   Problems with delta modulation.

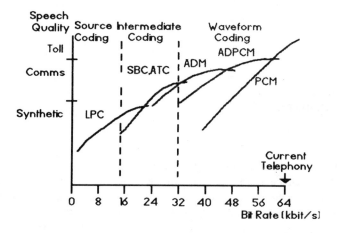

Figure 16.10   Comparison of speech coding systems.

16.4 INTERMEDIATE CODERS

Further techniques for bit rate reduction are the intermediate coding techniques such as sub-band coding (SBC) where the 3.4 kHz speech band is split into a small number (2-8) of sub-bands, Figure 16.11. It has been found that quantising the sub-bands can be accomplished with reduced accuracy to give overall communications quality transmission due to subjective noise masking where quantisation accuracy is set adaptively for best performance. Figure 16.11 provides typical numbers of bits/sample for 16, 24 and 32 kbit/s transmission rate systems.

The number of filters employed in SBC is often designed to be a power of 2 as it allows the use of quadrature mirror filter (QMF) designs. QMF allows a band to be split into two equal width sub-bands by employing a pair of FIR filters. With symmetrical and anti-symmetrical even tap number filter designs then the FIR coefficients are identical except for sign alteration permitting all the splitting to be performed in a single 32-stage FIR filter, which incorporates output downsampling or decimation in both the upper and lower sub-bands, Figure 16.12. The filters are designed such that their combined characteristic yields on all-pass response and the aliased distortion due to interband leakage and images are exactly compensated in the all-pass design [Jayant & Noll], Figure 16.13. Sub-band coding techniques are also being applied to obtain higher fidelity telephony transmission at 64 kbit/s by coding over wider bandwidths than 4 kHz.

An alternative technique is to perform a block transform on a set of input signal samples and adaptively assign the quantisation accuracy to the transformed data, Figure 16.14. This technique also achieves 16-32 kbit/s transmission rates, Figure 16.10, but it is more computationally demanding than sub-band coding. Transform coding is described further in the image processing lecture. The broad concepts of adaptive predictive and sub-band coding are next extended to lower bit rate (2.4 kbit/s) speech transmission by source coder or vocoder designs.

16.5 SOURCE CODERS

Introduction

Vocoders are sophisticated coders which extract, in an efficient manner, the significant components in the speech waveform. Speech basically comprises four formants, Figure 16.15 and the vocoder analyses the input information to find the position and magnitude of these with time. The analyser can again be a prediction error filter. Figure 16.7 showed the realisation of 3rd order forward and backward prediction error filters. In this instance we perform a full model of the input spectrum and transmit the model parameters rather than the ADPCM residual error samples.

The production of human speech, from a purely physical viewpoint, is governed by two fundamental mechanisms:

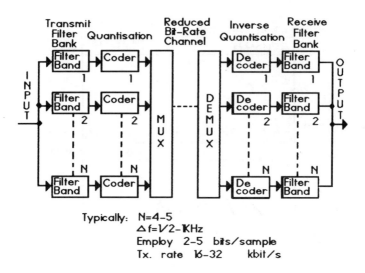

Typically: N=4-5
$\Delta f = 1/2 - 1 KHz$
Employ 2-5 bits/sample
Tx. rate 16-32   kbit/s

Figure 16.11   Sub-band coder design.

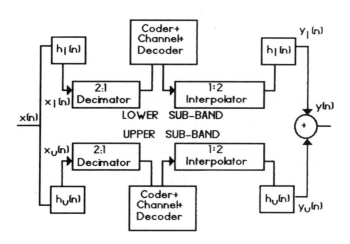

Figure 16.12   Quadrature-mirror filtering for splitting into two equal-width sub-bands.

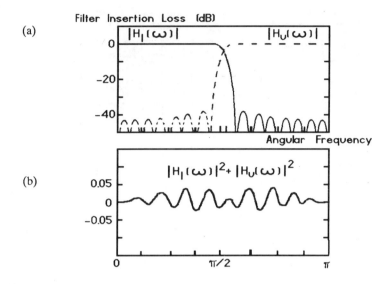

Figure 16.13 Illustration of amplitude-frequency responses in a quadrature mirror filter bank using FIR filters: (a) lowpass and highpass characteristics of individual 32-tap FIR filters; (b) approximately all-pass characteristic of the combination.

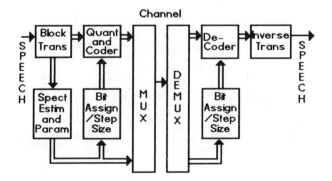

Figure 16.14 Block diagram on an adaptive transform coder.

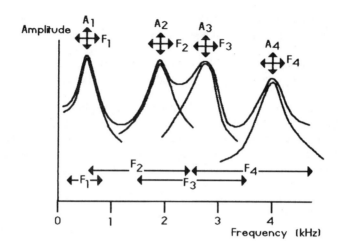

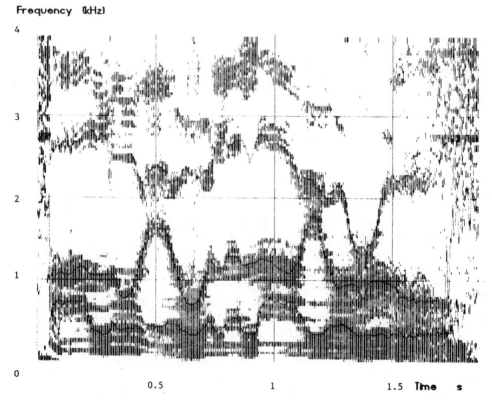

Figure 16.15   Typical spectral distribution of speech formants, and their variation with time (Spectrogram shows formant movement for two seconds of speech).

(i)   A source of fundamental excitation provided by the expulsion of air from the lungs, this excitation may be further modified by the action of the vocal chords.

(ii) The spectral shaping of this exciting broadband spectrum by the filtering action of the vocal tract formed by the mouth, tongue, teeth, lips and nasal canal, Figure 16.16.

The basic excitaton may be expulsion of air from the lungs with the vocal chords open, in which case the speech is said to be unvoiced. In this case the excitation may be modelled by white noise. On the other hand, if the vocal chords are closed they will vibrate providing an excitation which is a periodic pulse train, the periodicity being referred to as the voice pitch. The type of speech produced in this case is said to be voiced.

The spectrum of either of these excitations is then modified by the acoustic cavities formed by the vocal tract. The shaping of these cavities may be altered by altering the shape of the vocal tract using the tongue, lips, teeth and the glottis. With the glottis closed, no nasal sound, the transfer function of the vocal tract is all pole, i.e. purely auto-regressive (AR). In this case an inverse or whitening filter may be formed using a purely moving average (FIR) predictor, Figure 13.7. With the glottis open zeroes are introduced into the vocal tract transfer function and a true inverse would then also require poles (an ARMA model). However, this case is usually neglected due to the stability problems inherent in an adaptive ARMA process. So normally the vocal tract is assumed to be purely AR. This results in some degradation in reproduction of nasal sounds, however intelligibility in subjective tests is not noticeably degraded by this approximation.

The operation of a FIR prediction error filter cascade for parametric spectral analysis, Figure 13.5, is illustrated further in Figure 16.17. This shows how the output spectrum is whitened as one moves progressively down the cascade. In this example the filter is input with white noise convolved with the synthetic channel impulse response $0.28 + z^{-1} + 0.28z^{-2}$ to provide the filtered input power spectral density shown at the zero order in Figure 16.17.

Figure 16.18 shows the effect of applying this parametric spectral estimation or modelling to an input signal comprising five separate sinusoids. Again we progressively whiten the input signal and if, after convergence, the filter correlation coefficients are Fourier transformed, they yield a power spectral density analyzer response, chapter 13. Figure 16.18 shows the transformed output from prediction error filters whose order increased progressively from 1 to 10. These simulations show that each second-order stage can control the positions of a zero pair to model the generating pole pair corresponding to one sinusoid. Thus a filter of order 10 is required to model the inverse of this five sinusoid input signal.

The prediction error filter now fits appropriate zeros to model the input. This results in a progressive whitening of the spectrum as it emerges from each filter stage. Compared to Fourier analysis techniques, Figure 16.19, the adaptive parametric spectral estimation approach optimally identifies the locations of the input sinusoids, but it provides no detail in the regions in between. For a low signal-to-noise ratio at the input, the noise components in between the sinusoidal tones drive the filter from convergence, making this approach not as useful as

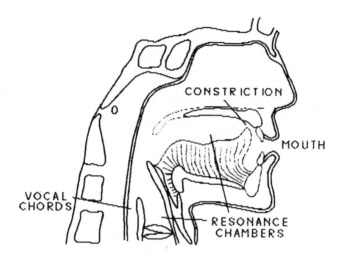

Figure 16.16   Schematic of vocal tract.

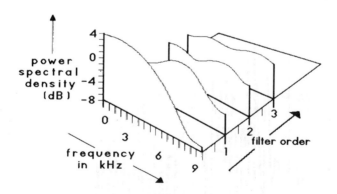

Figure 16.17   The power spectra of the outputs of autoregressive prediction error (PE) filters of increasing order, showing the progressive whitening of a signal.

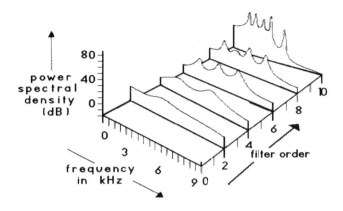

Figure 16.18   The inverse of the frequency response of PE filters of increasing order. The input signal is a collection of five sinusoids.

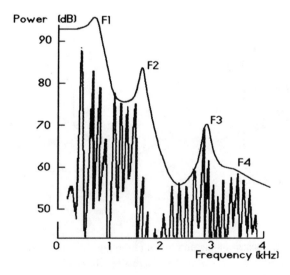

Figure 16.19   Comparison of smooth AR with FFT speech spectral modelling.

Fourier techniques for determining the input spectral response. Thus it is generally accepted that nonparametric Fourier analysis techniques are superior for broadband analysis with low input SNR. However, the resolution of this technique, which is proportional to the length of the observation window, is inferior. For time-varying spectra or short time series, such as speech the observation window has to be restricted, reducing the resolution of the Fourier approach, making parametric techniques more attractive.

Spectral estimation techniques are widely used in vocoders, which exploit the redundancy in the speech waveform to achieve low-bit-rate (< 2.4 kbit/s) transmission. Two major designs exist at present, the channel vocoder and the linear predictive coder (LPC). Although the LPC design has been implemented by the autocorrelation method [Makhoul], which uses adaptive transversal filters, a cascade of linear prediction error filters is the preferred approach, as it is less sensitive to coefficient inaccuracies.

Linear Predictive Coder (LPC)

In the LPC vocoder, Figure 16.20, the analyzer and encoder normally process the signal in 20-ms frames and subsequently transmit the coarse spectral information via the filter coefficients. The residual error (noise output from the prediction error whitening filter) is not transmitted, instead it is used to provide an estimate of the input power level which is sent along with the pitch information and an indication as to whether the input is voiced or unvoiced (Figure 16.20). The latter can be ascertained by examining whether the first lag of the autocorrelation function of the signal lies above or below a certain threshold. If above the threshold, the value of autocorrelation term provides the pitch information. The decoder and synthesizer apply the received filter coefficients to an AR synthesizing filter which is excited with impulses at the pitch frequency if voiced, or white noise if unvoiced. The excitation amplitude is controlled by the input power estimate information.

The adaptive lattice filter can be effectively applied to implement an all-pole filter representation of the physical lossless acoustic tube model of the vocal tract, Figure 16.21. This approach which outputs a continuous representation of the filter prediction error coefficients, has received most emphasis to date because it is a regular structure that is amenable to implementation with digital LSI circuits, and it compactly forms both forward and backward prediction error filters. The lattice filter of Figure 16.21 adaptively sets partial correlation or PARCOR (K) coefficients at each stage to remove the correlated signal components across the delay term. Thus it successive decorrelates the signal components down the lattice structure in a manner similar to the Gram-Schmidt decorrelation in adaptive arrays. The lattice structure uses less hardware for a given order number than an equivalent transversal filter design and, further, it is less sensitive to wordlength limitations in the K coefficients than the transversal design. The coefficients are adaptively updated with either the LMS or RLS algorithms, see adaptive filters chapter 10.

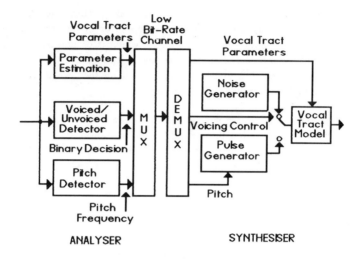

Figure 16.20   Block diagram of the linear predictive vocoder.

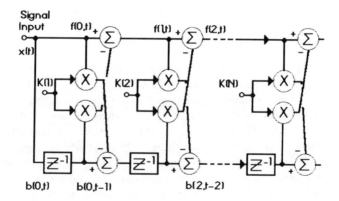

Figure 16.21   The lattice prediction error filter structure.

Figure 16.19 showed a 18th order LPC power spectrum clearly picking out the first three formats. In comparison the 1024 point FFT logarithmic power spectrum shows much higher resolution. The parametric estimator does not possess the fine detail of the swept-frequency response, due to the much shorter analysis time. Further investigation shows close agreement between approaches when estimating the overall spectral density, but the parametric analyzer is less accurate in estimating the absolute frequencies of the peaks. Figure 16.19 gives a broad comparison of the two approaches and shows how the adaptive zero fitting in the simpler autoregressive estimator provides a sufficiently accurate spectral representation for synthetic and possibly also communications-quality speech transmission. Toll-quality transmission requires more accurate sampling techniques, such as pulse-code modulation.

With delays in the vocal tract of about 1 ms and typical speech sample rates of 8 to 10 kHz the number of lattice stages is normally in the range 8 to 12, with 10 being the number adopted in the integrated LPC vocoder standard, which transmits at a 2.4 kbit/s rate. These vocoders normally require a multichip, or multiple e.g. 3 processor DSP design. In addition to these vocoder applications, digital lattice filters are used in several commercial speech synthesis systems.

The Channel Vocoder

Historically, the channel vocoder was invented in 1939 by Homer Dudley at Bell Telephone Laboratories and hence it is an older technique than LPC. A block diagram of the channel vocoder is shown in Figure 16.22. In the analyser, the main processing block is a bank of contiguous band-pass filters arranged to cover continuously the speech bandwidth (50 Hz - 4 kHz). The outputs from these filters are rectified and low-pass filtered so that an approximation to the short-time spectral envelope of the speech is available. Normally, the amplitude components of the smoothed spectral envelope are sampled, quantised logarithmically, multiplexed with pitch and voice/unvoice information into frames and transmitted serially to the synthesiser. Data reduction is achieved because phase information is not transmitted. Only the smoothed envelope of the voiced speech spectrum is transmitted, and both the amplitude and frequency are logarithmically quantised.

In the synthesiser, the received data are inversely decoded and fed in parallel to the appropriate circuit elements. Speech is synthesised by summing the outputs from an identical contiguous filter bank, which has been input with weighted versions of an excitation source. The particular source is selected by the voicing control and the period of the source excitation is given by the received pitch information. Finally, the synthetic speech is filtered to compensate for the excitation source and equalisation.

The channel vocoder fidelity depends on the design of the contiguous filter banks. Ideally, these should consist of steep sided filters narrow enough for no more than a single harmonic to enter any one filter during voicing. The disadvantage of this filter bank, is that relatively little bandwidth compression would result. For example, if the lower limit of the pitch frequency is 50 Hz then 80 parallel filters are required to analyze a 4 kHz bandwidth. The filter bandwidths are therefore increased so that the total number of filters can be reduced.

Channel vocoder designs typically employ between 16 and 32 logarithmically spaced filters to cover a 4 kHz bandwidth. The filter characteristics for the British 19-channel vocoder design are given in Figure 16.23 [Holmes]. The individual filter characteristic is also an important consideration. Most channel vocoders use a 2-pole Butterworth characteristic.

The cut-off frequencies of the low-pass filters which smooth or average the rectified band-pass filter outputs have to be chosen to follow the slowly varying spectral content of speech. Thus the smoothing filter is usually chosen to have a 3 dB attenuation at 25-35 Hz and an 18 dB/octave roll-off. It is generally accepted that the minimum data rate which can be achieved by a channel vocoder is in the order of 2.4 kbit/s. This requires that channel 1 be coded with 3-bit PCM and channels 2 to 19 with 2-bit DM. With 1-bit for the voice-unvoice decision, 6-bits for the pitch information and 2 engineering bits the total transmission bit rate for each 20 ms frame is 2.4 kbit/s. At this data rate, the speech has a mechanical quality but still maintains good intelligibility.

Formant Vocoder

Pitch information [Childers] can be obtained by calculating the cepstrum, which comprises two DFT based spectrum analysers interconnected by a logarithmic amplifier. Figure 16.24 shows a sample of input speech comprising part of the vowel "I", with pitch period of 7.2 ms which is sampled at 8 kHz rate. These simulations show that the spectrum has a line spacing of 139 Hz while the cepstrum exhibits a large peak at a quefrency of 7.2 ms. Cepstrum processing such as this also forms the basis of the homomorphic vocoder, Figure 16.25, which attempts further reduction in bit rate below 2.4 kbit/s.

16.6 SUMMARY

A comparison of all these speech coders in terms of transmission bit rate, quality and complexity is provided in Table 16.1, which covers waveform, intermediate and source coders. Low complexity implies a standard codec chip while high complexity demands a multiple DSP microprocessor solution, see chapter 19. Finally, it should be noted that analogue switched capacitor techniques, see chapter 18, are also applicable as filterbanks for speech analysis. The techniques described here also form the basis of speech recognition systems [McInnes & Jack] and, at present, LPC and formant synthesis are widely applied to efficiently store and recall synthetic speech.

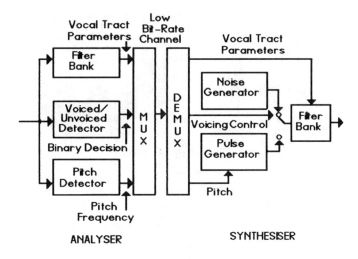

Figure 16.22   Block diagram of the channel vocoder.

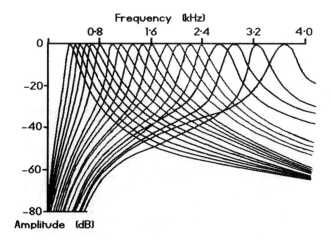

Figure 16.23   Channel vocoder filterbank details.

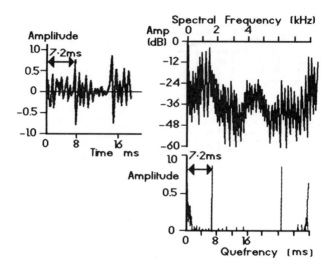

Figure 16.24   Example of spectrum and cepstrum computation.

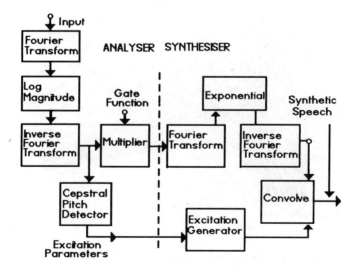

Figure 16.25   Block diagram of the homomorphic vocoder.

class	technique	bit-rate kbits/s	quality	complexity
waveform coders	PCM	64	excellent	low
	DM	32	very good	low
	DPCM	16	fairly good	low
intermediate coders	SBC	16	very good	medium
	ATC	16	very good	high
	ATC	4.8	fairly good	high
source coders	channel vocoder	2.4	fair	high
	LPC vocoder	2.4	fair	high
	formant vocoder	1.2		very high

Table 16.1 Current status of speech coder designs.

TUTORIAL Signal and Speech Coding

1. Two low-pass signals, each band-limited to 4kHz, are to be multiplexed into a single channel using pulse amplitude modulation. Each signal is impulse-sampled at a rate of 10 kHz. The time-multiplexed signal waveform is filtered by an ideal low-pass filter before transmission. (a) What is the minimum clock frequency of the system? *[20 kHz]* (b) What is the minimum cutoff frequency of the LPF? *[8 kHz < B < 12 kHz]*

2. Twenty-five input signals, each band-limited to 3.3 kHz, are each sampled at an 8 kHz rate then time-multiplexed. Calculate the minimum bandwidth required to transmit this multiplexed signal in the presence of noise if the pulse modulation used is: (a) PAM; (b) PPM with a required level resolution of 5%; or (c) binary PCM with a required level resolution of > 0.5%. (This higher resolution requirement on PCM is normal for speech-type signals because the quantisation noise is quite objectionable). *[(a) 100 kHz, (b) 2 MHz, (c) 800 kHz]*

3. For the n-bit μ-law companded system, where the output signal to noise ratio (SNR) is given by:

$$\frac{3.2^{2n}}{[\ln(1 + \mu)]^2}$$

Calculate the degradation in output SNR in dB for large signal amplitudes in an $n = 8$ bit companded PCM system with typical μ value when compared with a linear PCM system operating at the same channel transmission rate. *[10 dB]*

4.   An 8-bit A-law companded PCM system is to be designed with piecewise linear approximation as shown in Figure 16.5. If 13 segments are employed (with 4 colinear near the origin) and the segments join at 1/2, 1/4, etc. of the full scale value calculate the approximate SNR for full scale and small signal values with $A = 87.6$. *[full scale 36 dB, small signal 84 dB]*

Chapter 17
IMAGE PROCESSING AND CODING

17.1 INTRODUCTION

The general field of image processing involves topics such as coding, filtering for restoration and enhancement of degraded images, feature or pattern recognition and extraction. The discussion here is confined initially to the topic of image coding for bit rate reduction, following on from the theme developed previously for speech signals. The latter parts of this chapter examine 2-D filter techniques for enhancement of edge information.

Photodiode image sensor arrays for image capture can be fabricated with a standard MOS RAM semiconductor process, but the main emphasis is on analogue CCD based sensors as they can provide more flexible readout modes and lower noise. In most cases the image data is normally read out in raster scan format. Solid state imagers have now reached densities of $> 10^6$ pixels in large 5.5-by-5.5 cm chips. The achievement of 10^6 pixel imagers in more reasonable areas (1 cm^2) is expected shortly with the development of smaller 10-by-10 μm pixel areas.

Image processing is applied to individual pictures (facsimile) and to video which both present a two-dimensional distribution (2-D) of light intensity. The dynamic range of the raster scanned video signal is typically 50 dB (speech $\approx$80 dB) and the bandwidth for a black and white TV picture is 4-6 MHz. (For colour TV the chrominance signal requires approximately a 25% additional bandwidth requirement). The video is normally quantised in an 8-bit ADC operating at 8-20 MHz. In order to preserve the detail in video pictures spatial frequency resolution up to 250 cycles per scan line is required while for facsimile 500-2k cycle resolution is required as there is no time averaging [Haskell & Steele].

17.2 IMAGE TRANSFORM CODING

As individual images are 2-D in nature the image coding algorithms themselves must be 2-D and this further sophisticates the processing requirements and provides much of the thrust behind the development of array processor designs, chapter 19. Coding is normally achieved by transforming the signal to another domain so that the strong or significant signal components only occupy a limited number of locations which are less than the number of pixels transformed and hence the overall quantisation accuracy can be efficiently reduced, similar to SBC and channel vocoders.

The 2-D sampled data sequence

$$x = [x(n_1, n_2)]$$

is normally of finite extent i.e.,

$$0 \le n_1 < N_1 ; \quad 0 \le n_2 < N_2$$

such signals are usually characterised by looking at their frequency response. For a 2-D impulse response $h(n_1,n_2)$ the frequency response is given by the Fourier transform extended into two dimensions, ω_1 and ω_2.

$$H(\omega_1,\omega_2) = \sum_{n_1=-\infty}^{\infty} \sum_{n_2=-\infty}^{\infty} h(n_1,n_2) \, exp\,(-j\omega_1 n_1)\, exp\,(-j\omega_2 n_2) \qquad (17.1)$$

Figure 17.1 [Dudgeon & Mersereau] shows the frequency response for the impulse function

$$h(n_1,n_2) = \delta(n_1+1,n_2) + \delta(n_1-1,n_2) + \delta(n_1,n_2+1) + \delta(n_1,n_2-1) \qquad (17.2)$$

where δ is the Kronecker delta.

In fact this 2-D transform operation is performed directly by the optical lens when it focusses light. The 2-D $sin(x)/x$ response within the focussed spot provides the zero spatial frequency term from the constant illumination at the input plane, Figure 17.2. As the input is circularly symmetric so is the focussed spot. If the input plane had been optically intensity modulated with a checkerboard pattern (e.g. via a transparency) then a second $sin(x)/x$ response would result corresponding to the checkerboard spatial frequency, Figure 17.3, with significant components at odd harmonics of the inverse periodicity, n. This is a direct extension, into two dimensions, of the rectangular pulse train transform described earlier in chapter 2. Low spatial frequencies are imaged close to the constant illumination term while high spatial frequencies with rapidly changing contrast are widely separated from this point in the transform domain, Figure 17.4.

In practical imaging systems the input signals are usually time sampled so the 2-D Fourier transform of equation 17.1 reduces to the 2-D DFT

$$X(k_1,k_2) = \sum_{n_1=0}^{N_1-1} \sum_{n_2=0}^{N_2-1} x(n_1,n_2) \, W_{N_1}^{n_1 k_1} \, W_{N_2}^{n_2 k_2} \qquad (17.3)$$

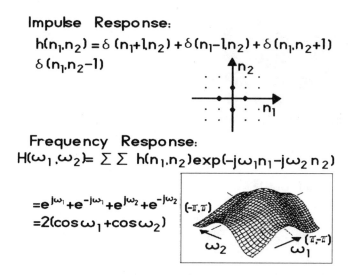

Impulse Response:

$$h(n_1,n_2) = \delta\,(n_1+1,n_2) + \delta\,(n_1-1,n_2) + \delta\,(n_1,n_2+1)$$
$$\delta\,(n_1,n_2-1)$$

Frequency Response:

$$H(\omega_1,\omega_2) = \sum \sum\, h(n_1,n_2)\exp(-j\omega_1 n_1 - j\omega_2 n_2)$$

$$=e^{j\omega_1}+e^{-j\omega_1}+e^{j\omega_2}+e^{-j\omega_2}$$
$$=2(\cos\omega_1 +\cos\omega_2)$$

Figure 17.1   Impulse & frequency response for a 2-D sampled data signal.

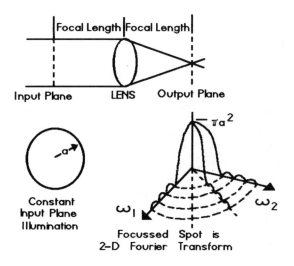

Figure 17.2   2-D spatial Fourier transform.

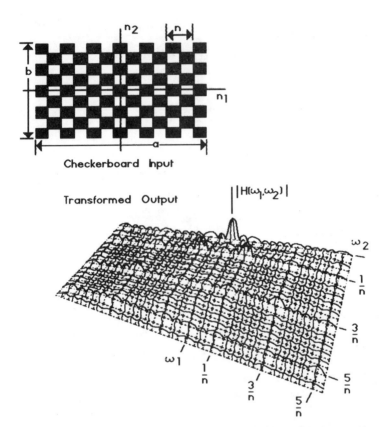

Figure 17.3   2-D Fourier transform for checkerboard intensity modulated input pattern.

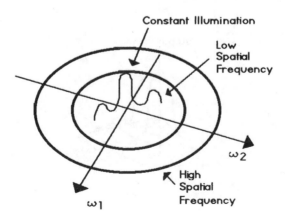

Figure 17.4   The spatial frequency concept.

for

$$0 \le k_1 \le N_1 - 1 \; ; \quad 0 \le k_2 \le N_2 - 1$$

and the complex exponential samples W_{N_1}, W_{N_2} are defined as in the Fourier transform chapter. In this case direct calculation of the DFT requires $N_1.N_2$ complex operations per sample or $N_1^2.N_2^2$ per 2-D transform. If the transform is M-dimensional then the number of operations is $N_1^2.N_2^2....N_M^2$.

Again fast algorithms have been developed to perform the DFT computations. The important property is that row-column decomposition

$$X(k_1,k_2) = \sum_{n_1=0}^{N_1-1} G(n_1,k_2) \, W_{N_1}^{n_1 k_2} \tag{17.4}$$

where

$$G(n_1,k_2) = \sum_{n_2=0}^{N_2-1} x(n_1,n_2) \, W_{N_2}^{n_2 k_2} \tag{17.5}$$

Here each column of G is the 1-D DFT of the corresponding column of x, and each row of X is the 1-D DFT of the corresponding row of G. Thus the 2-D DFT can be calculated as a set of 1-D DFT's followed by a data reordering or "corner turning" operation followed by another set of 1-D DFT operations, Figure 17.5. For a 1024-by-1024 point 2-D DFT direct computation requires 10^{12} complex multiply operations, row-column decomposition reduces this to 2×10^9, and the use of the FFT in place of the DFT further reduces this to 10^7 operations providing a saving factor of 10^5.

Just as the 1-D FFT decomposed the DFT into successively smaller transform sizes until two point transforms resulted to minimise the computations, the 2-D DFT can be decomposed in an identical manner to yield the 2-D vector-radix (vr) transform. This offers further savings, over row-column decomposition, which increases as the dimension M of the data set increases [Dudgeon & Mersereau].

In addition to the DFT which uses basis vectors comprising sampled sine and cosine functions other significant transforms are the discrete cosine transform (DCT) which uses only cosine functions with special amplitude and phase relationships. These are shown in Figure 17.6 for 8 point transforms. The DCT is especially significant in image coding where the data is usually real (i.e. not complex valued). The DCT is an orthonormal transform

$$C(k_1,k_2) = \sum_{n_1=0}^{N_1-1} \sum_{n_2=0}^{N_2-1} x(n_1,n_2) \cos\left(\frac{(2n_1+1)\,k_1\pi}{N_1}\right) \cos\left(\frac{(2n_2+1)\,k_2\pi}{N_2}\right)$$

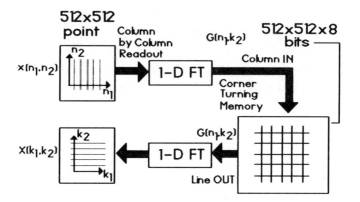

Figure 17.5   2-D DFT calculation via cascaded 1-D DFT's employing row-column decomposition techniques.

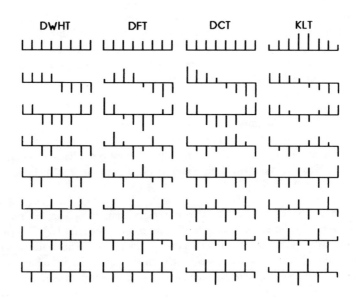

Figure 17.6 $N = 8$ point 1-D basis vectors for four distinct signal transform types.

where forward and backwards transforms have identical kernels except for a scale factor. Here the basis vectors are sampled cosines with phase shifts which are not given by the alternating 0 and $\pi/2$ sines and cosines of the DFT pattern. The basis vectors can be shown to be closely related to the eigenvectors of the autoregressive process [Jayant & Noll]. Hence the DCT is identical to the optimum KLT at low orders (e.g. 2). For order 2

$$^2C = \,^2F \quad (DFT)$$

For order 4

$$^4C = \frac{1}{2} \begin{bmatrix} 1 & 1 & 1 & 1 \\ a & b & -b & -a \\ 1 & -1 & -1 & 1 \\ b & -a & a & -b \end{bmatrix}$$

where $a = \sqrt{2} \cos\pi/8$ and $b = \sqrt{2} \cos 3\pi/8$ while

$$^4F = \frac{1}{2} \begin{bmatrix} 1 & 1 & 1 & 1 \\ 1 & -j & -1 & j \\ 1 & -1 & 1 & -1 \\ 1 & j & -1 & -j \end{bmatrix}$$

Basis vectors for order 8 are shown in Figure 17.6.

Alternatively the discrete Walsh Hadamard transform (DWHT) employs square wave basis vectors of different sequencies, which simplifies the computation to multiplication by only ± 1. The Hadamard transform of order 2 is:

$$^2H = \frac{1}{\sqrt{2}} \begin{bmatrix} 1 & 1 \\ 1 & -1 \end{bmatrix}$$

Higher order matrices are obtained by the recursive rule [Jayant & Noll]

$$^{2N}H = \frac{1}{\sqrt{2}} \begin{bmatrix} ^NH & ^NH \\ ^NH & -^NH \end{bmatrix}$$

thus for order 4 we obtain

$$^4H = \frac{1}{2} \begin{bmatrix} 1 & 1 & 1 & 1 \\ 1 & -1 & 1 & -1 \\ 1 & 1 & -1 & -1 \\ 1 & -1 & -1 & 1 \end{bmatrix}$$

Figure 17.6 showed the basis vectors for ^8H. The correlation functions for the rows (or columns) of a 1 dimensional 8-order Hadamard transform [Grant & Collins] clearly shows the orthogonality in autocorrelation and cross-correlation between these codes.

The Walsh transform differs from the Hadamard transform only in the ordering of the rows. For the sequency ordered Walsh Hadamard 4-order matrix we obtain:

$$^4H = \frac{1}{2} \begin{bmatrix} 1 & 1 & 1 & 1 \\ 1 & 1 & -1 & -1 \\ 1 & -1 & -1 & 1 \\ 1 & -1 & 1 & -1 \end{bmatrix}$$

where sequency is defined as half the number of sign changes in the sequence (i.e. like periods in a sinewave). Figure 17.7 shows the 16 basic images or optical masks for an 4-by-4 DWHT, where $+1$ is represented by white or transmission and -1 by black. Note that the upper right hand mask measures high spatial frequency in the n_1 dimension only, while the lower left mask performs the same measurement in n_2.

In practical systems the transforms which are employed are quite small e.g. 4-by-4 to 16-by-16 and these masks are slid across or convolved with the image and the transformed components are allocated different numbers of bits in the quantiser, depending on the statistics of the image. Using this technique quite acceptable quality picture can be achieved with $\simeq 2$ bits per picture Nyquist sample (pixel or pel) for a DWHT, compared with 8-bit quantisation in direct PCM.

The DFT, DCT and DWHT are all popular as fast algorithms exist already for their implementation [Rao]. Darby reports the application of the DCT to video processing in a military prototype datalink. Here a 16-point one-dimensional DCT or slant transform was applied to the lines of video and DPCM coding was applied between lines, Figure 17.8, to achieve an effective average transmission rate of less than one bit per pel. With reduced frame rate sampling, the low final bit rate of $\simeq 100$kHz was then spread into a wide bandwidth to provide ECCM protection of the video, see later chapter 20.

However, as these are all fixed transforms they are sub-optimal compared to adaptive transform coding techniques such as the Karhunen-Loeve transform (KLT). This eigenvector or Hotelling transform [Jayant & Noll] is defined by the fact that its rows are the eigenvectors of the signal autocorrelation matrix, R_{xx}, chapter 8. It thus has strong similarities with the lattice filters which are used so successfully in LPC vocoders [Jayant & Noll], and it is considered to be one of the best image coding techniques. However in practice it is very similar to the DCT, Figure 17.6 and so this latter transform is often used in practical system implementations.

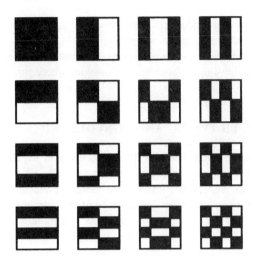

Figure 17.7   Set of 16 basis images or filter masks for calculating a 4-by-4 discrete Walsh transform.

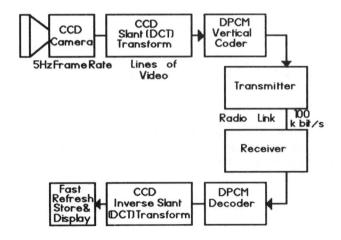

Figure 17.8   Low data rate link using 1-D DCT coding of video line data.

In order to assess the impact of coding on transmission bit rate reduction, [Haskell & Steele] give a summary of a large number of different coding techniques. They provide a good indication of the relative significance in practical systems of transform coding compared to other techniques for video and the simpler facsimile transmission, where run length coding is widely applied.

17.3 TWO-DIMENSIONAL FILTERING AND CONVOLUTION

For multi-dimensional filters the linear-phase FIR filter is the most popular design as it is always stable. In addition with purely real frequency responses there is no distortion to edges and line features in optical, radar and geophysical images. Several methods are available for the filter design. They fall basically into those based on window techniques, transformation from a 1-D into 2-D design and the optimised or minimax design techniques where the magnitude of the peak error is minimised or, for example, by applying a weighted least squares criterion, chapter 7. 2-D window techniques [Huang] commonly require a circularly symmetric filter design where a good 1-D window, such as rectangular, Hanning or Kaiser is rotated about the origin. Of these the Kaiser window, which is based on modified Bessel functions, is the most flexible as the sidelobe level in the stopband is adjustable via the precise detail on the window selected.

The second technique, which is superior to the window approach, transforms a good 1-D filter design into a 2-D filter design. This permits the use of established design techniques such as Chebyshev polynomials to produce equiripple filter designs. This design is generally simple but if there is a narrow transition region in high spatial frequency space then the filter requires an unnecessary high order.

The most powerful techniques, which are widely used today, are the optimised design approaches which offers the smallest passband and stopband deviations from the ideal response. In this approach an error is derived between the actual and ideal responses

$$E(\omega_1,\omega_2) = H(\omega_1,\omega_2) - I(\omega_1,\omega_2)$$

and a function of the error term is minimised to reduce the largest and most significant errors. There have been several distinct approaches such as minimax and weighted least squares design [Harris & Mersereau] which are applicable to simple filters up to 15-by-15 point designs with reasonable computational load.

Figure 17.9 shows the specification and responses for circular symmetric equiripple 5-by-5 and 11-by-11 point FIR filters with ideal frequency response

$$H(\omega_1,\omega_2) = 1 \quad (\omega_1^2 + \omega_2^2) < (0.4\pi)^2$$

$$= 0 \quad (\omega_1^2 + \omega_2^2) > (0.6\pi)^2$$

The unity gain passband is a disc of radius 0.4π and the stopband the exterior of the disc of radius 0.6π [Harris & Mersereau] relative to the sampling rate 2π. The filtering performance of the 11-by-11-point filter is clearly superior with a peak error magnitude of 0.057 for the nominal passband magnitude of unity.

2-D filters can also be realised as symmetric fan filter designs as well as a circularly symmetric design. These filters can in general be implemented by direct convolution

$$y(n_1,n_2) = \sum_{k_1} \sum_{k_2} h(k_1,k_2)\, x(n_1-k_1,n_2-k_2) \qquad (17.6)$$

or by the Fourier transform approach.

$$Y(\omega_1,\omega_2) = H(\omega_1,\omega_2) \cdot X(\omega_1,\omega_2) \qquad (17.7)$$

For small filter kernals e.g., 3-by-3 to 10-by-10 the direct approach is attractive with digital or analogue (CCD) techniques. If the data is held in a buffer memory then it can be fed successively through the 1-D FIR filter structure of Figure 17.10 to accumulate one row of 2-D output data samples. The output data rows then have to be multiplexed with respect to the filter weights to obtain the output data samples for the other rows. If the region of support is rectangular and the filter impulse response symmetrical then a digital implementation of Figure 17.10 can halve the total number of multiply operations. Integrated 2-D digital FIR filters are available which perform 3-by-3 to 8-by-8 convolutions at video rates. (These are a direct development of the general purpose DSP chips discussed in chapter 19).

If the Fourier transform approach is adopted then we experience the block processing problems reported later chapter 19 and require to use overlap-add or overlap-save techniques. It has been suggested [Twogood] that filters with regions of support in the range 30-by-30 to 80-by-80 samples should be implemented with 256-by-256 point block sizes. There are alternative methods to reduce the computational load in multi-dimensional filters [McClennan & Chan, Mersereau]. Figure 17.11 [Dudgeon & Mersereau] compares the computational complexity of direct convolution and row-column FFT decomposition, with the latter becoming attractive at large filter kernals e.g. 16-by-16 point and larger designs. With these available techniques for multi-dimensional transformation and convolution we next look at the functions which are commonly deployed in image processing.

17.4 IMAGE FEATURE ENHANCEMENT AND RESTORATION

Image enhancement comprises a collection of techniques that seek to improve the visual appearance of an image. The contrast in an image can be measured by examining the histogram of the image which plots the cumulative distribution function or the number of pixels containing a specific grey level against the grey level states, Figure 17.12. With this information it is possible to equalise the histogram to optimally use all the grey levels which are available in the display, to provide a contrast enhanced image. Histograms can also be sliced at a desired level to suppress a background for example, or sawtooth scaled to increase

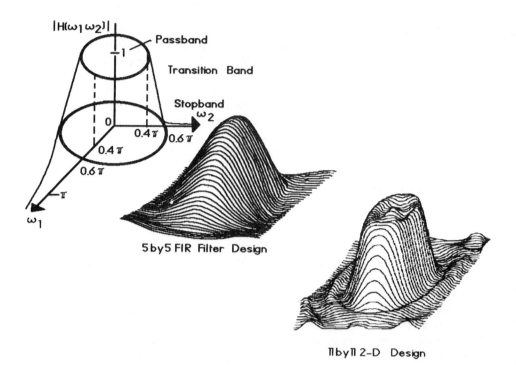

5 by 5 FIR Filter Design

11 by 11 2-D Design

Figure 17.9   Specification and practical responses for 5-by-5 and 11-by-11 low pass equiripple FIR filters.

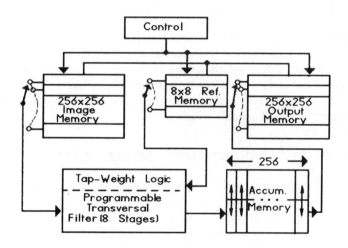

Figure 17.10   2-D FIR filtering via successive 1-D processing.

N	Direct Convolution	FFT Techniques
5	36	46
10	121	46
20	441	46
40	1681	46

Figure 17.11 Multiplications per output point when processing a 1024-by-1024 point image with a $(2N+1)$-by-$(2N+1)$ point FIR filter using direct convolution and FFT techniques.

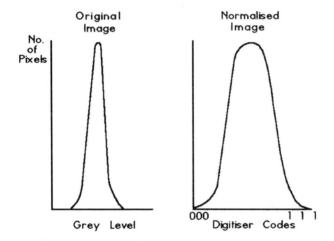

Figure 17.12 Histogram plotting number of pixels for each value of image intensity. Shows example of input and normalised histograms.

the contrast. Histogram measurement is a computationally demanding operation when performed digitally but it can also be implemented with analogue techniques before quantising the image, offering the possibility of more accurately setting the quantiser thresholds.

Noise reduction is possible in images which are subject to impulsive noise. Here a nonlinear median filter technique (rank order filter) is often adopted where an odd number of pixels are examined and the centre pixel value is replaced by the median of the pixel magnitude values in the filter. In comparison to mean filtering, nonlinear median filtering does not destroy the features in the image and it reduces the effect of impulsive noise, Figure 17.13, provided the number of noise samples are less than half the number of samples processed in the median filter. An alternative is to use a low-pass filter such as

$$H = \frac{1}{9}\begin{bmatrix} 1 & 1 & 1 \\ 1 & 1 & 1 \\ 1 & 1 & 1 \end{bmatrix} \text{ or } \frac{1}{10}\begin{bmatrix} 1 & 1 & 1 \\ 1 & 2 & 1 \\ 1 & 1 & 1 \end{bmatrix} \text{ or } \frac{1}{16}\begin{bmatrix} 1 & 2 & 1 \\ 2 & 4 & 2 \\ 1 & 2 & 1 \end{bmatrix} \qquad (17.8)$$

which involve the 3-by-3 linear convolutions which are now available as integrated circuits. Further these masks use power of two filter weights which can be implemented with shift rather than full multiply operations. Low-pass filtering inevitably destroys some of the high spatial frequency information blurring the image. If the SNR is high enough then the edges can also be enhanced by high pass filtering with filter masks such as

$$H = \begin{bmatrix} 0 & -1 & 0 \\ -1 & 5 & -1 \\ 0 & -1 & 0 \end{bmatrix} \text{ or } \begin{bmatrix} -1 & -1 & -1 \\ -1 & 9 & -1 \\ -1 & -1 & -1 \end{bmatrix} \text{ or } \begin{bmatrix} 1 & -2 & 1 \\ -2 & 5 & -2 \\ 1 & -2 & 1 \end{bmatrix} \qquad (17.9)$$

These masks are very similar to the edge detection operations discussed later.

Image restoration covers techniques to reduce distortions due to aliasing errors, pincushion and barrel distortions in the optics. However, the most significant restoration function is the recovery of blurred images due to relative motion of the camera with respect to the subject. There are a variety of techniques such as spatial inverse filters and Wiener filters which can be applied to obtain the desired restored response. You are referred to standard texts [Pratt, Rosenfeld & Kak] for details of these techniques. Other nonlinear processing techniques, such as logarithmic homomorphic filtering, are helpful for separating out multiplicative effects such as the illumination and reflectance or blurring in the original image.

17.5 IMAGE ANALYSIS AND FEATURE EXTRACTION

Machine vision systems [Ballard & Brown] rely on a hierarchy of processing techniques to recognise the objects or patterns which are present in the field of view. Pattern recognition or classification is based on statistically derived parameters [Duda & Hart 1973] and decision theory. We will concentrate here on filtering techniques for feature extraction, which initially look for edges or boundaries in the input scene. These techniques are partitioned into linear and nonlinear approaches.

A widely used linear technique is based on differential operators which are able to detect a step change in image intensity and produce a peak output at this point. Figure 17.14 shows the concept of a simple one dimensional differential or first derivative operator and gives masks for n_1 and n_2 differential detection which are balanced to provide no output on a constant contrast background. For 2-D images these filter masks are extended into the 3-by-3 point compass gradient set of 8 masks for edge detection and classification into 45° rotations, Figure 17.15. Here the edge information is measured between pixels with a 2 pixel separation. Note that south is not the polarity inverse of the north mask due to the balanced set of values used in the centre row. If these were all zero then the north and south would be the polarity inverse of each other. This redundancy is exploited in integrated circuit realisations, Figure 17.16 which perform these operations at 20 MHz video sample rates and include threshold control to output only the significant edge information.

The first derivative is unfortunately sensitive to the polarity of the intensity step. This can be overcome by developing a second derivative mask (formed from the difference of two spatially separated first derivatives, Figure 17.14), which outputs a zero crossing at the detected edge. This can be further extended to the circularly symmetric (isotropic) Laplacian operator which provides for rotation insensitive edge detection. Figure 17.17 also shows three examples of these when implemented as 3-by-3-point masks using power of two weight values [Pratt].

Recently [Marr] has reported how rotation in-sensitive edge detection can be accomplished on images by performing a convolution with two separate two-dimensional Gaussian filters or kernel functions and then taking the arithmetic difference which highlights the edges of objects in the image. Figure 17.18 illustrates this approximation to the Laplacian operator and Figure 17.19 shows how operators of different physical size or extent respond to different spatial frequencies in the image, larger ones detecting the lower spatial frequency components. The difference of Gaussian technique is receiving attention as it can easily be implemented within a CCD imager without requiring a dedicated FIR filter design. This approach is thus considerably simpler than the rotation sensitive operators of Figures 17.14.

Common nonlinear edge detection techniques are the Roberts square root cross operator, [Pratt].

$$g_R(n_1,n_2) = \left([x(n_1,n_2) - x(n_1+1,n_2+1)]^2 + [x(n_1,n_2+1) - x(n_1+1,n_2)]^2 \right)^{0.5} \quad (17.10)$$

Figure 17.20 shows this 2-by-2 filter implementation. He also has a modulus or magnitude operator using similar terms. Another nonlinear technique is the Sobel operator

$$g_S(n_1,n_2) = (A^2 + B^2)^{0.5} \quad (17.11)$$

where

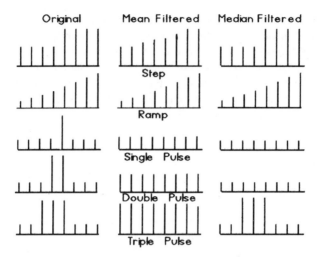

Figure 17.13   Comparison of 1-D linear mean filtering with nonlinear median filtering for impulsive noise reduction.

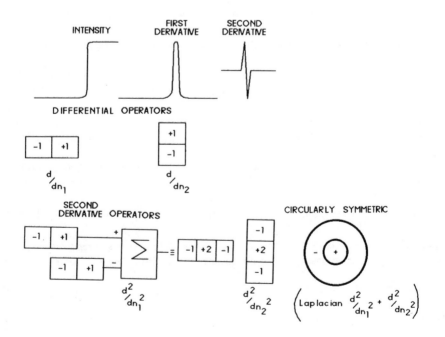

Figure 17.14   Examples of edge detection operators. Second derivatives use zero crossing detection or the rotationally insensitive Laplacian operator.

NORTH	1	1	1
	1	-2	1
	-1	-1	-1
NORTHEAST	1	1	1
	-1	-2	1
	-1	-1	1
EAST	-1	1	1
	-1	-2	1
	-1	1	1
SOUTH	-1	-1	-1
	1	-2	1
	1	1	1
WEST	1	1	-1
	1	-2	-1
	1	1	-1

Figure 17.15   Selection from eight 2-D gradient masks for edge detection.

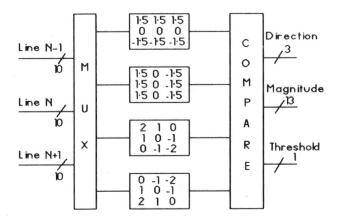

Figure 17.16   2-D integrated edge detector with 45° rotation measurement capability.

```
 0   -1    0
-1    4   -1
 0   -1    0

-1   -1   -1
-1    8   -1
-1   -1   -1

 1   -2    1
-2    4   -2
 1   -2    1
```

Figure 17.17   Examples of 3-by-3 point Laplacian edge detection masks.

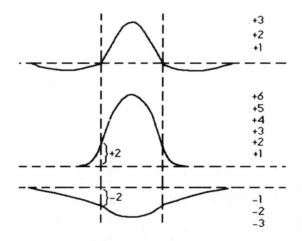

Figure 17.18   Edge detection via a difference of two Gaussian operators.

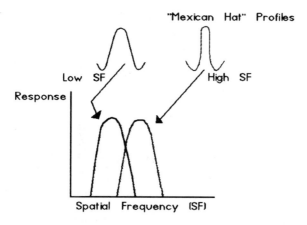

Figure 17.19   Edge operators with their associated spatial frequency.

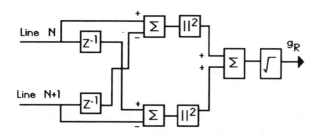

Figure 17.20   Roberts nonlinear square root 2-by-2 cross operator for edge detection.

$$A = x(n_1+1,n_2+1) + 2x(n_1+1,n_2) + x(n_1+1,n_2-1)$$

$$- x(n_1-1,n_2+1) - 2x(n_1-1,n_2) - x(n_1-1,n_2-1)$$

and

$$B = x(n_1-1,n_2+1) + 2x(n_1,n_2+1) + x(n_1+1,n_2+1)$$

$$- x(n_1-1,n_2-1) - 2x(n_1,n_2-1) - x(n_1+1,n_2-1)$$

with the pixels again defined as in Figure 17.1. In comparison with Figure 17.20 the Sobel operator, Figure 17.21, processes over 3-by-3 point convolutions with very similar square and square root spatial functions in the n_1 and n_2 directions. A comprehensive survey of these convolution based edge detection approaches and the edge fitting methods of [Heuckel] is given by [Davis]. At the present time integrated linear filter edge detectors, Figure 17.16, seem to be preferred in practice to nonlinear techniques, and there is further confusion as Sobel name is used as a general edge detection term and is often applied to describe linear operators.

Detection of edges and the current research on texture analysis (for region determination and the generation of artificial texture) form the primary input of machine vision systems. Subsequently similar features in adjacent pixels such as edges or regions are linked together to generate a simplified sketch representing only the significant features of the image. As edge detectors usually provide noisy outputs some of the information inevitably has to be discarded.

If line information is available with good SNR then lines can be collapsed into points by using the Hough transform [Duda & Hart 1972], which maps into a transform domain measuring the angle of the line and the length of its perpendicular intercept to the origin, Figure 17.22. A set of lines with a common intercept provides a parabola in transform space. The Hough transform can also recognise curved features.

However, for machine or computer vision applications [Ballard & Brown] it is normal to attempt to connect the line data to form shapes or symbols and then use artificial intelligence based techniques to detect the features which are present.

17.6 CONCLUSION

This brief summary of image processing and coding techniques has attempted to indicate how the 1-D signal processing techniques of earlier chapters can be extended to process 2-D images and other multi-dimensional signals. It has highlighted the significance of transform coding for transmission bit-rate reduction to fit video data into practical channel bandwidths and shown some of the linear FIR and nonlinear filtering techniques that are applied to better recognise and analyse digitised optical, sonar, seismic and other images. With further analysis over time, between individual image frames we can extend into a third dimension. Thus in the literature 2-D processing is considered as one class within the larger subject of multi-dimensional processing.

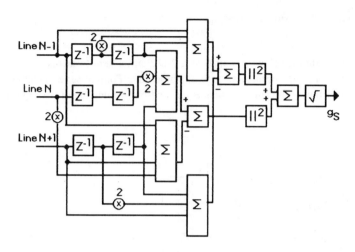

Figure 17.21   Sobel 3-by-3 nonlinear edge detection operator.

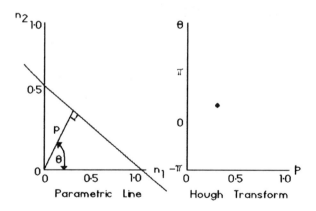

Figure 17.22   Hough transform for line detection.

TUTORIAL Image Processing and Coding

1.   The data field shown below is subject to a 2-D Fourier transform operation. Using 1-D
     Fourier transform of rectangular gate function and Fourier series analysis sketch the
     magnitudes of the significant components for a 64-by-64 sampling of the input data

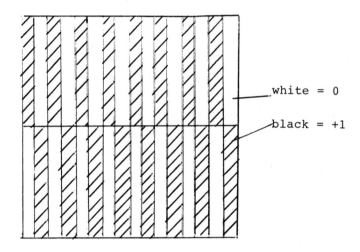

white = 0

black = +1

2.   Compare the results when the data field comprises only 16-by-16 pixels.

Chapter 18
ANALOGUE FILTER DESIGN

18.1 ANALOGUE SAMPLED-DATA SIGNAL PROCESSING

Sampled-data analogue techniques are attractive for realising integrated frequency filters. The most common approach is based on either switched capacitor design techniques or those using charge coupled devices (CCD's).

One possible approach to monolithic filters is to integrate in MOS technology conventional RC active circuits, Figure 18.1, with an operational amplifier. However, this is not attractive to any degree of accuracy, because the absolute value of the resistors cannot be

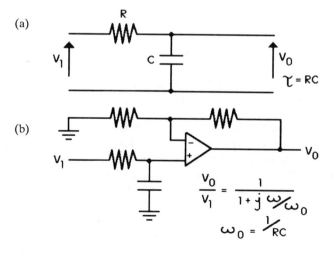

Figure 18.1   Low pass (a) passive and (b) active filters.

well controlled. Further, the device area per resistor would be large because these have to be produced from series combinations of diffusion tracks at about 50Ω per square. Typical variations in an MOS process yield parameter tolerances of the order of ±20%. However, what is significant is that an MOS process can produce close tolerance capacitor values, or even more significantly, precision capacitor ratios (∼ 0.1%) by careful design.

Switched Capacitor Techniques

A circuit that performs the function of a close tolerance series resistor which relies for its operation on capacitor ratios is shown in Figure 18.2(a). The operation of this "resistor" is as follows: the switch is initially in the left-hand position so that the capacitor C is charged to the voltage V_1. The switch is then thrown to the right and the capacitor is discharged to the voltage V_2. The amount of charge which flows into (or from) the capacitor is thus $Q = C(V_2 - V_1)$. If the switch is thrown back and forth every T_C seconds, then the net current flow, i_s, into V_2 will be

$$i_s = \frac{C(V_2 - V_1)}{T_C} \tag{18.1}$$

Thus the size of an equivalent resistor which would perform the same function as this circuit is $R = T_C/C$. The MOS realisation of the circuit is shown in Figure 18.2(a). Two MOSFET's in series are operated as switches which are pulsed with a two-phase non-overlapping clock (ϕ and $\overline{\phi}$) at a frequency f_C. The most important advantage of these switched capacitor resistors is the high accuracy of the RC time constants that can be obtained with their use. If a resistor, simulated by a capacitor C_1 which is switched at a clock rate of f_C, is connected to a capacitor C_2, the resultant time constant of this equivalent RC network, τ_{12}, is approximately

$$\tau_{12} = \frac{C_2}{C_1} \times \frac{1}{f_C} \tag{18.2}$$

For a given clock rate the value of τ_{12} is therefore determined by a ratio of capacitor values which makes it insensitive to processing variations.

The problem of implementing active filters in MOS technology is thus reduced to the question of what kind of active filter should be used. Frequently, the filter configuration chosen is the analogue computer simulation of the equations which describe a passive doubly-terminated RLC ladder. These filters are called "leapfrog" or "active ladder" filters in the active filter circuit literature and are closely related to wave-digital filters in the digital signal processing literature.

The basic building block of these filters is a differential integrator and summer, Figure 18.2(b). Figure 18.2(c) shows the circuit for a 5th order elliptic low-pass switched capacitor filter design. Switched-capacitor filters are obtained commercially with low-pass and bandpass characteristics, and typically one can integrate up to 100 poles of filtering into a single package. As these filters are sampled-data processors, their responses may be shifted with the clock

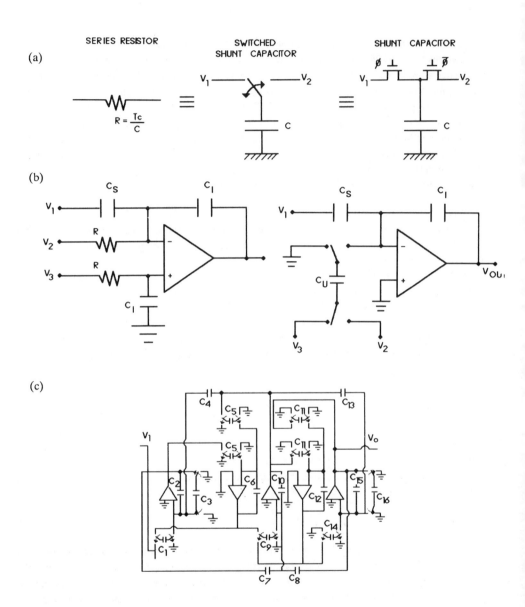

Figure 18.2 Switched capacitor filter principles and circuits: (a) switched capacitor realisation of series resistor; (b) RC integrator/summer design; (c) 5th order elliptic low-pass filter example.

frequency. However, because the simplest design techniques limit filters to low percentage bandwidths (say 3-10% corner frequency in a low-pass design) the maximum upper corner frequencies are typically 50 kHz (whilst clocking at over 1 MHz). Commercially, a series of these filters to Chebyshev and Bessel designs are available [Reticon] which, typically, have SNR values in the passband of over 80 dB, zero-dB insertion loss and can handle maximum peak-to-peak signals of 10V. Figure 18.3 shows a set of bandpass filter responses for different fractional bandwidths. The National Semiconductor MF8 is a second-order bandpass filter with 1.8 MHz gain-bandwidth product. It is a universal switched-capacitor filter design which can realise Butterworth or Chebyshev functions at speech bandwidth. Figure 18.4 shows a typical low-pass Butterworth switched capacitor filter response.

A vital, expanding market has developed for CODEC filters in PCM telephone systems which are fabricated in monolithic form. These require low-pass filtering, typically with several sections having a 5-pole, 4-zero elliptic filter characteristic. They may be realised in either CCD or switched capacitor forms, but in the latter realisation the silicon chip area required is now about half that required for CCD designs. Another key factor is that whereas a CCD normally requires a special double-level polysilicon gate NMOS process. Switched capacitor filters can be fabricated on widely available MOS RAM (random access memory) processes or even run on metal-gate NMOS processes. Therefore, undoubtedly, future solid-state frequency filtering requirements will be met by switched capacitor techniques, although time-domain transversal filtering will continue to be implemented by CCD technology particularly when a linear-phase response is required.

It is well known that microwave filters can be constructed by cascading sections of unequal impedance transmission line, as illustrated diagrammatically in Figure 18.5(a). Wave theory permits these networks to be realised with real resistances at baseband by time delays and adaptors. In Figure 18.5 the transmission delays are all assumed to equal T and the reflections at the discontinuities are modelled by the adaptors, Figure 18.5(b). The adaptors represent the discontinuities between the unit elements and they are designed to implement equations of the form.

$$B_1 = A_2 + \alpha(A_2 - A_1) \tag{18.3}$$

where $\alpha = (R_1 - R_2)/(R_1 + R_2)$ and R_1 and R_2 are the characteristic impedances of the unit elements to be connected; A_1 and A_2 are the incident waves, while B_1 and B_2 are the corresponding reflected waves. Note that $|\alpha| < 1$ for real positive unit element impedances. A corresponding approach to solving equation 18.3 performs the computation by an array of switches, capacitors and buffers. Referring to Figure 18.6, during time slot one (with switches 1 closed) C_1 is used to form the difference between A_1 and A_2 and, subsequently, in a second clock time, charge from C_1 which is now isolated is shared with an uncharged C_2 to produce the α-multiplier. The voltage across C_2 is then added to C_T which is precharged to A_2. The output signal is then fed via a unity-gain buffer to the next adaptor. Notice that in this approach to frequency filtering there is no fundamental requirement for differential-input operational amplifiers, which severely limit the layout area and performance of 'conventional'

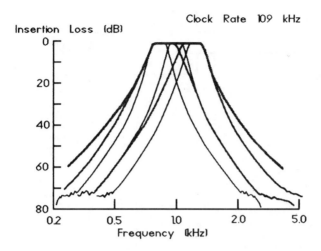

Figure 18.3   1/3, 1/2 and full octave switched capacitor bandpass filters, after Reticon.

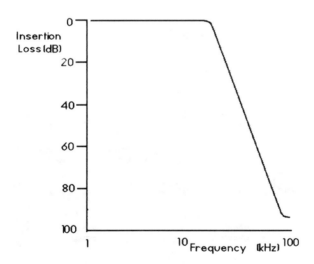

Figure 18.4   Typical low-pass Butterworth switched capacitor filter response.

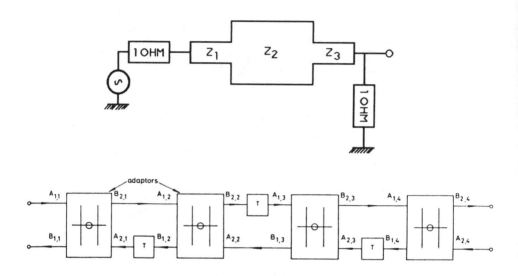

Figure 18.5   3rd order cascaded unit element model and equivalent wave filter structure.

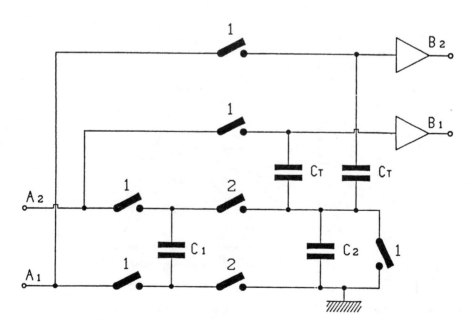

Figure 18.6   Schematic for wave filter adaptor.

switched capacitor designs. Further advantages of this wave filtering technique include: exact characteristic to the Nyquist frequency because the analysis is concise; modest capacitor ratios, 8/1 being typical; and accurate bandpass designs are possible at significant fractions of the clock frequency.

Prototype realisations of wave filters using sampled-data analogue techniques have been reported in the literature. The results show great promise although the dynamic range so far has been limited to about 60 dB, which should be greatly extended in future particularly in view of the potential of digital implementation. Results for a sampled-data analogue chip containing 3rd, 5th and 7th-order Chebyshev low-pass filters are given in Figure 18.7. The results indicate excellent agreement (± 0.1 dB) between theory and design in the filter passbands. Figure 18.8 illustrates a particular significant aspect of wave filters where the passband response is very insensitive to the accuracy of the internal arithmetic. This is the reason why they can be implemented with switched capacitor techniques but, further, wave filters are significant as digital filters as they can outperform IIR designs for the same accuracy or precision of arithmetic.

Charge-Coupled Devices

Charge-coupled devices (CCD's) were introduced in 1970 as a solid-state version of magnetic bubble, storage technology. The CCD is an integrated circuit which is usually fabricated using silicon, LSI MOS processes. Because of this, integrated CCD systems can be produced potentially in large numbers, very cheaply. They operate at low power and, consequently, provide a compact processor for many applications [Benyon & Lamb].

Operationally, information is represented in the CCD shift register by a quantity of electrical charge (minority carriers), as distinct from conventional circuits where current and/or voltage levels are generally employed. These signal charge 'packets' are stored and transferred in clocked, shift-register fashion under an array of closely spaced control electrodes or gates (see Figure 18.9). By applying a succession of carefully overlapped pulsed voltages to the CCD electrodes, a charge packet can be propagated in one direction and can be reversed in direction by readjusting the clocking sequence. The number of gates employed, and the rate with which the potentials on the gate are switched determines the time-bandwidth product and delay time of the CCD.

The maximum amount of signal charge which can be stored under any one electrode is related to the individual electrode area, the clock amplitude and the gate capacitance. For a surface channel device the maximum signal is usually less than 1pC or about 10^6 electrons. The signal-to-noise ratio (SNR), therefore, will be determined by the maximum charge handling capability and the CCD noise. A surface channel device and its associated peripheral circuitry usually has an equivalent noise magnitude of less than 5000 electrons and can be designed to be below 1000 electrons. The SNR for a full well is therefore predicted to be 80 dB, which is often achieved in practice.

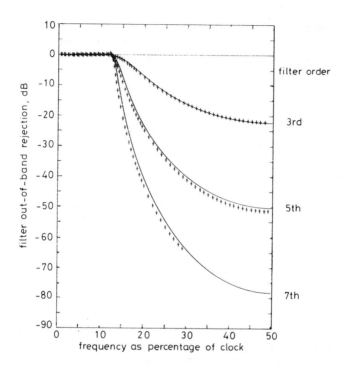

Figure 18.7   3rd, 5th and 7th order Chebychev low-pass wave filter responses.

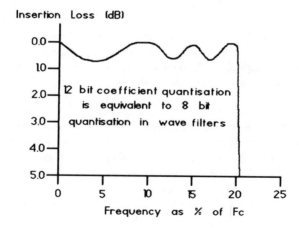

Figure 18.8   Shows relative insensitivity of response to accuracy in wave filter coefficients.

In practical CCD's the charge-transfer process is not perfect and charge may be lost and/or remain behind after each transfer. Fortunately, the efficiency of the charge-transfer can be made very high and, typically, more than 99.99% of any given charge packet is transferred to the next location after each clock phase. An important figure of merit for the CCD is thus the product of the total number of transfers, N, and the inefficiency, E. For analogue operation the NE product may be acceptable up to 0.1. Minimum clock rate is limited by dark current effects.

In a surface-channel CCD thermal diffusion tends to limit the charge-transfer efficiency and produce an increase in its low frequency value in the Megahertz range. In a practical device the 'fast surface states' also affect its high frequency performance. The bulk channel CCD, however, was conceived to reduce the surface state influence by causing the signal charge to be stored beneath the silicon surface, where the surface states no longer dominate the performance, and higher carrier bulk mobilities are obtained. Normal bulk channel CCD's have been operated successfully at data rates above 10 MHz and a variant of the technique called 'peristaltic CCD's' can process signals to above 100 MHz for basic delay line configurations. Although the upper frequency limit of silicon substrate CCD's is predicted to be above 1 GHz the problems of operating the device above 100 MHz, and the strong competition from passive SAW technology currently makes high frequency application very restricted. However, there is interest in high speed gallium arsenide based CCD's which take advantage of the extremely high mobilities of this material.

CCD techniques are used mainly for FIR transversal filter design. Fixed tap weight coefficient filters are frequently realised using the so-called 'split-gate' approach, illustrated in Figure 18.10. The desired impulse response is obtained by dividing one CCD gate per delay line bit in some proportion, which defines the particular impulse response. The two contributions per bit are each summed to a positive, $I+$, and a negative, $I-$, conductor or bus. The difference of the integrated current flow in each of the $I+$ and $I-$ buses yields the required impulse response. This is usually measured using a differential input integrator, configured with a number of operational amplifiers, which can be integrated monolithically with the CCD. CCD transversal filters, which are usually either low-pass or bandpass devices, are normally designed with a cut-off frequency approximately an order of magnitude less than the clock frequency. Figure 18.11 gives results for a CCD transversal filter which has a low-pass filtering shape, with a cut-off frequency at 1 kHz for a clock frequency of 10 kHz. In general, charge transfer inefficiency limits the number of transversal filter stages to $< 10^3$, and thus restricts the parameters of these frequency filters to the bounds shown later in Figure 18.20. Again, as for any sampled-data system, the CCD is programmable, through the clock waveform, and one filter design can be operated over a range of centre frequencies and absolute bandwidths. CCD frequency filters with variable responses may also be realised using programmable transversal filter (PTF) techniques.

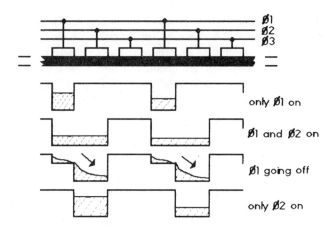

Figure 18.9   CCD electrode and clocking scheme.

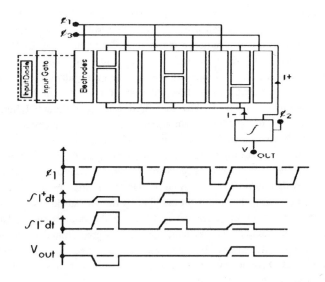

Figure 18.10   CCD transversal filter with split-gate tapping technique.

18.2 CONTINUOUS TIME ANALOGUE FILTERS

An interesting recent development is the continuous time analogue filter, which is realised with transconductance amplifier techniques. Figure 18.12 shows the response for such a 5th order Cauer filter whose cut-off frequency is electronically alterable in the range 10-100 kHz. The key attraction of these filters is that they are not sampled-data designs and hence can be deployed as anti-aliasing filters at the input and output of sampled-data CCD or switched capacitor filters.

Surface Acoustic Wave Devices

Acoustic waves in solids have been known and understood for a considerable period of time. They propagate with a velocity five orders of magnitude slower than electromagnetic waves and for crystalline materials it is possible to achieve low attenuation propagation up to UHF. The interest in surface acoustic waves (SAW) arises predominantly for two reasons. One is the development of the highly efficient interdigital electrode transducer (IDT), for operation on low loss, non-dispersive cuts of piezoelectric substrate materials. The other is the slow acoustic propagation velocity which permits a 3-μs signal, occupying 1 km as an electromagnetic wave, to be compressed into 1 cm on the solid, [Maines and Paige].

The IDT, which is basic to all SAW devices, consists of a set of interleaved metal electrodes, fabricated in a deposited metal film. In the simplest form the overlap and spacing of electrodes is equal and uniform throughout the pattern, as shown in Figure 18.13. Electrical excitation of the transducer produces, through the piezoelectric effect, a strain pattern of periodicity, L, the periodicity of the structure. If the excitation frequency is such that L approximates to the wavelength of the surface wave there is strong coupling and two surface acoustic wave beams of aperture, W, propagate normal to the IDT electrode. Peak output occurs at the synchronous frequency, f_o, where

$$f_o = \frac{v}{\lambda} \qquad (18.4)$$

when v = SAW velocity

λ = SAW wavelength, i.e. IDT periodicity, L, Figure 18.13.

For ST-X quartz substrate material v = 3158 m/s, hence at 100 MHz, λ = 32 μm. Thus the width of the IDT electrode fingers is 8 μm. At acoustic synchronism the stress contributions of the E electrodes in the IDT add in phase, analogous to an end fire array i.e.

$$stress\ output \propto E\ \frac{\sin E\,\pi(f-f_o)}{E\,\pi\,(f-f_o)} \qquad (18.5)$$

which illustrates the frequency selective property of the IDT. Delay lines are fabricated with two transducers, as shown in Figure 18.13, with the undesired signals terminated in acoustic absorbers.

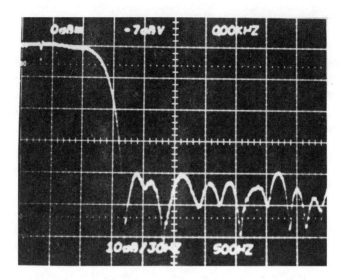

Figure 18.11   CCD low-pass filter frequency response at 10 kHz clock rate.

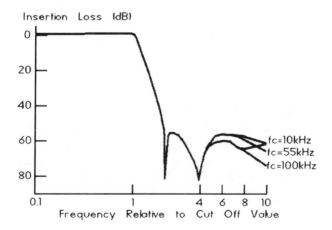

Figure 18.12   5th order Cauer low-pass continuous time filter response, after Wolfson Microelectronics.

The ability to arbitrarily place the IDT electrodes along the SAW propagation path results in these delay lines belonging to the general class of FIR (tapped) transversal filters in which the output is formed by weighting and summing the contributions from each electrode of the IDT. The output signal from such a filter is the convolution of the input signal with the device impulse response. Thus electrically impulsing the IDT shown in Figure 18.13 generates a rectangular shaped pulse of acoustic energy whose centre frequency is defined by the electrode spacing (equation (18.4)). Examination in the frequency domain shows the characteristic $sin(x)/x$ envelope (equation (18.5)) where the 3 dB bandwidth is determined by pulse length (number of electrodes). If, conversely, the IDT electrodes had incorporated amplitude weighting (variation of W) and phase weighting (in the L dimension) to generate in the time domain a $sin(x)/x$ impulse response, then the frequency domain characteristic would ideally exhibit a rectangular shaped response with a flat passband, sharp skirts and good suppression at all other frequencies (Figure 18.14). It is this characteristic of the IDT which forms the basis of the synthesis of SAW frequency filters, Figures 18.15 and 18.16

The attractiveness of SAW devices results predominantly from their ability to realise, with sophisticated computer-aided design (CAD) routines, complex device responses. The compatibility of fabrication with existing microelectronic techniques is also an important advantage. SAW device fabrication involves the evaporation onto a polished piezoelectric substrate of a thin metal film. This is subsequently coated with photoresist, exposed through the chromium mask, developed and etched to yield the IDT pattern. The single mask required for the IDT structure can often be generated directly from the CAD output tapes using standard photoreduction techniques.

Device performance is always constrained by the parameters of the selected piezoelectric substrate material. The commonly used ST-X cut of quartz has a very low temperature coefficient of delay (< 3 ppm/K), but its weak piezoelectric coupling limits the available bandwidth to 5-10%. Consequent delay line insertion loss is typically 10 dB, 6 dB arising directly from the bidirectional nature of the two IDT's. Another significant substrate is the closely coupled lithium niobate which permits the fabrication of delay lines with 8 dB insertion loss and 40% bandwidth. This substrate is less stable as its temperature coefficient of delay is 90 ppm/K. Both these materials can comfortably handle VHF/UHF signals between 10 MHz and 1 GHz. Other substrates of relevance are lithium tantalate, bismuth germanium oxide, PZT ceramics and deposited zinc oxide films.

The acoustic velocity achieved on these substrate materials permits up to 50 μs total delay to be accommodated within a 6" substrate. This, plus the relatively wide bandwidth and the ability to arbitrarily tap and modify the propagating wave, permits the design of many sophisticated devices. Minimum delay is limited by difficulties in isolating input and output matching networks to typically 100-500 ns. The maximum frequency is limited to 1 GHz by the 1 μm resolution restriction of photolithographically controlled etching. This can be overcome by techniques such as electron beam fabrication, or by operating at harmonics of the IDT. However, for operation above 1 GHz the high propagation loss results in low delay line efficiencies limiting filter Q. Low frequency operation is limited to approximately 10 MHz by

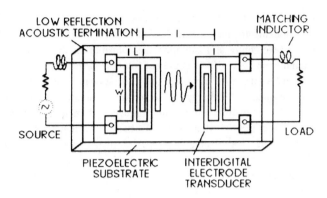

Figure 18.13   SAW delay line schematic.

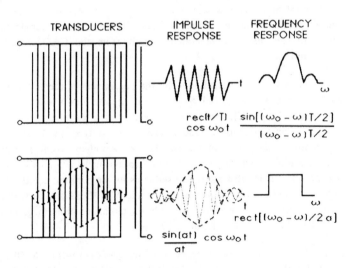

Figure 18.14   Principles of SAW frequency filtering.

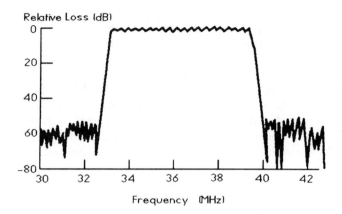

Figure 18.15   High Q SAW bandpass filter, after Signal Technology.

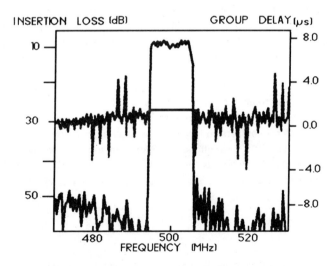

Figure 18.16   UHF SAW bandpass filter illustrating linear group delay response, after RF Monolithics, Dallas, TX.

acoustic diffraction and the substrate width required. For further details in design and operation of SAW devices see [Matthews, Morgan].

SAW Bandpass Filters

Due to the bi-directional transduction in the SAW IDT the minimum matched delay line insertion loss is 6 dB. However, multiphase excitation offers filters with theoretically no loss. With wide fractional bandwidths it is essential to mismatch to avoid the electrical Q restricting the filter bandwidth. Mismatch is also required to suppress the triple-transit response and reduce the amplitude and phase ripples in the passband [Lewis]. The selectivity of a bandpass filter is governed by the transition bandwidth which controls the achievable shape factors. This implies that the low shape factors with steep roll off to the stop band cannot be achieved in filters with extremely narrow passbands. The major sources of undesirable out of band responses are spurious bulk acoustic modes and direct electromagnetic breakthrough. Figure 18.15 shows the typical performance for a SAW low frequency bandpass with very sharp cut-off to the stop bands. Figure 18.16 shows a UHF filter to illustrate the linear group delay property of the SAW complex weighted FIR transversal filter, Figure 18.17. For IF filtering the designable and reproducible performance, coupled with the ability to synthesise independently almost any desired amplitude response whilst not compromising the phase response (group delay linearity) makes the SAW transversal filter very attractive. The SAW transversal filter has made a serious impact on TV IF filtering, Figure 18.18, where packaged and tested devices retail at < £1 each in 100,000 up quantities. At higher frequencies, 500 MHz, both the transversal filter and the low loss, high Q SAW resonator are especially attractive for equipment front-end filtering in TV, mobile radio and satellite communication equipments. The resonator is also important for stabilisation to low noise UHF and L-band oscillators.

The small physical size of the SAW filter make it possible to design contiguous filterbanks for frequency sorting in electronic surveillance receivers. The specification and performance capabilities of SAW transversal bandpass filters are summarised in Figure 18.19 and Table 18.1. Figure 18.20 provides a comparison of all the analogue filter design techniques reported here, as well as digital filters and conventional techniques in terms of bandwidth and centre frequency. A fundamental distinction is that SAW bandpass filters are fixed in centre frequency, bandwidth and delay while a sampled-data filter design is clock programmable, Figure 18.21.

18.3 SUMMARY

There are fundamental differences between the pole modelling switched capacitor filters and the FIR based CCD and SAW devices. In general full digital solutions can always offer superior dynamic range by employing high precision internal arithmetic, but they cannot achieve the high centre frequencies of SAW designs nor the compact size and low power consumption of CCD techniques.

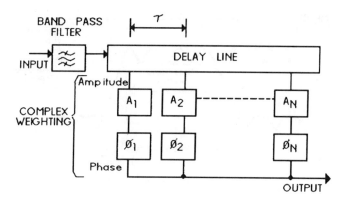

Figure 18.17   SAW complex FIR transversal filter.

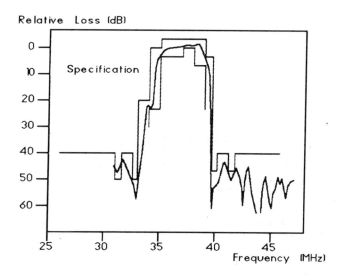

Figure 18.18   SAW PAL TV IF filter frequency specification and typical response.

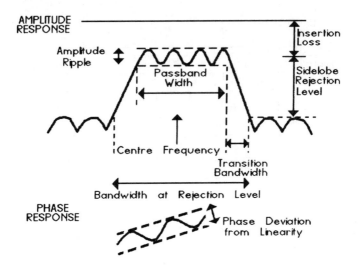

Figure 18.19   SAW bandpass filter specifications.

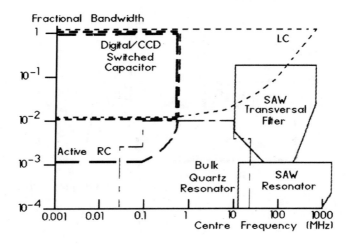

Figure 18.20   Performance bounds for frequency filters.

centre frequency (MHz)	10 - 1500
insertion loss (dB)	> 2.0
fractional bandwidth (%)	< 50
sidelobe rejection (dB)	80
passband width (kHz)	> 100
transition bandwidth (kHz)	> 100
shape factor	> 1.2 : 1
triple transit suppression (dB)	50
inband amplitude ripple (dB)	±0.05
inband phase ripple (° rms)	±0.05

Table 18.1 SAW bandpass filter performance capabilities.

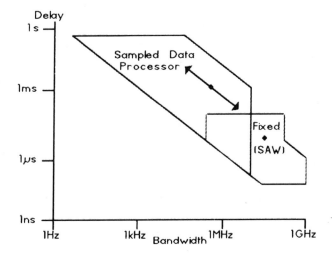

Figure 18.21   Shows how SAW filter performance is fixed while sampled-data processors are clock (and possibly also weight) programmable.

Chapter 19
DIGITAL SIGNAL PROCESSOR DESIGNS

19.1 INTRODUCTION

If one wishes to realise a filtering or Fourier transform function then the available DSP hardware approaches are:

(a)   Dedicated hardware design.

(b)   Standard microprocessors, e.g. Motorola 6809, 68000.

(c)   General purpose DSP microprocessors such as TI TMS 320, NEC 7720, Bell DSP 32.

(d)   Custom designed DSP chips, e.g. TRW TMC 2220, Plessey MS 2014, MEDL 7180.

(e)   Super computer or array processor implementations.

Dedicated hardware designs normally multiplex a few e.g. one or two fixed or floating point parallel multipliers with a shift register or RAM storage of signal sample and weight values. Using this technique one can relatively easily realise a FIR filter, Figure 19.1.

A FIR frequency or matched filter (for an $N = TB$ point correlation) requires N *complex* multiplies and accumulates to be performed each sample period. For speech bandwidth signals this can be accomplished with a single multiplexed high speed 8-16 bit parallel multiplier, as shown in Figure 19.1, in each of the four real (I and Q) processor channels. Such dedicated hardware FIR filters or correlators, i.e. approach (a), can be easily designed with prototype electronics for up to $N = 1,000$ points at sample rates of 10-50 kHz.

19.2 PROGRAMMABLE PROCESSORS

For more sophisticated operations such as DFT, FFT etc. it is attractive to use a microprocessor solution as the desired algorithm operations can be stored within the control microprogram, and they can be easily altered to perform other algorithms, Figure 19.2. Because it lacks a hardware multiplier the standard microprocessor approach is only applicable to low bandwidth processing, e.g. < 1 kHz bandwidth, such as medical applications, Table 19.1.

The next step in complexity is the signal processing microcomputer which incorporates an onboard multiplier. One series of devices which are widely used in the industry are the TMS 320 DSP microprocessors which are specially designed by Texas Instruments for high speed digital applications such as signal processing. The basic TMS 32010 processor is fabricated on a 3μm NMOS process with a total chip area of 45 mm ^{2}. Its most impressive feature is probably the high instruction rate of five million instructions per second. This allows a 16-by-16-bit multiply to be executed in 200 ns and it is this high speed which makes the DSP microprocessor well suited to digital signal processing applications. Later devices in the series are the 32020, CMOS 320C25 and the 320C30 processors.

The high speed of the TMS 320 series has been achieved by means of a single accumulator Harvard-type architecture. This architecture allows a very highly pipelined system and often an instruction is fetched while the previous two instructions are still executing. A strict Harvard architecture has completely separate program memory and data memory, Figure 19.3 and it is this which allows full overlapping of instruction fetch and execution. In the 320 series this architecture has been modified to load both data and program through the same input port and to allow limited transfer between data and program spaces. One use of this is to allow constants to be stored in program memory and then read into data memory thus eliminating the need for a separate coefficient ROM, which could be more limited in terms of size. The disadvantage of infringing the architecture in this manner is a speed penalty. To read and write from the program memory takes three instruction cycles whilst other instructions, excluding branches, take only one cycle. So these transfers should not be used in time critical parts of programs.

Internally the TMS 320 uses two's complement arithmetic and the arithmetic units: the arithmetic logic unit (ALU), the accumulator, the multiplier and the shifters all operate on data in this notation. The ALU operates on a 32 bit data word. It can add, subtract and perform logical operations with the accumulator being both one of the operands and also the result of the operation. Because the accumulator is the destination of all ALU operations it is also 32 bits wide and it is possible to save or load both the high and low order words of the accumulator. In addition, a wide variety of instructions are available to test the accumulator and branch on certain conditions.

The multiplier is a 16-by-16-bit fully parallel design, see later Figure 19.7, with two registers, the T register and the P register. The T register is a 16 bit design which stores the multiplicand and the P register stores the 32 bit product. The multiplier itself occupies a very significant part of the chip area. The TMS 320 RAM can be addressed either directly or indirectly via one of the two auxiliary registers. In direct addressing seven bits of the instruction word are concatenated with the one bit data page pointer to form the eight bit data

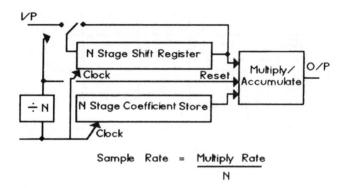

Figure 19.1 Implementation of FIR filter with single high speed multiplier.

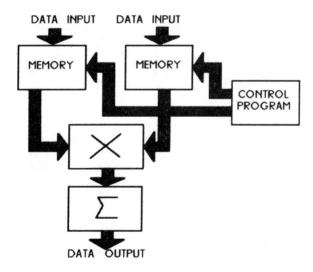

Figure 19.2 General purpose programmable processor.

PROCESSOR	6809 µP	68000 µP	TMS32010 DSP µC
ACCURACY (bits)	8	16	16
MULTIPLY TIME (us)	80	7	0.2
TIME FOR 256 POINT FFT (ms)	700	184	11
BANDWIDTH OF 8TH ORDER FILTER (kHz)	1	10	125

Table 19.1   Comparison of standard microprocessor capabilities for DSP.

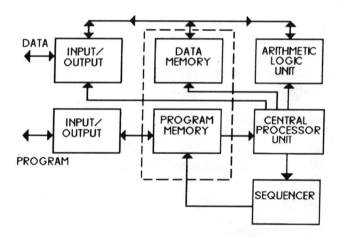

Figure 19.3   Full Harvard processor architecture.

memory address. Later versions of the series have larger amounts of on chip RAM and EPROM making programs simpler and faster to run. In indirect addressing the lower eight bits of an auxiliary register serve as the data memory address. These eight bits can access all 144 words and so no paging is necessary. Although it is possible to use program memory for data storage the difficulty in addressing it and the slow access time make this undesirable if at all possible. Thus the allocation of data memory is particularly important since it affects program structure and execution speed.

In terms of base operating speed or millions of arithmetic operations per second (MOPs) the TMS 320 is very impressive, providing benchmark figures which exceed a number of commercial computers and array processors, Table 19.2. However this is only achieved with limited accuracy 16-by-16-bit fixed-point arithmetic. There are now a number of fixed point DSP microprocessors with 16 to 24-bit precision (e.g. Motorola 56000) and also a move towards floating point 32-bit operation, Table 19.3.

When assessing the performance of these general purpose DSP microprocessors one must be careful in the choice of algorithm. In the TMS 320 multiplications are relatively quick in execution time, compared to other instructions such as branches. So although algorithms such as the FFT are more efficient in terms of multiplications than the direct implementation of a DFT, the FFT is a more complicated algorithm to control, which may well mean that it will execute more slowly. Thus, although the processor capability is 5 million instructions per second (MIPS) when typical algorithms are considered operation rate is typically 3/4 MOPs, Table 19.2. This allows these signal processing microprocessors to be used for real time voice bandwidth (10 kHz) processing. Other microprocessors for signal processing applications have also been developed using bit-slice architecture to implement a sum-of-products computing capability for array processing applications. Their fast speed however incurs more programming problems than are encountered when using the TMS 320 processor. Thus bit-slice approaches such as 2900 series and CMOS ADSP 1400 word slice series from Analog Devices are very fast but also more difficult to programme.

Table 19.4 provides benchmarks for various DSP microprocessors when performing standard FIR and IIR filter and FFT operations. Other significant processors are the array processor boards which operate on the VME bus. These use onboard floating-point array multipliers along with memory and interface controls. Their performance exceeds the DSP chips particularly in data and program storage but at a cost increase of 10 to 100 times.

19.3 FIXED PROCESSOR FUNCTIONS

The general purpose DSP microprocessor capabilities can also be exceeded by the specialised chips of (d) which are less flexible, but they trade this restriction for increased operating speed. Table 19.5 specifies the capabilities of a number of commercial FIR filter chips in terms of their input data, coefficient and accumulated product accuracy as well as sample rate and filter length. They all use the structure of Figure 19.4 in place of the canonical FIR filter form described earlier in chapter 7. These chips are directly applicable to

	MAX THEO	TYPICAL
CRAY-1	8-140	35
ILLIAC IV	40-80	9
AP-120B	6-12	6
CDC7600	5-15	3.3
IBM 370/168	2-4	0.9
TMS 32010	2-5	0.75
VAX 11/780	0.5	0.25

Table 19.2   Throughput rate in MOP's for various computing machines.

Manufacturer	TI	AD	NS	MOTO ROLA	WE/ BELL	NEC
Processor	TMS 32020	ADSP 2100	LM 32900	DSP 56000	DSP 32	77230
Multiplier(bits)	16x16 to32	16x16 to32	16x16 to32	24x24 to56	32bit FL-pt	32bit FL-pt
Clock Cycle /Execution (ns)	200	125	100	97.5	125/ 250	150
Prog.ROM Coeff.ROM Data.RAM	}Ext (4kx16) 544x16	}Ext 16kx16	}Ext	2kx24 512x24 514x24	}512x32 4kx32	2kx32 1kx32 1kx32
Technology	NMOS	1.5µm CMOS		1.5µm CMOS	1.5µm NMOS	1.5µm CMOS
Package /Power	68PGA 1.2W	100PGA .6W	72PGA .5W	88PGA	100PGA 2.7W	68PGA 1.7W

Table 19.3   DSP chip comparisons.

Processor		TI	AD	NS	MOTO ROLA	WE	NEC
		TMS 32020	ADSP 2100	LM 32900	DSP 56000	DSP 32	77230
Function	Unit						
Biquad Filter	μs	2.0	1.0	0.8	0.4	1.5	0.9
32ptFIR	μs	6		3.2	3.2	8	5.25
μ/ALAW	μs	0.4					
64pt COMPLEX FFT	ms	0.4			0.15		0.4
1024pt COMPLEX FFT	ms	14	7.2	13	5	14–20	10.75

Table 19.4   DSP chip performance benchmarks.

DEVICE	TRW TDC 1028	TRW TMC 2243	MEDL MA 7180	LSI L64240	INMOS IMS A100
Number of Taps	8	3	9(3x3)	64(8x8)	32
Input Data Accuracy (bits)	4	10	10	8	16
Tap Weight Accuracy (bits)	4	10	8	8	4–16
Output Signal Accuracy (bits)	13	16	16/22	22	24
Sample Rate (MHz)	20	20	20	20	10–25

Table 19.5   Examples of integrated digital FIR filters.

wideband linear-phase frequency and matched filtering. Table 19.6 compares the capabilities of selected FIR filter chips which possess only a binary $(+1/-1)$ weight capability. These correlator chips, Figure 19.5, which are simpler than the full FIR filter, are well suited to matched filtering of digitally phase-coded signals, see following chapter.

The early TRW 1004 binary-binary correlator, has now been superceded by the TMC 2220, which contains a 4 separate 1-bit 32-tap correlators which can be configured for 4-bit real or 2-bit complex processing at 20 MHz sample rate. MEDL also have a 4-by-1 bit 1½ W 64 stage real correlator (MA 7170) with a 10 MHz sample rate, which is extendable in length by cascading. This device performs its processing in a systolic array of individual processing elements, Figure 19.6, which are fed with time skewed data and correlator weight values [McCabe]. Here the latch functions are indicated by the dots in the correlator cell detail.

All these signal processing structures discussed so far have used array multipliers which operate with parallel arithmetic on N-bit wide data words. Figure 19.7 shows the design of such a 4-by-4 multiplier where an array of single bit full adders are deployed, along with carry save addition to implement the parallel arithmetic function. These 16-by-16 multipliers occupy a significant portion of the chip area in a DSP microprocessor and Table 19.5 showed that with simpler 8-by-8 or 8-by-10 multiplier designs we can only achieve a limited number of FIR filter stages per chip.

This constraint is alleviated by moving to serial-parallel arithmetic, Figure 19.8, where serial data is clocked past the parallel coefficient values [Denyer & Renshaw]. Further pipelining techniques can be incorporated to break the lower adder tree and permit these multipliers to be clocked at a faster data rate. Commercial serial-parallel multipliers do exist (AM 25 LS 14) which offer 8-by-8 multiplication at 2 MHz rate in a 40 MHz clock rate device. One example of a dedicated DSP chip incorporating serial-parallel arithmetic is the Plessey MS 2014 filter and detect (FAD) chip which is a TTL compatible dedicated biquadratic digital filter, Figure 19.9. This chip uses serial-parallel multiplier designs and hence its speed is not as fast as other earlier integrated DSP designs. However it is significant in telephony and more than 1 million are now installed in system and local exchanges as multi-tone signaling receivers. The FAD circuit can be designed as either a high sample rate (64 kbit/s) second-order filter section, Figure 19.9, or a low sample rate multiplexed high-order design [Adams].

Another bit-serial processor is the Inmos IMS A100 which is a 32 stage FIR filter. Input data wordlength is 16-bit and coefficient wordlength is extendible from 4 to 16-bits. This 40 MHz clock rate bit-serial processor gives an input sample rate of 40 MHz divided by the coefficient wordlength. Thus 10 Msamples/s is achievable for 4-bit coefficients and 2.5 M samples/s for 16-bit coefficients, Table 19.5.

Another multiplier implementation is the table look up read only memory (ROM), where all the products are stored in memory. This requires a large ROM for word sizes exceeding 8-bit inputs, and Figure 19.10 depicts one fast implementation which uses standard ROM parts.

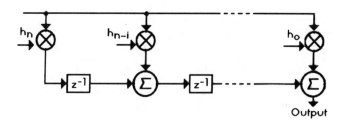

Figure 19.4 Architecture commonly adopted for FIR filters.

DEVICE	TRW 1004	TRW TMC2220	MEDL MA7170
Number of Taps	64	32(x4)	64
Input Data Accuracy (bits)	1	4-real 2-complex	4
Accumulator Accuracy (bits)	analogue	10	16
Sample Rate (MHz)	10	20	10

Table 19.6 Integrated binary correlator examples.

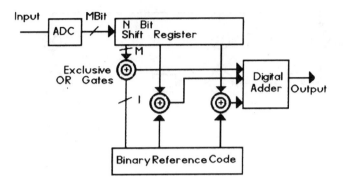

Figure 19.5   Integrated analogue-binary correlators.

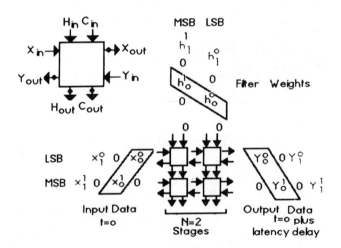

Figure 19.6   Bit-level systolic correlator design, after Marconi Electronic Devices Ltd. (MEDL).

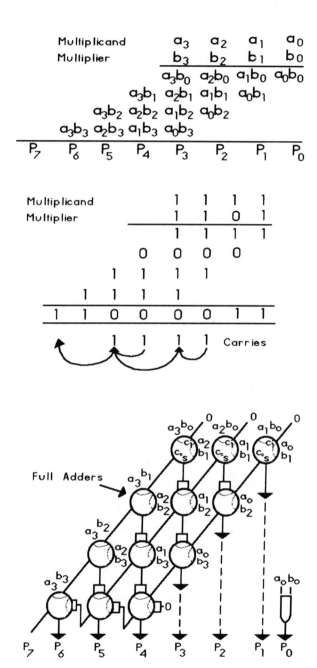

Figure 19.7   Multiplier principles and 4-by-4 adder array (parallel) multiplier hardware.

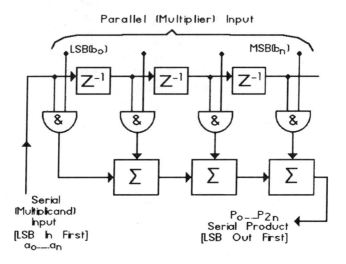

Figure 19.8   Serial-parallel multiplier design.

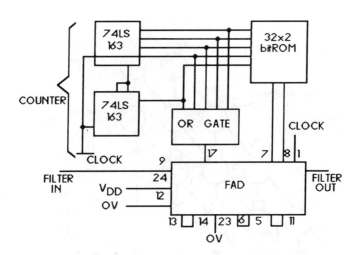

Figure 19.9   High sampling rate second-order integrated filter.

19.4 FFT BASED DIGITAL FILTER APPROACHES

The obvious difficulties in designing high speed FIR based programmable matched filters with adequate time bandwidth product or number of filter points can be overcome by replacing the time domain convolution approach by frequency domain multiplication, Figure 19.11. Although this requires two FFT processors interconnected via a fast digital multiplier and it introduces block processing problems, the FFT's do provide a considerable saving in the overall number of multiplications for the convolution of large time-bandwidth product waveforms. In addition the FFT can be pipelined for faster throughput and it offers the flexibility of more easily incorporating parallel channels to handle Doppler shifts. Hence the importance of FFT processor design extends beyond frequency analysis into frequency and matched filtering.

At present most FFT's are optimised via the sequential machine organisation where a single butterfly element is constructed and it is employed to serially process all the information. For an N-point FFT the data is stored in an N location memory from which sample pairs are extracted, processed in the butterfly, where one sample is multiplied by the appropriate Fourier weight W_N^k before being added to and subtracted from the other sample. Processed samples are then returned to the same memory location. Thus after $N/2$ of such operations the entire memory is updated processing a complete column ready for the next pass. These processors typically use a radix-2 or radix-4 design incorporating fast parallel multipliers. For a 10 MHz radix-2 complex multiply rate and an $N = 1024$ point transform the sample rate is 2 MHz. For a bit-slice based FFT with the same number of points, based on AMD 2900 components sample rate is 1/2 MHz. For higher speeds we must incorporate more than a single hardware multiplier into the processor. As the FFT processor requires $(N/2)\log_2(N)$ butterflies per transform the next processor complexity is the cascade design where one butterfly is incorporated for each column of the processor. This level of complexity is not always necessary as demonstrated by the impressive radix-4 FFT processor design [Swartzlander & Hallnor], which comprises 546 individual circuits, and has a 40 MHz throughout rate for a 4096 point transform. It uses a mix of commercial and semi-custom (gate array) circuits, and is based on 22-bit floating point arithmetic to give a theoretical dynamic range of 476 dB and precision of 96 dB.

FFT butterfly chip designs are thus exceptionally flexible as they can be cascaded or pipelined to realise FFTs of various sizes. Fully integrated DFT chips are presently much more restricted both in speed and in the fact that the transform size is fixed at design and is at present rather small e.g. 32-256 point. However this is likely to improve significantly over the next few years.

Linear and Circular Convolution in FFT Based Digital Filters

When the FFTs of the two sequences are multiplied together and the inverse FFT taken of the product, Figure 19.11, the result is the circular, rather than the customary linear, convolution of the two sequences.

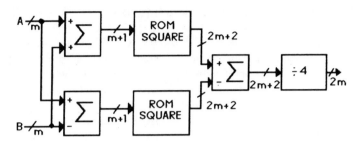

Figure 19.10   Quarter squares algorithm for ROM based multiplication.

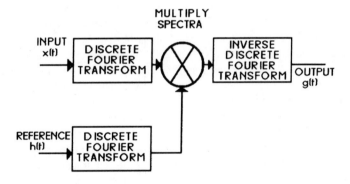

Figure 19.11   Frequency filter based on discrete Fourier transform signal processing.

Figure 19.12 shows in (a) and (b) the convolution of two sequences $x(n)$ and $h(n)$. For each shift, samples of x and h are multiplied point for point, and the M sub-products summed to produce an output sample. Due to the wrap around of h, the circular convolution differs from the linear convolution. However, only one of the output samples, Figure 19.12(a) is the same. Thus circular and linear convolution are different in all but *one* of the output samples. Thus for the arbitrary $h(n)$, each output of the circular convolution is a weighted sum of all M samples of $x(n)$. This problem is alleviated by using larger transforms and padding the data with zeros, Figure 19.13.

The overlap-save method is one way of using FFTs to produce the linear convolution of a long data sequence $x(n)$ with a relatively short sequence $h(n)$. If the short sequence is of length M, then we must choose the FFT size to be $N > M$, and pad $h(n)$ with enough zeros to make it of length N. The sequence $x(n)$ is partitioned into sections of length N, each overlapping the adjacent section by $M-1$ samples. The reason for the overlap will become apparent later. The FFT of one of these sections is computed and multiplied by the FFT of $h(n)$. The inverse FFT of the product is an N-point circular convolution. The last $N-M+1$ samples of the circular convolution are identical to those that would be obtained had we implemented linear convolution. We thus keep these samples and throw away the rest. Since we have produced $N-M+1$ output samples, the sequence $x(n)$ must be shifted by this amount before computing the next block of output. This produces an overlap of $M-1$ samples between successive sections. The normal optimum is the case where $N = 2M$, which achieves 50% overlap in the time domain samples. N-point data sections, $x(n)$, are convolved with M-point weight values (padded with zeros) and only the last M-points from the output section are used to obtain the convolved or filter output, $y(n)$. An alternative technique is overlap - add method where both $x(n)$ and $h(n)$ are padded with zeros and the partial products are added between successive frames to obtain the correct output samples [Clark et al].

19.5 MULTI-FUNCTION PROCESSORS

For radar signal processing it is attractive to consider all the receiver processing functions which must be performed such as Doppler analysis, matched filtering, constant false alarm rate (CFAR) detection, logical comparison, pulse repetition frequency (PRF)/Doppler ambiguity resolution etc. and combines all these into a single programmable processor. Current U.K. effort is being directed towards using an array of processing elements (PE) which incorporate nearest neighbour interconnections with all performing similar instructions on multiple data elements (SIMD machines). This distributed array processor (DAP) architecture, Figure 19.14, [Roberts] is used in ILLIAC 4, ICL/AMT DAP and Goodyear MPP computers and also new integrated processor designs based on transputer arrays, Figure 19.15. These array or vector processors are not optimised for any one processing function, but judged overall they are very efficient at multi-function processing and data re-ordering between functions.

The ICL second generation MSI DAP, Table 19.7 which has been optimised for stand alone operation rather than operating with a host mainframe computer, contains a 64-by-64 array of PE's, each with a 16 kbit RAM store, Figure 19.14. The Mil-DAP version, see Cross,

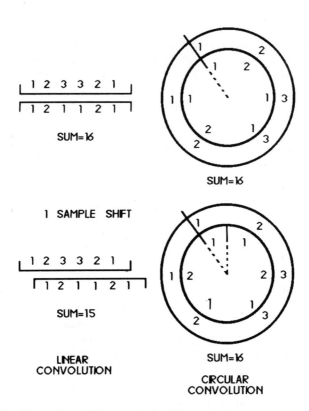

Figure 19.12   Comparison of linear and circular convolution.

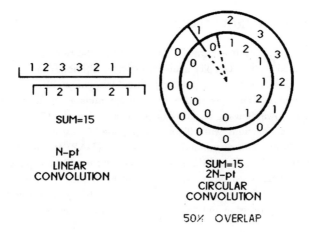

Figure 19.13   Circular convolution with zero padded data.

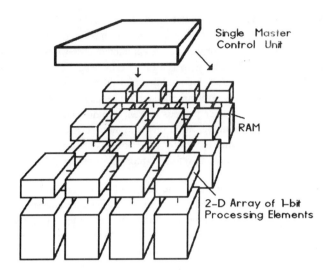

Figure 19.14   ICL/AMT DAP architecture.

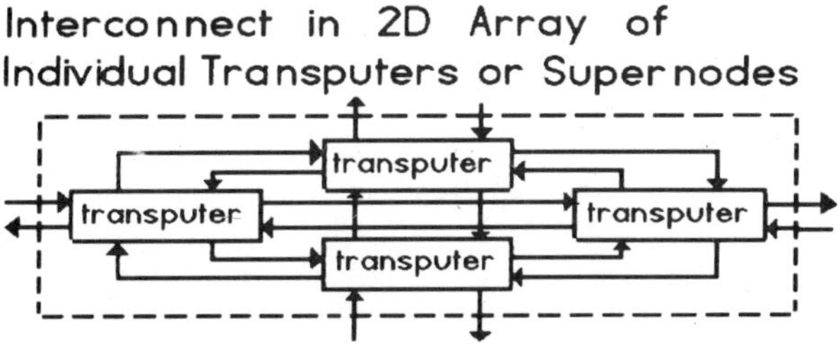

Interconnect in 2D Array of Individual Transputers or Supernodes

Figure 19.15   Transputers for array processor design.

	PE Array	Throughput Rate (MOPS)
DAP	64x64	0.5
MIL DAP	32x32	100-200
AMT 510	32x32	6-400
VLSI DAP		2k-20k

Table 19.7   DAP processor family.

chapter 33 in [Creasey] has a 32-by-32 array of 1-bit PE's, in a 750 W machine which occupies a 2 ATR case. The cycle time or broadcast rate from the master control unit is 145 ns which allows a full medium PRF search algorithm to be completed well within the dwell time of a scanning radar beam. In a 5 PRF radar with 100 range cells per PRF the 10 bit I and Q input data is weighted before 64-point DFTs, log-modulus and CFAR functions are calculated in 8 ms for all the 500 range gates. This gives an effective processing rate of 100-200 MOPs, Table 19.7. The speed of this DAP processor exceeds current commercially available floating point array processors, but the latters accuracy, at 32-bit, is higher. Further speed improvements of 20 to 200 times are expected from the third generation VLSI based DAP. Other DAP equipments are the commercial ones from Active Memory Technology (AMT), Table 19.7.

In addition to these radar applications the Mil-DAP is being used for connected word speaker recognition, image processing and pattern recognition, data encryption and also ESM signal sorting by association and recognition [Roberts]. In the latter application the 1-bit PE's which can be programmed for boolean, floating or fixed point operations give an overall G-bit/s logical comparison rates. Future developments aim to replace the DAP's hybrid PE designs by individual high speed CMOS bit-serial arithmetic integrated circuits. This will give an even more powerful and compact processor design, whose capabilities lie between second and third generation DAPs.

19.6 SUMMARY

This chapter has surveyed the application of various general purpose DSP microprocessors and selected array processors to a variety of programmable signal processing functions. In comparison to the single chip microprocessor solution, enhanced speed or signal bandwidth can be obtained for fixed processor functions, such as FIR filters and analogue-binary correlators, where very impressive rates are obtained from single and multi-chip integrated processor designs.

Chapter 20
CODING AND MATCHED FILTERS
FOR
RADAR AND COMMUNICATIONS

20.1 RADAR

In pulsed radar systems [Cook & Bernfeld] there is a conflicting requirement. Many transmitters are peak power limited and thus a long transmitter pulse duration is favoured to give a high output power and facilitate target detection at distant ranges. However the longer pulse degrades the range resolution of the radar as range resolution is proportional to transmitted signal bandwidth and longer pulses have narrower bandwidth, Figure 20.1. This problem can be overcome by coding the transmitted pulse and employing a matched filter to detect the received echoes, Figure 20.2.

The matched filter detection gives a processing gain or signal to noise ratio (SNR) improvement at the instant of correlation which is equal to the time bandwidth (TB) product of the coded signal.

$$Processing\ Gain\ =\ 10\ \log_{10} TB\ (Waveform\ duration\ \times\ bandwidth\ )\ dB \qquad (20.1)$$

It is this processing gain which is one of the prime attractions of matched filters.

The coding predominantly adopted in radar systems is a linear frequency modulated (FM) or chirp sweep. Here the instantaneous frequency is linearly swept across a bandwidth $B = \Delta f$ Hz during the time of the transmitted pulse, T sec, Figure 20.3. When the transmitted pulse is reflected from a target and detected in a filter, which is matched with an equal but opposite dispersive slope, then the received pulse of duration T sec is compressed by the coded waveform time bandwidth product (TB) into a pulse of $\dfrac{T}{TB} = \dfrac{1}{B}$ sec. Thus the range resolution of the radar is governed by the swept bandwidth Δf Hz, and not the pulse duration. Figure 20.4 shows a set of FM chirp filter responses for signals of different swept bandwidths, relative to the matched filter sample rate. The matched filter outputs the characteristic $sin\,(x\,)/x$ time domain envelope response, which is further modulated in time by the linear frequency sweep i.e. a quadratic phase law. The $sin\,(x\,)/x$ time sidelobes are

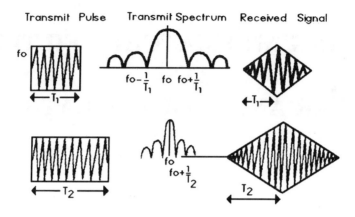

Figure 20.1   Receiver responses for an uncoded pulsed transmission system.

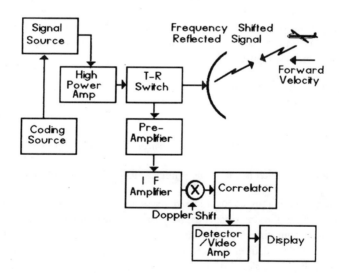

Figure 20.2   Coded waveform radar system.

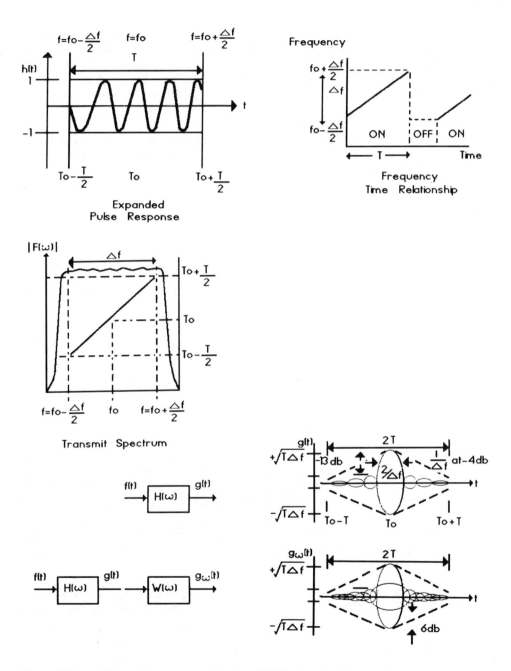

Figure 20.3   Linear frequency modulation (LFM) signals with unweighted and weighted receiver designs and output responses.

undesirable as a small target return, which is close to a large target, can easily be masked by the time sidelobes of the large target. However, as the sidelobes are at different frequencies from the main lobe they can be suppressed by following the pulse compression or matched filter by a separate, specially shaped, bandpass filter, Figure 20.3. Thus weighting techniques, similar to those described in the earlier FIR filters and FFT processor design chapters, are deployed.

For a coded signal waveform $f(t)$ the matched filter function is achieved by correlating the received echo return against a reference waveform $s(t)$, to give correlated output $R_{fs}(\tau)$:-

$$R_{fs}(\tau) = \int_{-\infty}^{\infty} f(t) \, s(t + \tau) \, dt \qquad (20.2)$$

This is achieved by multiplying together the two waveforms and performing the time integration. Two basic realisations of the receiver are possible: the active correlator, Figure 20.5(a) and linear matched filter, Figure 20.5(b). In Figure 20.5(a) an actively generated reference waveform is supplied and one value of the correlation function is calculated for a single relative delay value τ. Figure 20.5(b) employs a FIR filter which implements the convolution of $f(t)$ with the stored weights $h(t)$.

$$g(\tau) = \int_{-\infty}^{\infty} f(t) \, h(\tau - t) \, dt \qquad (20.3)$$

Here the stored weight values, $h(\tau - t)$, are a time reversed replica of the expected coded waveform $f(t)$, Figure 20.6. Thus it displays, in time, a complete set of matched filter output values for all values of τ, Figure 20.5(b). The filter is matched as its frequency response components exactly in amplitude and phase to the received signal.

In a pulsed radar receiver the timing of the received echo is unknown and hence the linear matched filter, Figure 20.5(b) solution, is required. Typical parameters to meet a radar requirements are: $T = 10$ μsec, $B = 10$ MHz with a matched filter whose dynamic range is in excess of 60 dB. Digital matched filters, have been devised and demonstrated. They will require ten 200 stage shift registers operating at 10 megabit rate with multipliers capable of performing a ten stage multiplication in less than 50 ns. At the present time the complexity of this device makes it poor competition for the simple but fixed coded, SAW pulse compression filters.

The main attraction of the SAW pulse compression filter is the ability to accurately phase match an expander and compressor pair. The expander is designed to generate a flat (constant amplitude) chirp for transmission in a limited TWT amplifier while the compressor incorporates the weighting to suppress the time sidelobes to <40dB with respect to the compressed pulse. Figure 20.7 shows the detected output pulse from a SAW pulse compression filter with and without sidelobe weighting. Figure 20.8 shows the typical close in sidelobes at −40dB in a weighted SAW pulse compression filter design. The fact that the compressor spectrum is weighted for sidelobe reduction gives a degradation in system bandwidth or compressed pulse

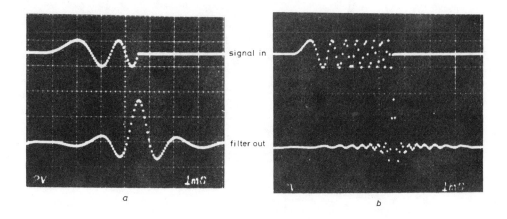

Figure 20.4   Receiver responses for LFM waveforms with swept bandwidths of (a) 1/16 and (b) 1/4 the sample rate.

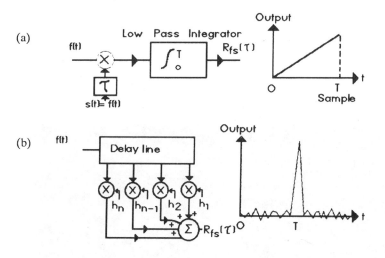

Figure 20.5   Comparison of receiver types: (a) active (time) correlator; (b) matched (FIR) filter.

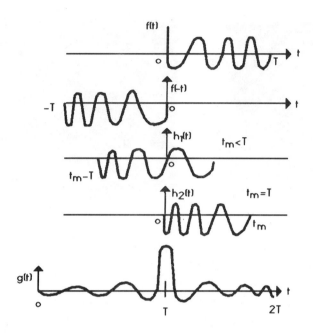

Figure 20.6   Generation of time reversed reference waveform and matched filter output for
the LFM waveform.

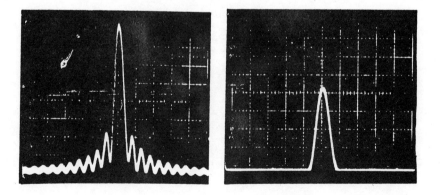

Figure 20.7   Detected output from the LFM pulse compression filter with and without time
sidelobe weighting.

width and hence receiver signal to noise or processing gain, compared to the true matched filter. Figure 20.9 shows how −40 dB sidelobe suppression incurs a 1.25 dB mismatch loss penalty, which is related to the Hamming window figures reported earlier [Butler].

There are cases however, such as airborne radar, where this 25% increase in transmitted power cannot be achieved. Here designers are utilising non-linear FM chirp coding, Figure 20.10, which can easily be implemented with SAW devices. Careful design of the non-linear law is required to retain the low weighted time sidelobes while also maintaining low sensitivity to Doppler. This can now be achieved for 20 kHz shifts equivalent to Mach 1 aircraft whose radars are operating at X band frequencies.

Low TB SAW chirp filters are realised with inline or inclined dispersive IDT's, Figure 20.11. An alternative method of realising SAW chirp filters which is of interest mainly for large TB devices, is the reflective array compressor (RAC) which has two sets of angled grooves, each with graded periodicity, Figure 20.12. The grooves reflect surface waves through $90°$, so that incident waves are reflected twice and reach the output transducer located next to the input transducer. For a particular frequency, reflection occurs mainly where the groove periodicity corresponds to the wavelength. The path length, and hence the delay, is thus a function of frequency. This type of device gives lower second-order effects than the conventional interdigital type, and time-bandwidth products up to 10^4 have been achieved, Table 20.1. Fabrication is more complex than for interdigital devices, so the RAC is normally considered only for large TB products, where the high stability and good aging are not of such primary importance. SAW linear FM pulse compression filters are admirably suited to TB products of a few hundred, currently employed in radar systems.

The maximum pulse length that can be processed by SAW devices is limited by the physical size of the substrate material: the longest reported dispersive delay being 100 μs, using a 300 mm substrate. Dispersion bandwidths 100 kHz to > 500 MHz are possible with SAW devices which normally operate at IF frequencies in the range 10 MHz to 1 GHz, Table 20.1.

For programmable radars, where the transmitted pulse duration and bandwidth is altered on a regular basis the SAW approaches cannot easily be altered for programmable correlation. Although SAW programmable correlator designs do exist in the laboratory and pilot production, they are considerably more sophisticated and expensive than fixed coded filters. Thus a digital solution is preferable but due to the large number of parallel multiplications needed to implement a FIR transversal filter, these take an alternative structure. Systems are normally configured with two back to back FFT's interconnected via a digital multiplier as it is simpler in digital hardware to implement the time domain correlation via a frequency domain multiplication, and further one can exploit the reduced multiplier requirements to the FFT to give a solution which offers an overall saving in hardware, (see chapter 19).

The performance of individual SAW devices is sufficiently accurate to allow the operation of matched pairs in parallel channels. This has potential application in for example adaptive antennas or coherent sidelobe canceller systems where a parallel channel is used for interference cancellation. Matched SAW chirp filters now allow wideband noise cancellation to be

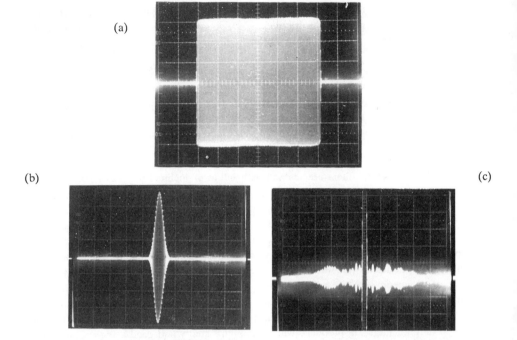

Figure 20.8   Waveforms from a SAW LFM expander - compressor pair: (a) expanded chirp
waveform (horizontal scale: 2 μs/div); (b) compressed pulse from a weighted
pulse compression filter (horizontal scale 0.5 μs/div); (c) amplified version of
(b) to show sidelobe detail (display centre line is equivalent to −40 dB sidelobe
level, horizontal scale 2 μs/div), after Racal-MESL Microwave.

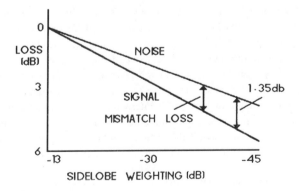

Figure 20.9   SNR loss in weighted matched filter receiver.

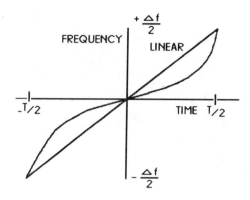

Figure 20.10   Linear and non-linear frequency modulation law.

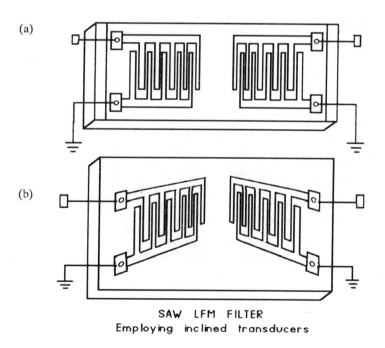

SAW LFM FILTER
Employing inclined transducers

Figure 20.11   SAW LFM (chirp) filter designs: (a) In line IDT; (b) Inclined IDT.

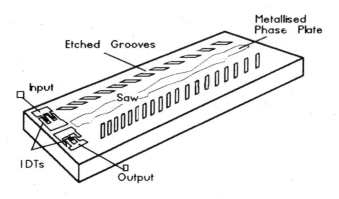

Figure 20.12   Reflective array compressor based chirp filter.

PARAMETER	I D T	R A C
Centre Freq. (MHz)	10-1200	60-1200
Bandwidth (MHz)	1-500	1-500
Dispersion (μs)	0.5-50	1-100
TΔf Product	10-1K	40-16K
Amp Ripple (dB p-p)	0.2	0.5
Phase Error (°rms)	0.5	0.8
Sidelobe Supp (dB)	-48	-35

Table 20.1   Comparison of capabilities of SAW LFM chirp filters.

incorporated along with pulse compression to give an overall processing gain of > 50 dB.

For wideband radar SAW device capabilities cannot exceed 500 MHz bandwidth. Other analogue techniques such as optical or superconductive components are possibilities. Superconductive electromagnetic pulse compression filters have been designed using backward wave couplers implemented on niobium-sapphire stripline substrates [Reliable]. Although they require cryogenic cooling to 4.2 K they do achieve > 1 GHz bandwidth with TB of > 100. Future designs using niobium-tin alloys promise more realistic operation at 10 K which can be achieved with a closed cycle refrigeration system.

Sonar

Systems for detecting underwater targets also utilise chirp modulation, but due to the propagation characteristics of the medium they use much lower frequencies and bandwidths than radar. Sonar frequencies [Dix et al] are typically in the range 2-20 kHz with pulse durations of 10 ms - 1 sec. This results in Doppler shifts being a much larger fraction of the transmitted bandwidth (e.g. up to 2%).

Here the simplified radar narrowband model of Doppler transformation, which assumes that target motion results simply in frequency shift of the received signals, is no longer accurate and the true effect of signal time expansion or compression must be considered. For wideband linear frequency modulated waveforms the Doppler effect produces a mismatch between received signal and matched filter which results in a distortion in the correlation response. For this reason the technique of linear period modulation or hyperbolic frequency modulation has application in sonar. Wideband linear period modulation exhibits a high Doppler tolerance since, here, Doppler produces only a time shift and does not modify the basic hyperbolic frequency law of the waveform. Thus, whereas a Doppler-shifted linear frequency-modulated waveform is mismatched to the receiver, a Doppler-shifted linear period modulation waveform remains matched with only a small amplitude change in the correlation waveform.

At the bandwidth of sonar systems, signals can be processed in either digital hardware, e.g. a microprocessor or in CCD transversal filters. CCD's cannot handle the extremely long (e.g. 1 sec) waveforms but they do provide low power, single chip programmable correlators for coded waveforms with TB's up to 256 and bandwidths up to a few MHz.

20.2 COMMUNICATIONS

Many electronic systems code the transmitted waveform in some manner so that on reception the signal can be more easily detected in the presence of noise and interference without introducing errors. Coding techniques for error detection and correction are well documented in the communications literature, and here we discuss the closely related coding techniques for cryptography and for improved detection by matched filters.

Coding and Cryptography

Cryptography [Beker & Piper] is a secret coding technique which is intelligible only to those possessing the 'key'. Communications security has been of great interest in the military environment for many years. Cryptography is used to prevent the enemy obtaining knowledge of the information contained in a transmission, and to provide authentication of message source and data plus a guarantee of the secrecy of the message. Authentication of the message source ensures that false transmission e.g. spoofing or misrouted traffic, will not be regarded as true information. The security required by a tactical transmission is, typically, that a cryptanalyst cannot decode the message in less than five minutes. A strategic transmission may be required to remain secret for tens of years.

There are two techniques, block ciphers and steam ciphers, for digitally enciphering and deciphering data. Although the data may be digitized speech or digital data from another source, voice communication is the most widely used technique in military applications. In a block cipher the data to be transmitted is partitioned into blocks of characters, say s characters long. These are then put through an algorithm controlled by a key which outputs the cipher text, also in s character long blocks. Deciphering is performed by inserting the cipher text into an algorithm controlled by a key which outputs plain data. The algorithm is termed symmetrical if the same algorithm is used to encrypt and decrypt the information.

The data encryption standard (DES) [Beker & Piper], is a publicly disclosed symmetrical algorithm, where the security of messages is provided by maintaining the secrecy of the key used. This is sponsored by the National Bureau of Standards to give compatibility and standardisation between systems. DES encrypts 64-bit blocks of plain text into 64-bit blocks of cipher text. This is controlled by a 56-bit key which is chosen by the sender with the knowledge of the recipient. This allows one 64-bit block of plain text to be converted into a possible 70 quadrillion versions of 64-bit encrypted text. This algorithm can be efficiently implemented in microprocessors, peripherals and dedicated chips, to perform the required operations.

Stream ciphers on the other hand do not propagate errors, each bit of data is independent of the rest of the message. A stream cipher takes a serial stream of data and modulo 2 adds (exclusive or's) it to a continuous known sequence, controlled by a key and algorithm, to give the cipher text. Periodic pseudo noise (PN) sequences are frequently used for enciphering. These are generated by linear feedback registers, see later Figure 20.17, where the key is controlled by the feedback connection. The sequence generator is required to produce one output bit for each data bit. This means that the period of the sequence, which is determined by the length of the key, must be greater than any message. For a N-bit key, the maximum period before repetition is $K = 2^N - 1$ bits, the true period is often less. It is also important that the number of available keys is large in order to prevent an interceptor from trying all the possible keys. Synchronisation of the code sequence is required to ensure that the message is correctly deciphered. Synchronisation can be performed continuously, by periodic transmission of synchronisation information or by synchronisation at the start of each transmission.

Spread Spectrum Techniques

Uncoded bit matched filters are used extensively in digital communications for optimising the SNR over each bit of data. Coded matched filters are used in another class of communication systems based on spread spectrum wideband modulation techniques, Figure 20.13.

One multiple access techniques widely adopted in communication systems, frequency division multiple access (FDMA), allocates to each subscriber a narrow frequency slot within the available channel. An alternative technique allocates the entire channel bandwidth to a subscriber but constrains him to transmit only regular short bursts of wideband signal (TDMA). Both these accessing techniques are well established for long haul terrestrial and satellite communications as they offer very good utilisation of the available bandwidth.

The inflexibility of these co-ordinated accessing techniques has resulted in the development of new systems based on the unco-ordinated spread spectrum concept [Dixon]. In these systems the bits of slow speed data traffic from each subscriber, are multiplied by a high chip rate spreading code, forcing the narrowband signal to fill the complete channel bandwidth. Spreading ratios, i.e. transmitted (chip) bandwidth to data (bit) bandwidth are typically between 100 and 10,000. Many subscribers can then be accessed by allocating a unique spreading code to each subscriber. The signals may be summed in a repeater to give a flat noise-like spectrum where each individual transmission is hidden in the multiple access interference, Figure 20.13.

In the receiver, detection of the desired signal is achieved by correlation against a local reference code which is identical to the particular spread spectrum coding employed prior to transmission. Matched filter detection gives a processing gain or SNR improvement equal to the spreading ratio.

$$Processing\ Gain\ =\ 10\ \log_{10} \left[\frac{Transmitted\ signal\ bandwidth}{Original\ data\ bandwidth} \right] dB \qquad (20.4)$$

Figure 20.13 shows the receiver implemented with the active correlator, Figure 20.5(a), as the range to the transmitter and hence signal time of arrival is known in advance. With suitable choice of the correlation properties of the spread spectrum codes selected for the different subscribers, the receiver will discriminate against multiple access interference. The effectiveness of wide or narrow band interference is reduced by a factor equal to the receiver processing gain, Figure 20.14, hence the system will operate in hostile environments. Multipath rejection can also be obtained if the differential propagation delay exceeds the chip time of the spreading code.

The requirement for a large number of unique coded waveforms for allocation to the different subscribers means that coding techniques other than linear frequency modulated chirp must be employed. It is common to utilise PN coding and modulate this with either phase shift keying (PSK) or frequency shift keying i.e. frequency hopping of the carrier oscillator, Figure

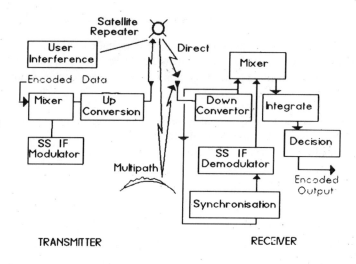

Figure 20.13   Typical spread spectrum system.

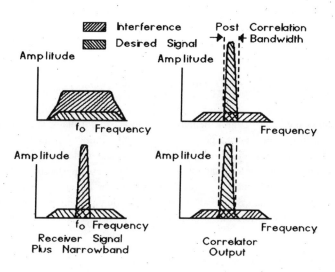

Figure 20.14   Suppression of wide and narrow band interference in a spread spectrum receiver.

20.15. In contrast to the rectangular chirp spectrum the PSK spectrum has a $sin(x)/x$ shape but it again yields a compressed pulse in the matched filter whose width is inversely proportional to the spread bandwidth. With frequency hopping the time on each frequency, T_2, is longer than with PSK and in consequence the spectrum comprises a number of individual $sin(x)/x$ responses. Frequency separation Δf is typically $1/T_2$. The attraction of PN coding is that a large number of codes exist, for any given length, which have low cross correlation properties and hence are suitable for use in multi-subscriber communications, or in spread spectrum navigation (ranging) systems such as NAVSTAR, Figure 20.16.

Digital Coding for Waveform Programmability

Digital phase modulation, with a PN code, Figure 20.17, offers many possible waveform designs for a given code length and bandwidth, and when combined with a programmable receiver can provide a radar system with a pulse to pulse code agility capability [Dixon]. PN codes exhibit very low time sidelobes (1 relative to the autocorrelation peak of amplitude K, where K is the code length) for maximal length periodic or repetitive sequences, Figure 20.18. However in pulsed radar or sonar only a short burst of code is normally transmitted. These systems must therefore use burst or aperiodic transmission of an $K = 2^N - 1$ maximal length PN code and not the continuous coded transmission used in communications and CW radar. This increases the sidelobe amplitude from unity into the range $\sqrt{K}$ to $2\sqrt{K}$ relative to the correlation peak of amplitude K, Figure 20.18. For a single unique code with zero Doppler shift, time sidelobes of slightly less than $\sqrt{K}$ can be achieved, while for the restricted set of codes in a waveform agile radar the peak sidelobes levels are more typically $2\sqrt{K}$.

The key attraction of this set of codes is that this sidelobe level can also be retained for cross-correlation between the different codes. However as the sidelobe level is code length (K) dependent the resulting dynamic range (for sidelobes of amplitude $2\sqrt{K}$) is 15 dB for a $K = 127$ chip code improving to 27 dB for a $K = 2047$ chip code. In an agile radar which selected a different code for each transmitted pulse the return from a follower jammer which incorporates a complete pulse repetition period delay would only appear at the cross correlation sidelobe level giving ECCM protection equivalent to the receiver code limited dynamic range. However these waveforms have two further drawbacks for radar applications. Firstly the sidelobes are randomly distributed across the autocorrelation function, implying that this relatively high level persists over $K = TB$ range gates each side of a return echo correlation peak. In comparison the time sidelobes of the linear FM waveform can be weighted to reduce their magnitude with offset from the compressed pulse peak, giving > 40 dB suppression in adjacent or closely spaced range cells, Figure 20.3.

In addition the radar target and/or platform can be in relative motion and there is often a Doppler frequency shift on the return echo, Figure 20.2. The correlator or matched filter output of equation (20.2) must now be extended into the third dimension or ambiguity surface by introducing the Doppler (ω) return.

(a)   (b)

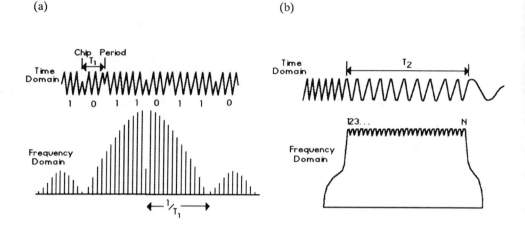

Figure 20.15   Typical spread spectrum modulation techniques: (a) phase shift keying; (b) frequency hopped transmission.

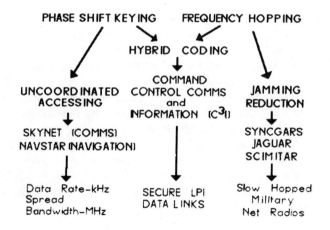

Figure 20.16   Classification of spread spectrum systems.

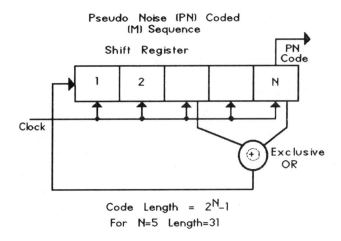

Figure 20.17   Pseudo-noise (PN) code generation.

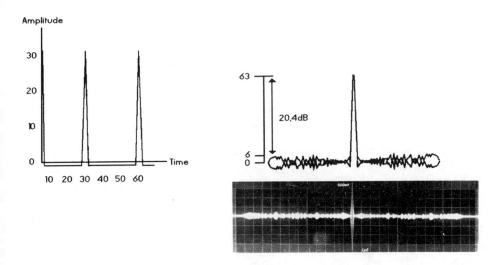

Figure 20.18   Autocorrelation function for 31 chip continuous transmissions. Complex aperiodic responses are obtained from a 63 chip asynchronous SAW PN-PSK matched filter.

$$| \chi_{fs}(\tau,\omega) | = | \int_{-\infty}^{\infty} f(t)\, s(t+\tau)\, cos(\omega t)\, dt | \qquad\qquad (20.5)$$

Examination of the ambiguity response for the LFM chirp waveform, shows that it has a ridge type response, Figure 20.19(a). The Doppler offset introduces a range error and hence range and Doppler information cannot be uniquely measured without ambiguity for this waveform type.

The ambiguity surface of the PN code has a thumbtack response, Figure 20.19(b), in comparison with the linear FM ridge. The small area under the thumbtack response implies that the matched filter output reduces to zero for relatively small Doppler offset of $1/T$, where T is the waveform duration. This allows unambiguous measurement of range and velocity but the Doppler capability is very restricted compared to linear FM. Figure 20.19(c) shows how the low sidelobe performance of the repetitive PN code, Figure 20.18, is only obtained for zero Doppler shift, quickly degrading with Doppler to the burst waveform case.

The codes normally employed in spread spectrum communications are again the PN maximal length (m) sequences used as stream ciphers in cryptography. The difference is that here several chips of fast PN code are multiplied by each data bit. The unique codes selected for use in the direct sequence spread spectrum system are obtained either as disjoint subsequences from very long m sequences, or by adding, with an exclusive or gate, two separate PN sequences to obtain a Gold code. In this latter case subscribers can use different relative delays between two common PN sequences, to obtain codes with auto and cross correlation properties which are appropriate for the unco-ordinated code division multiple access (CDMA) system.

PN coding techniques are also used in spread spectrum navigation (ranging) systems such as NAVSTAR, where the transmitted data comprises precise timing and position information from the satellite. Other codes of significance in spread spectrum are the Barker codes (up to 13 bits long) [Barker] which are used for synchronisation and the Reed-Solomon codes which are used for coding frequency hopped signal transmissions [Reed & Blasbalg].

The alternative to PSK modulation techniques is to alter, hop or shift the transmitter frequency in discrete steps across the spread bandwidth, Figure 20.15. With these frequency hopped (FH) techniques a spread spectrum communication system can be designed, in principle, with any desired number of frequency slots, several hundred being typical. Individual frequencies are selected in the synthesiser by detecting several adjacent chips of code and decoding the word to identify the transmit frequency. Orthogonality between adjacent frequency slots is ensured if the dwell time on each frequency equals the reciprocal of the slot separation. FH offers much flatter transmitted spectrum than PSK, Figure 20.15, and for a given rf bandwidth, the FH dwell time is much longer than the equivalent chip time when PSK techniques are used, which eases synchronisation acquisition in the FH system.

For slow FH systems, such as the Racal Jaguar, Marconi Scimitar and US Syncgars combat net radios, coherence between hops is not required [Pinches & Munday]. In systems

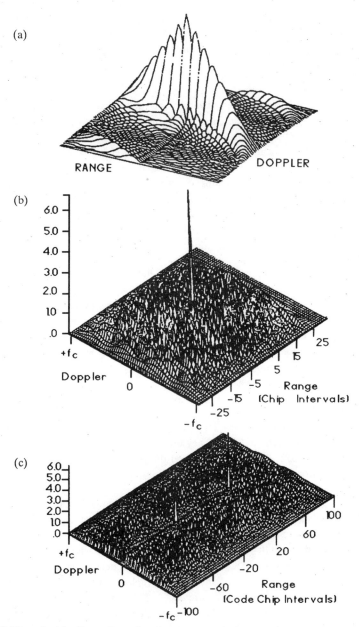

Figure 20.19 Ambiguity surface showing autocorrelation performance of coded waveforms with frequency offset (Doppler) on received signal: (a) linear frequency modulation ($TB = 8$); (b) 31-chip PN sequence; (c) 31-chip periodic PN sequence.

which hop within the bit interval the FH synthesiser must be both fast switched and phase coherent from hop to hop. Other coding techniques are time hopping, and hybrids, e.g. PSK/FH systems, which are applied in secure military data links, Figure 20.16.

Correlators and Matched Filters Receivers

PN coded waveforms can be detected most easily in an active correlator, Figure 20.5(a) but this requires a synchronised reference waveform generator. If synchronisation is not available then this is obtained through serial search techniques where the reference is slid past the received signal in the correlator. Synchronisation time is equal to receiver time uncertainly multiplied by the processing gain. Alternatively a matched filter receiver, Figure 20.5(b), searches simultaneously over all the chips of code in the filter to provide much faster synchronisation. For a PSK or on/off keyed IF signal the matched filter can be realised with the FIR transversal filter. Matching to a biphase coded signal requires each tap to be spaced apart by a delay, T, equal to the modulation (chip) period, with equal amplitude weighting and $+1$, or -1, e.g. 0 or π tap phase weighting.

CCD FIR filters designed for matching to the PN codes used in spread spectrum are implemented with an analogue-binary correlator design. Integrated devices have been realised which can handle up to 512 chip waveforms at 25 MHz rates [Mavor & Grant, Grant & Withers]. These low cost modems do require separate I and Q demodulation, but CCDs have been shown to exhibit only 1 dB degradation from the theoretical peak-to-sidelobe ratio when detecting 512 chip aperiodic coded sequences. The CCD approach also compares most favourably with one-bit and two-bit quantized digital correlators in terms of chip area and power consumption. With the move to smaller semiconductor process geometries several e.g. 4-8 CCD correlators will be designed on a single integrated circuit.

SAW fixed coded matched filters for PN coded waveforms have been designed with tapped delay line structures [Grant 1982]. They offer 10-50 MHz bandwidth and TB products or tap numbers up to $\simeq$ 512. Figure 20.18 showed the IF autocorrelation response for a SAW 127 tap passive asynchronous matched filter.

The digital equivalent of the SAW transversal filter would require the input to be demodulated to baseband in I and Q channels, and 4 real digital tapped delay lines, are required to handle complex input signals. In addition the input must be converted to digital words in an ADC and the shift registers expanded to 8-12 bits width to give the filter an adequate dynamic range. As the PSK reference waveform is demodulated into a bipolar data stream, multipliers are not required and they can be replaced by exclusive or logic gates to complement the outputs when required, Figure 19.5. This realisation is much more complex than the active correlator, Figure 20.5(a), but never the less a number of FIR integrated binary correlations do exist, Table 19.6. True digital matched filter receivers for linear FM waveforms have to adopt the DFT approach, which employs frequency domain multiplication to simplify the overall multiplier requirements, Figure 19.11.

20.3 SUMMARY

Figure 20.20 illustrates the typical arithmetic rates required in military signal processing applications and Table 20.2 compares the performance of the digital and analogue matched filter components described here. It is clear from these figures that analogue techniques can easily outperform digital processors in terms of bandwidth, size, power consumption, etc, but their accuracy is much reduced and, further, the analogue techniques do not usually offer the flexibility or programmability of digital processors.

TUTORIAL Coding and Matched Filters for Radar and Communications

1. A radar system is to be designed with a coded waveform of 1 MHz bandwidth and a pulse length in the range 10 - 64 μs. Given that the recurrent production costs for SAW matched filters are £1k each, and that ADC's with 1 - 2 MHz sample rate are available at £50 each and 16 x 16 bit multipliers are obtainable for £200 each which can multiply and accumulate in 50 ns, calculate (neglecting other costs) the breakpoint in coded waveform time bandwidth product where the SAW matched filter becomes competitive over the digital matched filter approach. *[20]*

2. A TTL 4 bit shift register is connected with feedback from delay stages number 4 and 1 though an exclusive or gate into the shift register input. Show that when switched on with a random pattern of 1's and -1's in the register the clock pulses generate at the 4th delay a maximal length 15-bit pseudo noise sequence. How can one synchronise an oscilloscope to check the generated code? Show that the continuous or periodic autocorrelation response of this sequence is two valued.

3. In comparison with question 2 above show the form of the burst or aperiodic autocorrelation response.

4. Comment on the differences between the autocorrelation responses for the pseudo noise sequence in question above with the aperiodic autocorrelation response for the 13 bit Barker code (+1 +1 +1 +1 +1 −1 −1 +1 +1 −1 +1 −1 +1). Why is the latter preferred for pulsed range detection systems? Given a free space propagation velocity of 300,000 km/s what bit rate would be required for a system ranging accuracy of 100 m? *[3 Mbit/s]*

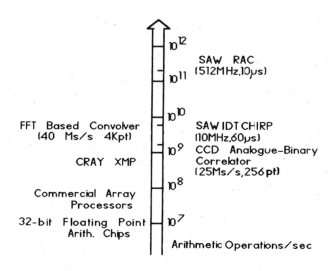

Figure 20.20   Arithmetic requirements for military signal processors.

Functions	RADAR			SONAR	VIDEO
	Sorting	Pulse Comp	MTI Doppler	Spect Anal	2-D FFT
Wordlength (bits)	5–8	8–10	8–12	1–12	8
Signal TΔf	100–500	50–200	100–500	250–1k	200–500
Throughput (MWord/s)	10–50	5–10	1–2	1–2	5–10
Computation Speed (MFLOPS)	2k–8k	1k–2k	50–100	50–100	200–500

Table 20.2   Comparison of computation rates for analogue and digital signal processors.

Appendix

MATRIX THEORY

The purpose of this appendix is to present the basic matrix conventions and operations which are used in this text. Dealing first with column matrices or vectors, we define a vector of order N as a column vector composed of N elements:

$$\underline{x} = \begin{bmatrix} x_o \\ x_1 \\ \cdot \\ \cdot \\ x_{N-1} \end{bmatrix} \tag{A.1}$$

The transpose of this vector is a row vector of order N:

$$\underline{x}^T = [x_o x_1 \cdots x_{N-1}] \tag{A.2}$$

The scalar, inner or dot product of 2 such vectors is given by:

$$\underline{x}^T \underline{y} = \sum_{i=0}^{N-1} x_i y_i = \underline{y}^T \underline{x} \tag{A.3}$$

The vector or outer product of these 2 vectors is given by:

$$\underline{x} \underline{y}^T = \underline{y} \underline{x}^T = \underline{A} \tag{A.4}$$

Where the matrix $\underline{A}$ is an $(N \times N)$ square matrix. In general such an $(N \times N)$ square matrix is defined as follows:

$$\underline{A} = \begin{bmatrix} a_{00} & a_{01} & \cdot\cdot & a_{0,N-1} \\ a_{10} & a_{11} & \cdot\cdot & \cdot \\ \cdot & \cdot & & \cdot \\ \cdot & \cdot & & \cdot \\ a_{0,N-1} & a_{N-1,1} & \cdot\cdot & a_{N-1,N-1} \end{bmatrix} \tag{A.5}$$

Transposition of the matrix A is achieved by reflection about the leading diagonal.

Example A.1

$$A = \begin{bmatrix} a_{00} & a_{01} & a_{02} \\ a_{10} & a_{11} & a_{12} \\ a_{20} & a_{21} & a_{22} \end{bmatrix}$$

$$B = A^T = \begin{bmatrix} a_{00} & a_{10} & a_{20} \\ a_{01} & a_{11} & a_{21} \\ a_{02} & a_{12} & a_{22} \end{bmatrix}$$

The matrix A is termed as symmetric when $A^T = A$. The operation of transposition has the following properties:

$$(A^T)^T = A$$

$$(A + B)^T = A^T + B^T$$

$$(AB)^T = B^T A^T \tag{A.6}$$

Multiplication of 2 square, $(N \times N)$ matrices leads to a product matrix which is also square and $(N \times N)$:

$$C = A B = \sum_{k=0}^{N-1} \begin{bmatrix} (a_{0k} \quad b_{k0}) & (a_{0k} \quad b_{k1}) & (a_{0k} \quad b_{k,N-1}) \\ \cdot & \cdot & \cdot & \cdot & \cdot \\ (a_{N-1,k} \quad b_{k,N-1}) & \cdot & \cdot & (a_{N-1,k} \quad b_{k,N-1}) \end{bmatrix} \tag{A.7}$$

The properties of multiplication are:

$$A B \neq B A$$

$$A B = A C \text{ does not imply } B = C$$

$$A (B C) = (A B) C$$

$$A (B + C) = A B + A C \tag{A.8}$$

Every square matrix A has associated with it a determinant which is a scalar defined as $|A|$. It is defined as the sum of the products of the elements in any row or column of A with the respective cofactors c_{ij} of that element a_{ij}. The cofactor, c_{ij}, is defined as $(-1)^{i+j} m_{ij}$ where m_{ij} is the determinant of the $(N-1) \times (N-1)$ matrix formed by removing the ith row and jth column of A. The properties of the determinant of A are

$$|A| = 0 \text{ if one row is zero or 2 rows are identical}$$

$$|\underline{A}\ \underline{B}| = |\underline{A}|\ |\underline{B}|$$

$$|\underline{A}^{-1}| = |\underline{A}|^{-1} \tag{A.9}$$

Example A.2

$$\underline{B} = \begin{bmatrix} 3 & 1 & 0 \\ -1 & 2 & 4 \\ 5 & 6 & -2 \end{bmatrix}$$

$$|\underline{B}| = 3\,(-28)\,-1\,(-18)\,+\,0.0$$

$$= -66$$

The inverse of a matrix $\underline{A}$ is defined by:

$$\underline{A}^{-1}\,\underline{A} = \underline{A}\,\underline{A}^{-1} = \underline{I} \tag{A.10}$$

where

$$\underline{I} = \begin{bmatrix} 1 & 0 & 0 & 0 \\ 0 & 1 & 0 & 0 \\ 0 & 0 & 1 & 0 \\ 0 & 0 & 0 & 1 \end{bmatrix}$$

is the identity matrix.

$$\underline{A}^{-1} = \frac{1}{|\underline{A}|}\, adj\,(\underline{A}) \tag{A.11}$$

where $adj\,(\underline{A})$ is the adjoint matrix of $\underline{A}$ and is the transpose of the matrix of the cofactors of $\underline{A}$. The properties of the inverse are:

$$(\underline{A}^{-1})^{-1} = \underline{A}$$

$$(\underline{A}\ \underline{B})^{-1} = \underline{B}^{-1}\,\underline{A}^{-1}$$

$$(\underline{A}^{-1})^T = (\underline{A}^T)^{-1} \tag{A.12}$$

For a square matrix $\underline{A}$ a non zero vector $\underline{a}$ is an eigenvector if a scalar λ exists such that:

$$\underline{A}\,\underline{a} = \lambda\,\underline{a}$$

$$(\underline{A} - \lambda\,\underline{I})\,\underline{a} = 0 \tag{A.13}$$

where λ is an eigenvalue of $\underline{A}$. Equation A.13 yields a non-trivial eigenvector only if:

$$|\underline{A} - \lambda\,\underline{I}| = 0 \tag{A.14}$$

This is the so-called characteristic equation for A and its roots are the eigenvalues of A. The properties of eigenvalues are:

$$|A| = \prod_{i=0}^{N-1} \lambda_i$$

$$trace\ (A) = \sum_{i=0}^{N-1} \lambda_i \qquad\qquad (A.15)$$

More details on matrix theory can be found in texts such as [Broyden].

REFERENCES

Adams, P.F., et al, "A MOS Integrated Circuit for Digital Filtering and Level Detection", IEEE Journal SC-16, No.3, pp.183-190, June 1981.

Assefi, T., 'Stochastic Processes and Estimation Theory with Applications', Wiley, New York, 1979.

Ballard, D.H. and Brown, C.M., 'Computer Vision', Prentice Hall, Englewood Cliffs, NJ, 1982.

Barker, R.H., "Group Synchronisation of Binary Digital Systems" in W. Jackson (ed.), 'Communication Theory', Academic Press, London, 1953.

Beker, H. and Piper, F., 'Cypher Systems for the Protection of Communications', Wiley, London, 1982.

Bellanger, M., 'Digital Processing of Signals', Wiley, New York, 1984.

Beynon, J.D.E. and Lamb, D.R., 'Charge-Coupled Devices and their Applications', McGraw-Hill, London, 1980.

Blahut, R.E., 'Theory and Practice of Error Control Codes', Addison-Wesley, Reading, MA, 1983.

Bode, H.W. and Shannon, C.E., "A Simplified Derivation of Linear Least Square Smoothing and Prediction Theory", Proc. IRE, Vol.38, No. 4, pp.417-425, 1950.

Bozic, S.M., 'Digital and Kalman Filtering', Edward Arnold, London, 1979.

Bracewell, R., 'The Fourier Transform and its Applications', McGraw Hill, New York, 1965.

Brigham, E.O., 'The Fast Fourier Transform', Prentice Hall, Englewood Cliffs, NJ, 1974.

Broyden, C.G., 'Basic Matrices' McMillan Press, UK, 1975.

Butler, M.B.N., "Radar Applications of SAW Dispersive Filters", IEE Proc., Vol.127, Part F, No.2, pp.118-124, April 1980.

Candy, J.V., 'Signal Processing - The Model Based Approach', McGraw-Hill New York, 1986.

Childers, D.G., et al, "The Cepstrum", Proc. IEEE, Vol. 65, No.10, pp.1428-1443, October, 1977.

Clark, G.A., Parker, S.R. and Mitra, S.K., "A Unified Approach to Time- and Frequency-Domain Adaptive Digital Filters", IEEE Trans. ASSP-31, No.5, pp.1073-1083, October 1983.

Clark, G.C. and Cain, J.B., 'Error-correction Coding for Digital Communications' Plenum Press, New York, 1981.

Cook, C.E. and Bernfeld, M., 'Radar Signals', Academic Press, New York, 1967.

Cooley, J.W. and Tukey, J.W., "The Fast Fourier Transform Algorithm ..." in Rabiner, L.R. and Rader, C.M. (ed.) 'Digital Signal Processing', pp.271-293, IEEE Press 1972.

Cowan, C.F.N. and Grant, P.M., 'Adaptive Filters', Prentice Hall, Englewood Cliffs, NJ, 1985.

Creasey, D.J. (ed.), 'Advanced Signal Processing in Radar, Sonar and Communications', Peter Peregrinus, London, 1985.

Darby, B.J., et al, "ECCM Protection of Video Data Links", AGARD Symposium on Guidance and Control of RPV's, Paper 4.4, Florence 1976.

Davis, L.S., "A Survey of Edge Detection Techniques", Computer Graphics & Image Proc., Vol.4, pp.248-270, 1975.

Denyer, P.B. and Renshaw, D., 'VLSI Signal Processing: a Bit-Serial Approach', Kluwer Academic, Norwood, MA, 1985.

Dix, J. et al, "Applications of CCD's in Sonar Systems", IEE Proc. Vol. 127, Part F, No.2, pp.125-131, April 1980.

Dixon, R.C., 'Spread Spectrum Systems', Wiley, New York, 1977.

Duda, R.O. and Hart, P.E., "Use of the Hough Transform to Detect Lines and Curves in Pictures", Comm., ACM, Vol.15, p.11, January 1972.

Duda, R.O. and Hart, P.E., 'Pattern Classification and Scene Analysis', Wiley, New York, 1973.

Dudgeon, D.E. and Mersereau, R.M., 'Multidimensional Signal Processing', Prentice Hall, Englewood Cliffs NJ, 1985.

Dudley, W.W., "The Vocoder", Bell Labs., Record, 1939, Vol.17, pp.122-126, 1939.

Gordon, B.M., "Linear Electronic Analog of Digital Conversion ... IEEE Trans. CAS-25, No. 7, p. 391, July, 1978.

Grant, P.M. and Withers, R.S., "Recent Advances in Analog Signal Processing", IEEE Trans. AES Vol. 25, No... 1989.

Grant, P.M. and Collins, J.H., "Synchronisation Acquisition and Data Transfer in a SAW PAMF", Electronics Letters, Vol. 18, No. 12, pp.299-301, May 1972.

Grant, P.M., "The Potential Application of Analogue Matched and Adaptive Filters in Spread Spectrum Communications", Radio and Electronic Engineer, Vol.52, No.5, pp.246-258, May 1982.

Gray, A.H. and Markel, J.D., 'Linear Prediction of Speech', Springer-Verlag, Berlin, 1976.

Hamming, R.W., 'Digital Filters', Prentice Hall, Englewood Cliffs NJ, 1983.

Haykin, S.S., 'Adaptive Filter Theory', Prentice Hall, Englewood Cliffs, NJ, 1986.

Harris, D.B. and Mersereau, R.M., "A Comparison of Algorithms for Minimax Design of 2-D Linear Phase FIR Digital Filters", IEEE Trans. ASSP-25, No.6, pp.492-500, December 1977.

Harris, F.J., "On the Use of Windows for Harmonic Analysis with the Discrete Fourier Transform", Proc. IEEE, Vol.66, No.1, pp.51-83, January 1978.

Haskell, B.G. and Steele, R., "Speech and Video Bit Rate Reduction", IERE Conf. Proc. No.49, pp. 395-412, April 1981.

Heuckel, M.H., "An Operator Which Detects Edges in Digitized Pictures", J. ACM, Vol. 18, p.120, February 1975.

Hill, R., 'A First Course in Coding Theory', Clarendon Press, Oxford, 1986.

Holmes, J.N., "The JSRU Channel Vocoder", IEE Proc. Vol.127, Part F, No. 1, pp.53-60, January 1980.

Honig, M.L. and Messerschnmitt, D.G., 'Adaptive Filters: Structures, Algorithms and Applications', Kluwer Academic, Norwood, MA, 1984.

Huang, T.S., 'Two-Dimensional Digital Signal Processing', Springer-Verlag, Berlin, 1981.

Jackson, L.B., 'Digital Filters and Signal Processing', Kluwer 1989, (second edition).

Jayant, N.S. and Noll, P., 'Digital Coding of Waveforms', Prentice-Hall, Englewood Cliffs, NJ, 1984.

Johnson, D.E., Johnson, J.R. and Moore, H.P., 'A Handbook of Active Filters', Prentice Hall, Englewood Cliffs, NJ, 1980.

Kalman, R.E., "A New Approach to Linear Filtering and Prediction Problems", Trans. ASME, Journal J. of Basic Engineering, pp.35-45, March 1960.

Kalman, R.E., and Bucy, R.S., "New Results in Linear Filtering and prediction", Trans. ASME Journal of Basic Engineering, pp. 95-108, March, 1961.

Kay, S.M., 'Modern Spectral Estimation', Prentice Hall, Englewood Cliffs, NJ, 1988.

Kuo, F.F., 'Network Analysis and Synthesis', Wiley, New York, 1966.

Lathi, B.P., 'Modern Digital and Analog Communication Systems', Holt Reinhart and Winston, New York, 1983.

Lawrence, R.E. and Kaufman, H., "The Kalman Filter for the Equalisation of a Digital

Communications Channel", IEEE Trans. COM-19, No. 12, pp.1137-1141, December 1971.

Lewis, B.L., Kretschmer, F.F. and Shelton, W.W., "Aspects of Radar Signal Processing", Artech House, Denham, MA, 1986.

Lewis, M.F. et al, "Recent Developments in SAW Devices", IEE Proc., Vol.131, Part A, No.4, pp.186-215, June 1984.

McCabe, M.M., et al, "New Algorithms and Architectures for VLSI", GEC Journal of Science and Technology, Vol. 48, No.2, pp.68-71, 1982.

McClellan, J.H. and Chan, D.S.C., "A 2-D Filter Structure Derived from the Chebyshev Recursion" IEEE Trans. CAS-24, No.7, pp.372-378, July 1977.

McClellan, J.H. and Rader, C.M., 'Number Theory in Digital Signal Processing', Prentice Hall, Englewood Cliffs, NJ, 1979.

McClellan, J.H. and Parks, T.W., "A Unified Approach to the Design of Optimum FIR Linear Phase Digital Filters", IEEE Trans. CT-20, No. 6, pp.697-701, November 1973.

McClellan, J.H. et al, "FIR Linear Phase Filter Design Program", in 'Programs for Digital Signal Processing', IEEE Press, New York, 1979.

McInnes, F. and Jack, M.A., 'Automatic Speech Recognition using Word Reference Patterns', Chapter 1 in Jack, M.A. and Lavor, J., 'Aspects of Speech Technology', Edinburgh University Press, 1988.

MacWilliams, F.J. and Sloane, N.J.A., 'The Theory of Error Correcting Codes', North Holland, Amsterdam, 1977.

Marr, D., 'Vision', Freeman, San Fransisco, 1982.

Makhoul, J., "Linear Prediction : A Tutorial Review", Proc. IEEE, Vol.63, No.4, pp.561-580, April 1975.

Marple, S.L., 'Digital Spectral Analysis', Prentice Hall, Englewood Cliffs, NJ, 1987.

Matthews, H., 'Surface Wave Filters', Design Construction and use, Wiley, New York, 1977.

Mavor, J. and Grant, P.M., "Operating Principles and Recent Developments in Analogue and Digital Signal Processing Hardware" IEE Proc., Vol. 134, Part F, No. 4, pp. 305-334, July 1987.

Mersereau, R.M., "Two-Dimensional Nonrecursive Filter Design", in Huang, T.S., (ed), 'Two-Dimensional Digital Signal Processing', Springer-Verlag, Berlin, 1981.

Oppenheim, A.V., 'Applications of Digital Signal Processing', Prentice Hall, Englewood Cliffs, NJ, 1978

Oppenheim, A.V., Willsky, A.S. and Young, I.T., 'Signals and Systems', Prentice Hall, Englewood Cliffs, NJ, 1983.

Parks, T.W. and McClellan, J.H., "Chebychev Approximation for Nonrecursive Digital Filters", IEEE Trans. CT-19, No. 2, pp.184-194, March 1972.

Peled, A. and Liu, B., 'Digital Signal Processing : Theory Design and Implementation', John Wiley, New York, 1976.

Pinches, M.C. and Munday, P.J., "Jaguar-V Frequency Hopping Radio", IEE Proc., Vol. 129, Part F, No.3, pp.213-222, June 1982.

Pratt, W.K., 'Digital Image Processing', Wiley, New York, 1978.

Rabiner, L.R., and Gold, B., 'Theory and Application of Digital Signal Processing', Prentice Hall, Englewood Cliffs, NJ, 1975.

Rao, K.R., (ed), 'Discrete Transforms and their Applications', Van Nostrand Rienhold, New York, 1985.

Reed, I.S. and Blasbalg, H., "Multipath Tolerant Ranging and Data Transfer Techniques for Air-Ground and Ground-Air Links", Proc. IEEE, Vol. 58, No. 3, pp.422-429, March 1970.

Reticon Corp. Sunnyvale, C.A.

Rice, S.O., "Mathematical Analysis of Random Noise (1)", Bell System Tech. Journal, Vol.23, pp.282-333, July 1944, see below.

Rice, S.O., "Mathematical Analysis of Random Noise (2)", Bell System Tech. Journal, Vol.24, pp.96-157, January 1945. or see:-

Wax, N., 'Selected Papers on Noise and Stochastic Processes', [Reprints of Rice Papers], Dover, New York, 1954.

Roberts, J.B.G. et al, "Signal Processing Applications of a Distributed Array Processor", IEE Proc., Vol.131, Part F, No.6, pp.603-609, October 1984.

Rosenfeld, A. and Kak, A.C., 'Digital Picture Processing', 2nd Edition, Academic Press, New York, 1982.

Spiegel, M.R., 'Mathematical Handbook for Formulas and Tables', Schaum's Outline Series Pub. McGraw-Hill.

Swartzlander, E.E. and Hallnor, G., "Frequency Domain Digital Filtering with VLSI", Chapter 19 in Kung, S.Y., Whitehouse, H.J. and Kailath, T., (ed), 'VLSI and Modern Signal Processing', Prentice Hall, Englewood Cliffs, NJ, 1985.

Twogood, R.E., et al., "Optimal Sectioning Procedure for the Implementation of 2-D Digital Filters", IEEE Trans. CAS-25, No.5, pp.260-269, May 1979.

Widrow, B., and Stearns, S.D., 'Adaptive Signal Processing', Prentice Hall, Englewood Cliffs, NJ, 1984.

Wiener, N., 'Extrapolation, Interpolation and Smoothing of Stationary Time Series', Wiley, New York, 1949.

Williams, C.S., 'Design of Digital Filters', Prentice Hall, Englewood Cliffs NJ, 1986.

Zverev, A.I., 'Handbook of Filter Synthesis', Wiley, New York, 1967.

INDEX

Peter M Grant

Peter Grant was awarded the BSc degree in electronic engineering from the Heriot-Watt University, Edinburgh, in 1966, and the PhD degree from the University of Edinburgh in 1975.

From 1966 to 1970 he worked as a development engineer with the Plessey Company Ltd, at both the Allen Clark Research Centre, Towcester and Avionics and Communications Division, Havant, designing frequency synthesisers and standards for mobile military communications. In 1971 he was appointed to a research fellowship at the University of Edinburgh to study the applications of surface acoustic wave and charge-coupled devices in communication systems. He was subsequently appointed to a faculty position, with responsibility for teaching electronic circuits, signal processing and communication systems. He presently holds the chair of Electronic Signal Processing, leading research in this area with personal interests in adaptive filtering, waveform coding and pattern recognition.

During academic year 1977-78, he was the recipient of a James Caird Travelling Scholarship and as a visiting assistant professor he researched in acoustic imaging and surface acoustic wave storage correlator applications at the Ginzton Laboratory, Stanford University, CA. In 1985-86 he was appointed as a visiting staff member at the MIT Lincoln Laboratory, Lexington, MA., studying the application of Neural Networks to pattern recognition. Professor Grant is also a Fellow of the I.E.E., where he serves as one of the honorary editors of the I.E.E. Proceedings Part F, Radar and Signal Processing, on the Editorial Advisory Panel for the Electronics and Communications Engineering Journal and, separately, as an elected member of the Electronics Divisional Board.

Colin F N Cowan

Colin Cowan is currently a lecturer in Electrical Engineering at Edinburgh University. He was awarded the degrees of BSc and PhD in Electrical Engineering by Edinburgh University in 1977 and 1980 respectively.

Since 1977 he has been an active researcher in the general area of signal processing with specific interests in adaptive systems and telecommunications systems. He has authored numerous articles in this area and co-authored two authoritative books on the subject of adaptive filters.

He is a member of the I.E.E. and chairman of the 1st I.E.E. International Conference on Artificial Neural Networks. He is also a member of the editorial board of the European journal "Signal Processing".

Bernard Mulgrew

Bernard Mulgrew received the BSc Hons first class degree in Electrical and Electronic Engineering from Queen's University Belfast in 1979 and the PhD degree in electrical engineering from the University of Edinburgh in 1987.

From 1979 to 1983, he worked in the Radar Systems Department of Ferranti plc, Edinburgh, on digital hardware design and tracking algorithms for airborne radar. From 1983 to 1986 he was a research associate in the Department of Electrical Engineering at the University of Edinburgh, studying the performance and design of adaptive filter algorithms. He is currently a lecturer in the department. His research interests are in adaptive signal processing and estimation theory and in their application to radar and communications systems. He is co-author of the text *Adaptive Filters and Equalisers* (Kluwer Academic Publishers, 1988).

Dr Mulgrew is an associate member of the I.E.E. and a member of the I.E.E.E.

James H Dripps

James Dripps received a BSc degree in Electrical Engineering from Queen's University of Belfast in 1970 and a PhD degree from Strathclyde University, Glasgow in 1977, studying modulation methods for digital data transmission on HF ionospheric links. From 1970 to 1972 he worked on circuit design with Short Bros (Aircraft and Missiles) Belfast and from 1977 to 1980 on FFT processor design for radar at Ferranti, Edinburgh. He is currently a lecturer in the Department of Electrical Engineering at Edinburgh University. His research interests are in the application of signal processing techniques to communication and medical electronics systems.

Handbook of Electronics *by J. de Sousa Pires*

an integrated reference source on:

Analog electronics
Digital electronics
Personal computers
Communication
Mathematics

Although written in an easily understood manner, this book is not a low-level description of Electronics. It covers the ground between hobbyist and specialist. The author has created an *environment* where the reader will find answers to not only those problems directly related to Electronics, but also to those in related areas, *in the same book.*

Analog Electronics
Theory and practice of basic circuits. Ohm. Joule. Thevenin. Norton. Bridges. Filters. Diodes. Voltage controlling. Oscillators.

Digital Electronics
Basic concepts and theorems. Bases. Base transforming. Boolean algebra. Codes. Randomized sequences. Circuit categories. Circuit simulation using spreadsheets.

Personal Computers
Covering PC's, software, technology, peripherals and accessories, with advice and hints on faster and more efficient programs.

Communications
Shannon's and Nyquist's theorem. CW. Modems. Parity. Morse. Kansas City format. ASCII code. EBCDIC code. RTTY. Baudot code. AMTOR code.

Mathematics
For those who may not recall all the formal techniques and concepts. Reverse Polish Notation. Least-square. Adjustment of measure data. Vectors. Differential equations. Logarithms.

Tables and Standards
MIDI-standard. Frequencies of the notes. Synthesizers. Constants. Prefixes. Units.

800 pages, hardback, 1989, ISBN 0-86238-061-8

Fourier Transforms in Action *by Frank Pettit*
Contains more than 100 videographs of waveforms and Fourier Spectra with Accompanying explanatory text. The presentation is based on *graphical* rather than *mathematical* treatments so as to give the reader a real understanding of the practicalities of Fourier Transforms. Attention is focussed on the validity of application of a widely misused and misinterpreted subject.
Contents: List of figures; Preface; About signals; Sampling techniques; Fourier transforms; The Fourier transform software kit; On waves and windows; Transforms of non-integral waves; Waveforms from spectra; Window functions; The FT kit in practice; The fast Fourier transform; Applications for FFTs; (Appendices; Complex numbers; Fortran-80).
1986, 133 pages, ISBN 0-86238-088-X

Beta Maths Handbook by Lennart Rade and Bertil Westergren

BETA is a comprehensive mathematics handbook for scientists, engineers and university students. It presents, in a lucid and accessible form, classical areas of mathematics such as algebra, geometry and analysis. Furthermore, areas of particular current interest are covered, such as discrete mathematics, probability and statistics, optimization, programming and numerical analysis. BETA concentrates on definitions, results, formulas and tables. The importance of computers in modern applied mathematics is also considered.

Contents: Fundamentals; Discrete Mathematics; Algebra; Geometry and Trigonometry; Linear Algebra; The Elementary Functions; Differential Calculus (one variable); Integral Calculus; Sequences and Series; Ordinary Differential Equations (ODE); Multidimensional Calculus; Vector Analysis; Orthogonal Series and Special Functions; Numerical Analysis and Programming; Probability Theory; Statistics; Miscellaneous; History.

Hardback, 1988, 425 pages, ISBN 0-86238-140-1

Computer Display Designer's Handbook by Eric Wagner

Introduces systems designers and programmers - those who provide process control systems - and to end users of those systems, to computer-based information design. These systems can provide many new and imaginative ways of displaying information. The important point is that man's abilities and limitations in perceiving and processing visual information be taken into account. The author, a professional industrial designer, has been involved in design of MMC equipment and display design for ASEA Automation.

Contents: Introduction; Visual Perception; General Visual Concepts; General Colour Concepts; Human Information Processing Theory; Human Performance - an overview; Display Design; Principles of Graphic Design; Graphic Illustration Techniques; Display Design - Some Practical Examples; Display Hierarchy; Information Structure; Design of Graphic Display Elements; System Dialogue; Bibliography; Index.

1988, approx 300 pages, ISBN 0-86238-171-1

Programmable Control Systems by Goran Johannesson

Industry today has a great need for control systems for automating of processes and machines. The programmable control system (PCS) has become more and more common and today spans the region from simple relay controls up to tasks for micro- and mini-computers. Some general principles of control systems using relays, logic circuits and computers are discussed. A detailed description of the design and functioning of different types of PC systems is then given. This book is designed to be used in industry and technical educational institutes as an introduction to the applications of PC systems.

Contents: Aims; Control systems; What is a control system? Conventional types of binary control systems; PC systems; Comparison between different types of control systems; Exercises: Programming PC systems; Basis for programming; Programming language; Programming interlocks; Programming of sequences; Programming equipment; Exercises: Design of PC systems; Problem definition; Choosing a control system; Electrical design and installation; Programming; Process simulation; Commissioning; Documentation; Exercises: Solutions to exercises; PC glossary; Installation instructions for PBS and computer equipment.

1985, 136 pages, ISBN 0-86238-046-4

Computer Networks: Fundamentals and Practice by M. D. Bacon, A.V. Stokes & J. Bacon

This introduction to the fundamentals of data transmission and computer networks is divided into three sections. The first deals with the technology of transmitting data, from simple synchronous and asynchronous transmission to various switching methods and methods of sharing one communications link between many different users. One chapter is devoted to the problem of errors. Section two examines the historical development of computer networks then concentrates on hardware and software, with special reference to network protocols, and changes in network technology (especially satellite and LANS) are discussed. The final section examines relationships between multiprocessing and networking in the context of distributed processing and gives numerous examples of such systems.

Contents: PART 1 - DATA TRANSMISSION; Introduction to Data Transmission; Data Transmission; Data Transmission Systems; Switching Techniques; Multiplexing; Modulation; Errors: PART 2 - COMPUTER NETWORKS; An Introduction; Network Hardware and Software; Recent Advances in Networking: PART 3 - DISTRIBUTED PROCESSING; Networks as Distributed Processes (Appendices: CCITT Recommendations; Some Acronyms and Abbreviations).

Comments on this edition by UK Lecturers
" ... very lucid and helpful introduction" " ... excellent, straightforward and broad-based" " ... cheap, concise, what more can you ask for" " ... a sound basis for this syllabus topic"
1984, 109 pages, ISBN 0-86238-028-6

Datacommunication: Datanet, Protocols and Design   by Ewald, Westman
Aiming to give a general knowledge of data communication without going too deeply into the subject, this introductory book explains common terms and concepts. The contents may be regarded to some extent as a reference book, while at the same time dealing, among other things, with the technology, protocols and types of network which exist today.

Contents: Introduction to data communication; Cables and wires; Conductor theory; Data communication; Protocols and line procedures; Private and public data networks; Distributed data networks; Local data networks; Transaction systems, queues and queuing theory; Data and telephone connections; Terminals; Communication computers; Modems and modulation; DCE and DATEX; Test instruments; Glossary; References; Bibliography; Index.
1988, 350 pages, ISBN 0-86238-092-8

Telecommunications: Telephone Networks 1   by Ericsson, Televerket
The worldwide telephone network must be one of the largest and most complex technical systems existing. Moreover, it is an essential part of the infrastructure and is a vital prerequisite in the development of a country. In order to work in this field, basic knowledge of the telephone network is required. These books have therefore been produced by Ericsson Telecom and the Swedish Telecommunication Administration and are widely used in their basic training, in Sweden and throughout Europe. The emphasis is on fundamental principles and concepts rather than on the technical details of any particular system. Certainly the best introductory books in the field.

Contents: Networks for telecommunication; Basic requirements of the telephone network; Demands on the telephone network; PCM-technology; Transmission media; SPC-technology in digital and analogue environments; CCITT; Fundamental plans; Numbering plan; Changing plan; Other fundamental plans; Network design; National digital networks; Network functions - introduction; The telephone and the subscriber line network; Functions of the local exchange; Functions of other types of exchange; Signalling; Subscriber signalling; Channel associated signalling; Line and register signalling; The R2 (MFC) register signalling system; Common channel signalling; The signalling network; The synchronisation network; Mobile telephony.
1986, 147 pages, ISBN 0-86238-093-6

Telecommunications: Telephone Networks 2   by Ericsson and Televerket
Contents: Transmission; Transmission parameters; Transmission techniques; Transmission media; Transmission systems - example; Subscriber equipment; Equipment in the subscriber line net; Digital coupling; Digital coupling systems; Equipment for signalling; Control; Subscriber switches; Traffic theory; Prognosis; Optimising; Operation and maintenance - introduction; Operation; Maintenance; Example from operating and maintenance of a digital net; Organisation of operation and maintenance; ISDN; Subscriber equipment for ISDN; Applications

in ISDN; Techniques and functions in ISDN.
1987, 176 pages, ISBN 0-86238-113-4

Fundamentals of Microprocessor Systems by Philip A Witting

This complete guide for designing microprocessor-based equipment considers all the hardware and software issues to be resolved during design. The theory is explained in a manner which is not specific to any particular processor and such references in the main text are kept to an absolute minimum. However, two chapters have been specifically dedicated to illustrating the theory by reference to the Motorola 6800 family of devices. These chapters are paralleled by two appendices which consider the Intel 8080/8085 family. Thus one book contains both the general concepts and their specific application to the two most popular families of devices.

"It is almost certainly the best of the books on microprocessor systems design currently on the market. I would strongly recommend it for all second and final-year courses in microprocessor systems design. Owing to its size, it covers all the topics likely to be found in such courses." - Microprocessors and Microsystems

Contents: Introduction; The sequential processor; Data representation and number systems; Binary arithmetic processes; Methods of addressing; Memory systems; Input-output operations I; Input-output operations II; The architecture and instruction set of the MC68000; Techniques for communications; Techniques for bulk storage of data; Multi-processor systems; Memory management; Peripheral support devices for use with microprocessors; Program development; Microprocessor system development techniques; Single-chip and special-purpose microprocessors; Bit-slice processors; (Appendices: The architecture and instruction set of the 8085 processor; Support devices for the 8080 and 8085 processors; Digital systems components; Semiconductor fabrication techniques; Modulo-2 arithmetic) References; Index.

1984, 525 pages, ISBN 0-86238-030-8

Dictionary of Computer and Information Technology Terms by Don Lynch

Concise and easily understood brief explanations of over 2500 of the most common words, terms, jargon, acronyms, abbreviations and codes. It makes the terminology and jargon of computer and information science readily understandable and available to the non-expert.

1987, 225 pages, ISBN 0-86238-128-2

Information Technology Dictionary of Acronyms and Abbreviations
by Don Lynch

Unexplained abbreviations and acronyms are on the increase. Even topic experts are sometimes in the dark. The solution is this comprehensive, low-cost source of reference for meanings of OVER 6000 common abbreviations and acronyms associated with Information Technology.

1988, 270 pages, ISBN 0-86238-153-3

Authors

Chartwell-Bratt are keen to hear from new authors in Computing and related disciplines. If you think you could write a worthwhile book, or even a textbook classic, we would be delighted to hear from you! We are able to offer you fast production times, high royalty rates, worldwide distribution and low selling prices.

If you would like to discuss the possibility of authorship please ring Philip Yorke on 01-467 1956, or write to him at Chartwell-Bratt, Old Orchard, Bickley Road, Bromley, Kent, BR1 2NE, United Kingdom.

Computing Books from Chartwell-Bratt

GENERAL COMPUTING BOOKS

Compiler Physiology for Beginners, M Farmer, 279pp, ISBN 0-86238-064-2
Dictionary of Computer and Information Technology, D Lynch, 225 pages, ISBN 0-86238-128-2
File Structure and Design, M Cunningham, 211pp, ISBN 0-86238-065-0
Information Technology Dictionary of Acronyms and Abbreviations, D Lynch, 270pp, ISBN 0-86238-153-3
The IBM Personal Computer with BASIC and PC-DOS, B Kynning, 320pp, ISBN 0-86238-080-4

PROGRAMMING LANGUAGES

An Intro to LISP, P Smith, 130pp, ISBN 0-86238-187-8
An Intro to OCCAM 2 Programming, Bowler, *et al,* 109pp, ISBN 0-86238-137-1
Cobol for Mainframe and Micro, D Watson, 177pp, ISBN 0-86238-082-0
Comparative Languages: 2nd Ed, J R Malone, 125pp, ISBN 0-86238-123-1
Fortran 77 for Non-Scientists, P Adman, 109pp, ISBN 0-86238-074-X
Fortran 77 Solutions to Non-Scientific Problems, P Adman, 150pp, ISBN 0-86238-087-1
Fortran Lectures at Oxford, F Pettit, 135pp, ISBN 0-86238-122-3
LISP: From Foundations to Applications, G Doukidis *et al,* 228pp, ISBN 0-86238-191-6
Programming Language Semantics, C Rattray, 135pp, ISBN 0-86238-066-9
Prolog versus You, A Johansson, *et al,* 308pp, ISBN 0-86238-174-6
Simula Begin, G M Birtwistle, *et al,* 391pp, ISBN 0-86238-009-X
The Intensive C Course, M Farmer, 167pp, ISBN 0-86238-114-2
The Intensive Pascal Course, M Farmer, 111pp, ISBN 0-86238-063-4

ASSEMBLY LANGUAGE PROGRAMMING

Coding the 68000, N Hellawell, 214pp, ISBN 0-86238-180-0
Computer Organisation and Assembly Language Programming, L Ohlsson & P Stenstrom, 128pp, ISBN 0-86238-129-0
What is machine code and what can you do with it? N Hellawell, 104pp, ISBN 0-86238-132-0

PROGRAMMING TECHNIQUES

Discrete-events simulations models in PASCAL/MT+ on a microcomputer, L P Jennergren, 135pp, ISBN 0-86238-053-7
Information and Coding, J A Llewellyn, 152pp, ISBN 0-86238-099-5
JSP - A Practical Method of Program Design, L Ingevaldsson, 204pp, ISBN 0-86238-107-X
JSD - Method for System Development, L Ingevaldsson, 248pp, ISBN 0-86238-103-7

Linear Programming: A Computational Approach: 2nd Ed, K K Lau, 150pp, ISBN 0-86238-182-7

Programming for Beginners: the structured way, D Bell & P Scott, 178pp, ISBN 0-86238-130-4

Software Engineering for Students, M Coleman & S Pratt, 195pp, ISBN 0-86238-115-0

Software Taming with Dimensional Design, M Coleman & S Pratt, 164pp, ISBN 0-86238-142-8

Systems Programming with JSP, B Sanden, 186pp, ISBN 0-86238-054-5

MATHEMATICS AND COMPUTING

Fourier Transforms in Action, F Pettit, 133pp, ISBN 0-86238-088-X

Generalised Coordinates, L G Chambers, 90pp, ISBN 0-86238-079-0

Statistics and Operations Research, I P Schagen, 300pp, ISBN 0-86238-077-4

Teaching of Modern Engineering Mathematics, L Rade (ed), 225pp, ISBN 0-86238-173-8

Teaching of Statistics in the Computer Age, L Rade (ed), 248pp, ISBN 0-86238-090-1

The Essentials of Numerical Computation, M Bartholomew-Biggs, 241pp, ISBN 0-86238-029-4

DATABASES AND MODELLING

Database Analysis and Design, H Robinson, 378pp, ISBN 0-86238-018-9

Databases and Database Systems, E Oxborrow, 256pp, ISBN 0-86238-091-X

Data Bases and Data Models, B Sundgren, 134pp, ISBN 0-86238-031-6

Text Retrieval and Document Databases, J Ashford & Willett P, 125pp, ISBN 0-86238-204-1

Towards Transparent Databases, G Sandstrom, 192pp, ISBN 0-86238-095-2

Information Modelling, J Bubenko (ed), 687pp, ISBN 0-86238-006-5

UNIX

An Intro to the Unix Operating System, C Duffy, 152pp, ISBN 0-86238-143-6

Operating Systems through Unix, G Emery, 96pp, ISBN 0-86238-086-3

SYSTEMS ANALYSIS AND DEVELOPMENT

Systems Analysis and Development: 2nd Ed, P Layzell & P Loucopoulos, 232pp, ISBN 0-86238-156-8

SYSTEMS DESIGN

Computer Systems: Where Hardware meets Software, C Machin, 200pp, ISBN 0-86238-075-8

Distributed Applications and Online Dialogues: a design method for application systems, A Rasmussen, 271pp, ISBN 0-86238-105-3

HARDWARE

Computers from First Principles, M Brown, 128pp, ISBN 0-86238-027-8
Fundamentals of Microprocessor Systems, P Witting, 525pp, ISBN 0-86238-030-8

NETWORKS

Communication Network Protocols: 2nd Ed, B Marsden, 345pp, ISBN 0-86238-106-1
Computer Networks: Fundamentals and Practice, M D Bacon *et al,* 109pp, ISBN 0-86238-028-6
Datacommunication: Data Networks, Protocols and Design, L Ewald & E Westman, 350pp, ISBN 0-86238-092-8
Telecommunications: Telephone Networks 1, Ericsson & Televerket, 147pp, ISBN 0-86238-093-6
Telecommunications: Telephone Networks 2, Ericsson & Televerket, 176pp, ISBN 0-86238-113-4

GRAPHICS

An Introductory Course in Computer Graphics, R Kingslake, 146pp, ISBN 0-86238-073-1
Techniques of Interactive Computer Graphics, A Boyd, 242pp, ISBN 0-86238-024-3
Two-dimensional Computer Graphics, S Laflin, 85pp, ISBN 0-86238-127-4

APPLICATIONS

Computers in Health and Fitness, J Abas, 106pp, ISBN 0-86238-155-X
Developing Expert Systems, G Doukidis, E Whitley, ISBN 0-86238-196-7
Expert Systems Introduced, D Daly, 180pp, ISBN 0-86238-185-1
Handbook of Finite Element Software, J Mackerle & B Fredriksson, approx 1000pp, ISBN 0-86238-135-5
Inside **Data Processing: computers and their effective use in business,** A deWatteville, 150pp, ISBN 0-86238-181-9
Proceedings of the Third Scandinavian Conference on Image Analysis, P Johansen & P Becker (eds) 426pp, ISBN 0-86238-039-1
Programmable Control Systems, G Johannesson, 136pp, ISBN 0-86238-046-4
Risk and Reliability Appraisal on Microcomputers, G Singh, with G Kiangi, 142pp, ISBN 0-86238-159-2
Statistics with Lotus 1-2-3, M Lee & J Soper, 207pp, ISBN 0-86238-131-2

HCI

Human/Computer Interaction: from voltage to knowledge, J Kirakowski, 250pp, ISBN 0-86238-179-7
Information Ergonomics, T Ivegard, 228pp, ISBN 0-86238-032-4
Computer Display Designer's Handbook, E Wagner, approx 300pp, ISBN 0-86238-171-1

INFORMATION AND SOCIETY

Access to Government Records: International Perspectives and Trends, T Riley, 112pp, ISBN 0-86238-119-3
CAL/CBT - the great debate, D Marshall, 300pp, ISBN 0-86238-144-4
Economic and Trade-Related Aspects of Transborder Dataflow,
R Wellington-Brown, 93pp, ISBN 0-86238-110-X
Information Technology and a New International Order, J Becker, 141pp, ISBN 0-86238-043-X
People or Computers: Three Ways of Looking at Information Systems,
M Nurminen, 1218pp, ISBN 0-86238-184-3
Transnational Data Flows in the Information Age, C Hamelink, 115pp, ISBN 0-86238-042-1

SCIENCE HANDBOOKS

Alpha Maths Handbook, L Rade, 199pp, ISBN 0-86238-036-7
Beta Maths Handbook, L Rade, 425pp, ISBN 0-86238-140-1
Handbook of Electronics, J de Sousa Pires, approx 750pp, ISBN 0-86238-061-8
Nuclear Analytical Chemistry, D Brune *et al,* 557pp, ISBN 0-86238-047-2
Physics Handbook, C Nordling & J Osterman, 430pp, ISBN 0-86238-037-5
The V-Belt Handbook, H Palmgren, 287pp, ISBN 0-86238-111-8

Chartwell-Bratt specialise in excellent books at affordable prices.

For further details contact your local bookshop, or ring Chartwell-Bratt direct on **01-467 1956** (Access/Visa welcome.)

Ring or write for our *free* catalogue.

Chartwell-Bratt (Publishing & Training) Ltd, Old Orchard, Bickley Road, Bromley, Kent, BR1 2NE, United Kingdom.
Tel 01-467 1956, Fax 01-467 1754, Telecom Gold 84:KJM001,
Telex 9312100451(CB)